MODERN BIOLOGY

Assessment Item Listing

HOLT, RINEHART AND WINSTON

A Harcourt Classroom Education Company

Austin · New York · Orlando · Atlanta · San Francisco · Boston · Dallas · Toronto · London

Cover Image
© Manfred Danegger/Okapai/Photo Researchers, Inc.

Copyright © by Holt, Rinehart and Winston

Printed in the United States of America

ISBN 0-03-064664-2

4 5 6   066   05 04 03

CONTENTS

CONTENTS

Introduction

The *Modern Biology* Test Generator and Assessment Item Listing

The *Modern Biology* Test Generator consists of a comprehensive bank of more than 3,500 test items and the ExamView Pro 3.0 Test Builder software, which enables you to produce your own tests based on these items and those items you create yourself. Both Macintosh® and Windows® versions of the Test Generator are included on the *Modern Biology One-Stop Planner CD-ROM with Test Generator*. Directions on pp. vi-vii of this book explain how to install the program on your computer. This Assessment Item Listing is a printout of all the test items in the Test Generator.

ExamView Pro 3.0 Software

The ExamView Pro 3.0 Test Builder program enables you to quickly create printed tests. You can enter your own questions and customize the appearance of the tests you create. The ExamView Pro 3.0 Test Builder program offers many unique features and provides numerous options that allow you to customize the content and appearance of the tests you create.

Test Items

The *Modern Biology* Test Generator contains a file of test items for each chapter of the textbook. The test items are in a variety of formats, including true/false, multiple choice, completion, problem, and essay. Each item is correlated to the chapter objectives in the textbook and by difficulty level.

Item Codes

As you browse through this Assessment Item Listing, you will see that all test items of the same type are gathered together under an identifying head. Each item is coded to assist you with item selection. Following is an explanation of the codes.

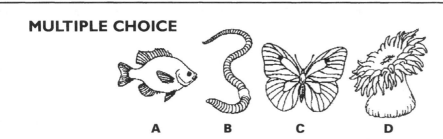

MULTIPLE CHOICE

A   B   C   D

1. Refer to the illustration above. Which organism in the diagrams captures its prey using nematocysts?

    a. Organism "A"   c. Organism "C"
    b. Organism "B"   d. Organism "D"

    ANS: A   DIF: I   OBJ: 16-1.1

defines the difficulty of the item.
requires recall of information.
requires analysis and interpretation of known information.
requires application of knowledge to new situations.

OBJ lists the chapter number, section number, and objective.
(21-2.2 = Chapter 21, Section 2, Objective 2)

INSTALLATION AND STARTUP

The ExamView Pro 3.0 test generator software is provided on the One-Stop Planner CD-ROM. The ExamView test generator includes the program and all of the questions for the corresponding textbook. Your ExamView software includes three components: Test Builder, Question Bank Editor, and Test Player. The **Test Builder** includes options to create, edit, print and save tests. The **Question Bank Editor** lets you create or edit question banks. The **Test Player** is a separate program that your students can use to take on-line* (computerized or LAN-based) tests. Please refer to the ExamView User's Guide on the One-Stop Planner CD-ROM for complete instructions.

Before you can use the test generator, you must install the program and the test banks on your hard drive. The system requirements, installation instructions, and startup procedures are provided below.

SYSTEM REQUIREMENTS

To use the ExamView Pro 3.0 test generator, your computer must meet or exceed the following minimum hardware requirements:

Windows®
- Pentium computer
- Windows 95®, Windows 98®, Windows 2000® (or a more recent version)
- color monitor (VGA-compatible)
- CD-ROM and/or high-density floppy disk drive
- hard drive with at least 7 MB space available
- 8 MB available memory (*16 MB memory recommended*)
- *If you wish to use the on-line test player, you must have an Internet connection to access the Internet testing features.*

Macintosh®
- PowerPC processor, 100 MHz computer
- System 7.5 (or a more recent version)
- color monitor (VGA-compatible)
- CD-ROM and/or high-density floppy disk drive
- hard drive with at least 7 MB space available
- 8 MB available memory (*16 MB memory recommended*)
- *If you wish to use the on-line test player, you must have an Internet connection with System 8.6 (or more recent version) to access the Internet testing features.*

You can use the on-line test player to host tests on your personal or school Web site or local area network (LAN) at no additional charge. The ExamView Web site's Internet test-hosting service must be purchased separately. Visit www.examview.com to learn more.

INSTALLATION

Instructions for installing ExamView from the CD-ROM:

Windows®
Step 1
Turn on your computer.
Step 2
Insert the One-Stop Planner disc with the ExamView test generator into the CD-ROM drive.
Step 3
Click the **Start** button on the *Taskbar,* and choose the *Run* option.
Step 4
The ExamView software is provided on the One-Stop Planner CD-ROM under the drive letter that corresponds to the CD-ROM drive on your computer (e.g., **d:\setup.exe**). The setup program will automatically install everything you need to use ExamView.
Step 5
Follow the prompts on the screen to complete the installation process.

Macintosh®
Step 1
Turn on your computer.
Step 2
Insert the One-Stop Planner disc with the ExamView test generator into the CD-ROM drive.
Step 3
Double-click the *ExamView* installation icon to start the program.
Step 4
Follow the prompts on the screen to complete the installation process.

Instructions for installing ExamView from the One-Stop Planner Menu (Macintosh® or Windows®):

Follow steps 1 and 2 from above.
Step 3
Click on **One-Stop.pdf.** (If you do not have Adobe Acrobat® Reader installed on your computer, install it before proceeding by clicking on **Reader Installer.**)
Step 4
Click on the **Test Generator** button.
Step 5
Click on **Install ExamView.**
Step 6
Select the operating system you are using (Macintosh® or Windows®).
Step 7
ExamView will launch the installer. Follow the prompts on the screen to complete the installation process.

GETTING STARTED

After you complete the installation process, follow these instructions to start the ExamView test generator software. See the ExamView User's Guide on the One-Stop Planner for further instructions on the options for creating a test and editing a question bank.

Startup Instructions

Step 1
Turn on the computer.
Step 2
Windows®: Click the **Start** button on the *Taskbar*. Highlight the **Programs** menu, and locate the *ExamView Test Generator* folder. Select the *ExamView Pro* option to start the software.
Macintosh®: Locate and open the *ExamView* folder. Double-click the *ExamView Pro* program icon.
Step 3
The first time you run the software, you will be prompted to enter your name, school/institution name, and city/state. You are now ready to begin using the ExamView software.
Step 4
Each time you start ExamView, the **Startup** menu appears. Choose one of the options shown.
Step 5
Use ExamView to create a test or edit questions in a question bank.

Technical Support

If you have any questions about the Test Generator or need assistance, call the Holt, Rinehart and Winston technical support line at 1-800-323-9239, Monday through Friday, 7:00 A.M. to 6:00 P.M., Central Standard Time. You can contact the Technical Support Center on the Internet http://www.hrwtechsupport.com or by e-mail at tsc@hrwtechsupport.com.

TRUE/FALSE

1. The study of biology can help you better understand human reproduction.

   ANS: T   DIF: I   OBJ: 1-1.1

2. Almost all organisms ultimately get their energy for survival from the sun.

   ANS: T   DIF: I   OBJ: 1-1.2

3. All living things are composed of chemicals.

   ANS: T   DIF: I   OBJ: 1-1.3

4. Refer to the illustration above. Both species are multicellular.

   ANS: F   DIF: II   OBJ: 1-1.3

5. Refer to the illustration above. Both species have DNA in their cells.

   ANS: T   DIF: II   OBJ: 1-1.3

6. Refer to the illustration above. Reproduction ensures the ongoing success of both species.

   ANS: T   DIF: II   OBJ: 1-2.1

7. Refer to the illustration above. The sand dollar and paramecium both show organization.

   ANS: T   DIF: II   OBJ: 1-2.2

8. Refer to the illustration above. Unlike the sand dollar, the paramecium does not have to maintain a stable internal environment.

   ANS: F   DIF: II   OBJ: 1-2.3

9. Scientists have not discovered any new species on Earth in more than 20 years.

   ANS: F   DIF: I   OBJ: 1-2.3

10. A scientist who performs an experiment has no idea what the outcome of the experiment is going to be.

ANS: F   DIF: I   OBJ: 1-3.2

11. A theory is a hypothesis that has been proven true.

ANS: F   DIF: I   OBJ: 1-3.2

12. A theory is an assumption made by scientists and implies a lack of certainty.

ANS: F   DIF: I   OBJ: 1-3.2

13. Publication of the results of scientific investigations enables other scientists to verify these results.

ANS: T   DIF: I   OBJ: 1-3.3

14. Scientific investigations always follow a series of rigidly defined steps.

ANS: F   DIF: I   OBJ: 1-3.4

15. Resolution is a microscope's power to increase an object's apparent size.

ANS: F   DIF: I   OBJ: 1-4.1

16. The resolution power of an electron microscope is limited by the physical characteristics of light.

ANS: T   DIF: I   OBJ: 1-4.1

17. Units of time are not measured in metric units, so time measurements are not accepted for use with SI units.

ANS: F   DIF: I   OBJ: 1-4.2

MULTIPLE CHOICE

1. Biology is the study of
   a. minerals.
   b. life.
   c. the weather.
   d. energy.

ANS: B   DIF: I   OBJ: 1-1.1

2. All organisms possess DNA. DNA
   a. creates energy for the cells.
   b. allows sensitivity to environmental stimuli.
   c. contains information for growth and development.
   d. captures energy from the sun.

ANS: C   DIF: I   OBJ: 1-1.1

3. Instructions for development that are passed from parents to offspring are known as
   a. a species plan.
   b. organ codes.
   c. genes.
   d. natural selections.

   ANS: C   DIF: I   OBJ: 1-1.1

4. As a characteristic of all living things, homeostasis relates most directly to which of the following biological themes?
   a. interacting systems
   b. stability
   c. evolution
   d. scale and structure

   ANS: B   DIF: I   OBJ: 1-1.1

5. Homeostasis means
   a. a change over long periods of time.
   b. keeping things the same.
   c. rapid change.
   d. the same thing as evolution.

   ANS: B   DIF: I   OBJ: 1-1.1

6. Ecology
   a. refers to change in species over time.
   b. refers to a delicate internal balance within organisms.
   c. is inconsistent with evolution.
   d. is the study of communities or organisms in relation to their environment.

   ANS: D   DIF: I   OBJ: 1-1.1

7. Which of the following is a means by which heterotrophs can obtain energy?
   a. using water, carbon dioxide, and energy from the sun to produce sugars
   b. using water and carbon dioxide to produce energy-rich compounds
   c. consuming autotrophs
   d. consuming simple chemicals from the environment and using them to assemble complex chemicals and structures needed by the organism

   ANS: D   DIF: II   OBJ: 1-1.2

8. Which of the following is *not* necessarily a distinct property of living things?
   a. homeostasis
   b. metabolism
   c. complexity
   d. reproduction

   ANS: C   DIF: I   OBJ: 1-1.3

9. The smallest units that can carry on all the functions of life are called
   a. molecules.
   b. cells.
   c. organelles.
   d. species.

   ANS: B   DIF: I   OBJ: 1-1.3

10. Living things
    a. need energy for life processes.
    b. have the ability to reproduce.
    c. are composed of cells.
    d. All of the above

    ANS: D   DIF: I   OBJ: 1-1.3

11. All organisms are composed of
    a. diatoms.
    b. cellulose.
    c. cells.
    d. None of the above

    ANS: C   DIF: I   OBJ: 1-2.1

12. All living things maintain a balance within their cells and the environment through the process of
    a. growth.
    b. development.
    c. homeostasis.
    d. evolution.

    ANS: C   DIF: I   OBJ: 1-2.1

13. Which of the following is characteristic of all living things?
    a. movement
    b. growth
    c. development
    d. cellular organization

    ANS: D   DIF: I   OBJ: 1-2.2

14. Which of the following is *not* a partial explanation for our lack of understanding of many of the living things on Earth?
    a. Many organisms are microscopic in size and therefore difficult to observe.
    b. Many organisms are so different from other organisms that it is difficult to understand them.
    c. Many organisms live in areas of the world that are difficult to explore.
    d. Tropical rain forests contain many species, and it is difficult to find all of them in these dense forests.

    ANS: B   DIF: II   OBJ: 1-2.3

15. A scientist noticed that in acidic pond water some salamanders developed with curved spines. This was a(n)
    a. hypothesis.
    b. theory.
    c. observation.
    d. control.

    ANS: C   DIF: I   OBJ: 1-3.1

16. Which example of scientific methodology is *incorrect*?
    a. Observation—A number of people in Zaire dying of a disease outbreak
    b. Measurement—A record of the number of people with symptoms of the disease and the number of people who had died from the disease
    c. Analysis of data—Comparison of the effects of mixing monkey cells with virus-containing blood in test tubes and the effects of mixing of liquid from these test tubes with fresh monkey cells
    d. Inference making—Identification of the Ebola virus as the cause of the disease by taking electron micrographs of substances found in the blood of persons affected with the disease

    ANS: D   DIF: II   OBJ: 1-3.1

17. The English physician Ronald Ross wanted to try to find the cause of malaria. Based on his observations, Dr. Ross suggested that the *Anopheles* mosquito might spread malaria from person to person. This suggestion was a
    a. prediction.
    b. hypothesis.
    c. theory.
    d. scientific "truth."

    ANS: B   DIF: I   OBJ: 1-3.2

18. Dr. Ross knew that the parasite *Plasmodium* was always found in the blood of malaria patients. He thought that if the *Anopheles* mosquitoes were responsible for spreading malaria, then *Plasmodium* would be found in the mosquitoes. This idea was a
    a. prediction.
    b. hypothesis.
    c. theory.
    d. scientific "truth."

    ANS: A   DIF: I   OBJ: 1-3.2

19. Scientific hypotheses are most often tested by the process of
    a. communicating.
    b. inferring.
    c. experimenting.
    d. analyzing data.

    ANS: C   DIF: I   OBJ: 1-3.2

20. A hypothesis is
    a. a definite answer to a given problem.
    b. a testable possible explanation of an observation.
    c. a proven statement.
    d. a concluding statement.

    ANS: B   DIF: I   OBJ: 1-3.2

21. A unifying explanation for a broad range of observations is a
    a. hypothesis.
    b. theory.
    c. prediction.
    d. controlled experiment.

    ANS: B   DIF: I   OBJ: 1-3.2

22. A hypothesis that does not explain an observation
    a. is known as an inaccurate forecast.
    b. often predicts a different observation.
    c. is rejected.
    d. None of the above

    ANS: C   DIF: I   OBJ: 1-3.2

23. Scientists usually design experiments
    a. with a good idea of the expected experimental results.
    b. based on wild guesses.
    c. in order to develop new laboratory tools.
    d. All of the above

    ANS: A   DIF: I   OBJ: 1-3.2

24. A scientific theory
    a. is absolutely certain.
    b. is unchangeable.
    c. may be revised as new evidence is presented.
    d. is a controlled experiment.

    ANS: C   DIF: I   OBJ: 1-3.2

25. The word *theory* used in a scientific sense means
    a. that of which the scientist is most certain.
    b. a guess made with very little knowledge to support it.
    c. an absolute scientific certainty.
    d. None of the above

    ANS: A   DIF: I   OBJ: 1-3.2

26. observation : hypothesis ::
    a. theory : observation   c. certainty : investigation
    b. guess : hypothesis   d. theory : control

    ANS: C   DIF: I   OBJ: 1-3.2

27. Which of the following components of a scientific investigation would benefit from communication between scientists?
    a. observing   c. analyzing data
    b. measuring   d. All of the above

    ANS: D   DIF: I   OBJ: 1-3.3

28. Most typically, the order in which the steps of the scientific method are applied is
    a. observations, predictions, hypothesis, controlled testing, theory, verification.
    b. predictions, observations, hypothesis, theory, controlled testing, verification.
    c. observations, hypothesis, predictions, controlled testing, theory, verification.
    d. observations, hypothesis, predictions, controlled testing, verification, theory.

    ANS: C   DIF: I   OBJ: 1-3.4

29. A light microscope that has an objective lens of 10× and an ocular lens of 20× has a magnification of
    a. 30×.   c. 300×.
    b. 200×.   d. 2000×.

    ANS: B   DIF: I   OBJ: 1-4.1

30. Which of the following associations between an SI base unit abbreviation and its base quantity is incorrect?
    a. A—area   c. s—second
    b. m—length   d. mol—amount of a substance

    ANS: A   DIF: II   OBJ: 1-4.2

COMPLETION

1. _____ is the study of a complex community of organisms in relation to their environment and each other.

   ANS: Ecology   DIF: I   OBJ: 1-1.1

2. Photosynthetic organisms include _____.

   ANS: plants, algae, and some bacteria   DIF: 1   OBJ: 1-1.2

3. All living things must maintain a constant internal environment to function properly through the process of _____.

   ANS: homeostasis   DIF: I   OBJ: 1-2.1

4. In most multicellular organisms, cells are organized according to their _____.

   ANS: function   DIF: II   OBJ: 1-2.2

5. A single gram of _____ may contain as many as 2.5 billion unicellular organisms.

   ANS: soil   DIF: I   OBJ: 1-2.3

6. An educated guess, or _____, may be tested by experimentation.

   ANS: hypothesis   DIF: I   OBJ: 1-3.2

7. Stating in advance the result that may be obtained from testing a hypothesis is called _____.

   ANS: predicting   DIF: I   OBJ: 1-3.2

8. A unifying explanation for a broad range of observations is a _____.

   ANS: theory   DIF: I   OBJ: 1-3.2

9. The main means by which scientists communicate with each other are _____.

   ANS: publishing in scientific journals and presenting at scientific meetings

   DIF: I   OBJ: 1-3.3

10. A _____ experiment is one in which the condition suspected to cause the effect is compared to the same situation without the suspected condition.

    ANS: control   DIF: I   OBJ: 1-3.4

11. The base unit for length in the Systeme International d'Unites is the

_____.

ANS: meter   DIF: II   OBJ: 1-4.2

PROBLEM

1. Some scientists conducted an experiment in which they evaluated various measurements of human health in people who drank at least one cup of coffee a day. They found no significant differences in these health indicators in the subjects who drank only one cup of coffee a day and those who drank as many as 20 cups a day. They concluded that coffee has no adverse effects on human health. Write your answers to the following in the spaces below.
   a. What were the independent and dependent variables in this experiment?
   b. Was this a controlled experiment? If so, what were the control and experimental groups?
   c. Do you agree with the conclusion the scientists' drew from their results? Why or why not?

   ANS:
   a. The independent variable was the number of cups of coffee a subject drank each day; the dependent variables were the indicators of human health measured.
   b. This was not a controlled experiment because there was no group of subjects who drank zero cups of coffee a day.
   c. Students should disagree with the scientists' conclusion because this was not a controlled experiment (there could be something harmful in coffee that would be effective when only one cup of coffee was consumed each day).

   DIF: III   OBJ: 1-3.1

ESSAY

1. Briefly discuss some of the major themes in biology that we will examine this year. Write your answer in the space below.

   ANS:
   Major themes are: cell structure and function; stability and homeostasis; heredity; matter, energy, and organization; evolution; and interdependence. Stability refers to the control of cells and homeostasis. Heredity is the study of the transmission of characteristics from parent to offspring. Matter, energy, and organization refers to the need all living things have for energy. Evolution refers to changes in species over time. Interdependence refers to ecology and the interaction of organisms with each other and the environment.

   DIF: II   OBJ: 1-1.1

2. Name five characteristics that are considered distinct properties of all living things. Write your answer in the space below.

ANS:
Each organism is composed of one or more cells. All living things carry out metabolic reactions that involve the use of energy. Reproduction is characteristic of all living things, as is homeostasis, the maintenance of a constant internal environment. All organisms pass on genetic information to offspring.

DIF: II   OBJ: 1-2.1

3. Toads that live in hot, dry regions bury themselves in the soil during the day. How might this be important to the toad? Write your answer in the space below.

ANS:
The toad must maintain a constant internal environment (homeostasis) in order to function properly. Burying themselves in the soil is a way to keep their body temperature from rising too high and to keep their bodies from drying out.

DIF: II   OBJ: 1-2.1

4. The results of an experiment do not support the hypothesis that the experiment was designed to test. Was the experiment a waste of time? Explain. Write your answer in the space below.

ANS:
No, the experiment was not a waste of time. A scientist works by systematically showing that certain hypotheses are not valid when they are not consistent with the results of experiments. The results of experiments are used to evaluate alternative hypotheses. An experiment can be successful if it shows that one or more of the alternative hypotheses are inconsistent with observations.

DIF: II   OBJ: 1-3.2

CHAPTER 2—CHEMISTRY

TRUE/FALSE

1. The types of particles that are located in the nucleus of an atom are protons and neutrons, and the types of particles that are located in the energy levels surrounding the nucleus are electrons.

   ANS: T   DIF: I   OBJ: 2-1.2

2. The atomic number of carbon is 6, so it must contain 12 electrons.

   ANS: F   DIF: II   OBJ: 2-1.2

3. Most elements are stable if their outermost energy level contains an even number of electrons.

   ANS: F   DIF: I   OBJ: 2-1.3

4. Atoms in a gas move more rapidly than atoms in a liquid or a solid do.

   ANS: T   DIF: I   OBJ: 2-2.1

5. The products of an endergonic chemical reaction possess more energy than the reactants from which they are produced.

   ANS: T   DIF: I   OBJ: 2-2.2

6. The amount of energy needed to cause a chemical reaction to start is called activation energy.

   ANS: T   DIF: I   OBJ: 2-2.2

7. When an enzyme binds with its substrate, the activation energy needed for the chemical reaction to occur is raised.

   ANS: F   DIF: I   OBJ: 2-2.3

8. Enzymes speed up a chemical reaction by increasing the activation energy of the reaction.

   ANS: F   DIF: I   OBJ: 2-2.3

9. Without enzymes, chemical reactions necessary for life would not occur at a rate sufficient to sustain life.

   ANS: T   DIF: I   OBJ: 2-2.3

10. Free hydrogen ions can react with water molecules and form a positively charged ion, the hydronium ion.

    ANS: T   DIF: I   OBJ: 2-3.2

11. Bases tend to have a sour taste, while acids tend to have a bitter taste.

ANS: F   DIF: I   OBJ: 2-3.3

12. Buffers can neutralize acids, but they do not affect bases.

ANS: F   DIF: I   OBJ: 2-3.5

MULTIPLE CHOICE

1. Atoms are composed of
   a. protons with a positive charge.
   b. neutrons with no charge.
   c. electrons with a negative charge.
   d. All of the above

   ANS: D   DIF: I   OBJ: 2-1.1

2. The smallest particle of matter that can retain the chemical properties of carbon is
   a. a carbon molecule.
   b. a carbon macromolecule.
   c. a carbon atom.
   d. an element.

   ANS: C   DIF: I   OBJ: 2-1.1

3. A substance that is composed of only one type of atom is called a(n)
   a. nucleus.
   b. cell.
   c. element.
   d. molecule.

   ANS: C   DIF: I   OBJ: 2-1.1

4. All matter in the universe is composed of
   a. cells.
   b. molecules.
   c. atoms.
   d. carbon.

   ANS: C   DIF: I   OBJ: 2-1.1

5. The electrons of an atom
   a. are found in the nucleus along with the protons.
   b. orbit the nucleus in various energy levels.
   c. have a positive charge.
   d. are attracted to the positive charge of neutrons.

   ANS: B   DIF: I   OBJ: 2-1.2

6. Atoms that have gained energy
   a. have protons and neutrons that move farther apart.
   b. lose neutrons from the nucleus.
   c. have electrons that move to higher energy levels.
   d. absorb electrons into the nucleus.

   ANS: C   DIF: I   OBJ: 2-1.3

7. Which of the following states of matter contain(s) particles that are tightly linked together in a definite shape?
a. solid
b. liquid
c. gas
d. solid and liquid

ANS: A DIF: II OBJ: 2-1.3

Assume that each of the atoms below requires eight electrons to fill its outer energy level.

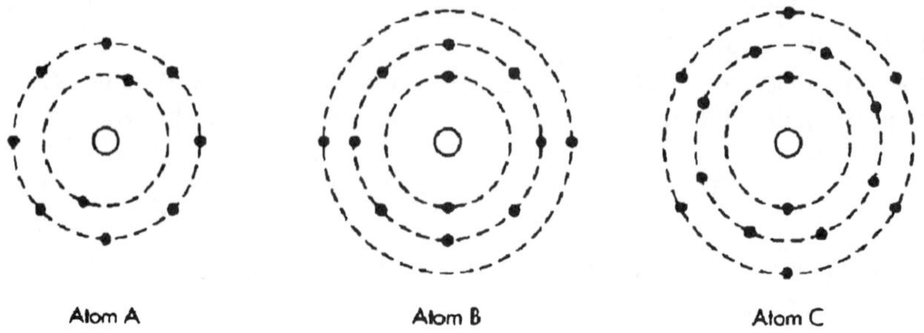

Atom A   Atom B   Atom C

8. Refer to the illustration above. Which of the atoms is chemically stable?
a. Atom "A"
b. Atom "B"
c. Atom "C"
d. None of the above

ANS: A DIF: II OBJ: 2-1.3

9. Refer to the illustration above. If Atom "C" interacted with Atom "B" to form an ionic bond, Atom "C" would
a. lose 6 electrons.
b. gain 2 electrons.
c. gain 5 electrons.
d. move 4 electrons into the nucleus.

ANS: B DIF: II OBJ: 2-1.4

10. Refer to the illustration above. If Atom "B" interacted with Atom "C" to form an ionic bond, Atom "B" would
a. gain 6 electrons.
b. lose 4 electrons.
c. lose 2 electrons.
d. move 2 electrons into the nucleus.

ANS: C DIF: II OBJ: 2-1.4

11. Because carbon has four electrons in its outer energy level,
a. it can form bonds with carbon atoms only.
b. these atoms are naturally chemically stable.
c. it can react with up to four other atoms to form covalent bonds.
d. it cannot react with anything other than organic molecules.

ANS: C DIF: I OBJ: 2-1.4

12. The bond formed when two atoms share a pair of electrons is called a
    a. hydrogen bond.
    b. nonpolar bond.
    c. covalent bond.
    d. water bond.

    ANS: C   DIF: I   OBJ: 2-1.4

13. Sharing of electrons in the outer energy levels of two atoms
    a. results in ion formation.
    b. occurs in covalent bonds.
    c. only occurs if both are atoms of the same element.
    d. is found only among carbon atoms.

    ANS: B   DIF: I   OBJ: 2-1.4

14. An atom that has gained or lost electrons is called a(n)
    a. molecule.
    b. nucleon.
    c. ion.
    d. element.

    ANS: C   DIF: I   OBJ: 2-1.4

15. Which of the following statements most accurately describes the difference between an ionic bond and a covalent bond?
    a. Atoms held together by ionic bonds separate when placed in water while atoms held together by covalent bonds do not separate in water.
    b. Ionic bonds hold together atoms of two different types, while covalent bonds hold together atoms of the same type.
    c. Electrons are exchanged between atoms held together by an ionic bond, but they are shared between atoms held together by a covalent bond.
    d. Ionic bonds form between atoms that carry opposite charges, while covalent bonds form between uncharged atoms.

    ANS: C   DIF: I   OBJ: 2-1.4

16. A reaction in which the products have less energy than the reactants is
    a. an endergonic reaction.
    b. an exergonic reaction.
    c. a filamentous reaction.
    d. impossible.

    ANS: B   DIF: I   OBJ: 2-2.2

17. If the products of a chemical reaction contain less energy than the reactants, the reaction must
    a. involve the release of energy.
    b. result in the production of sugar.
    c. be an energy-storing reaction.
    d. occur in the cytoplasm of cells.

    ANS: A   DIF: I   OBJ: 2-2.2

18. All of the activities occurring within cells
    a. are driven by chemical reactions.
    b. result from the random mixing of enzymes.
    c. cause the fluids in the cell to bubble and fizz.
    d. result in the production of enzymes.

    ANS: A   DIF: I   OBJ: 2-2.2

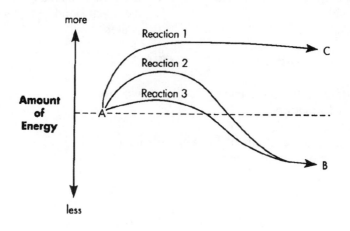

19. Refer to the graph above. Reaction "1" in the graph
    a. is an energy-storing reaction.
    b. requires a greater activation energy than Reaction "2."
    c. may use the same initial reactant condition needed to form Product "B."
    d. All of the above

    ANS: D   DIF: II   OBJ: 2-2.2

20. Refer to the graph above. Reaction "3" in the graph
    a. probably occurred in the presence of a catalyst.
    b. requires a greater activation energy than Reaction "2."
    c. is the same as Reaction "1," but faster.
    d. takes longer than Reaction "2."

    ANS: A   DIF: II   OBJ: 2-2.2

21. Refer to the graph above. Which of these statements is true regarding the graph?
    a. Reaction "2" occurs faster than Reaction "3" because Reaction "2" requires more
       energy than Reaction "3."
    b. The difference in the graphs shown for Reaction "2" and Reaction "3" is due to a
       difference in the activation energy needed for these reactions.
    c. Reactant "A" contains more energy at the beginning of the reaction than Product
       "C" has after the reaction.
    d. All of the above

    ANS: B   DIF: II   OBJ: 2-2.2

Modern Biology Assessment Item Listing
14

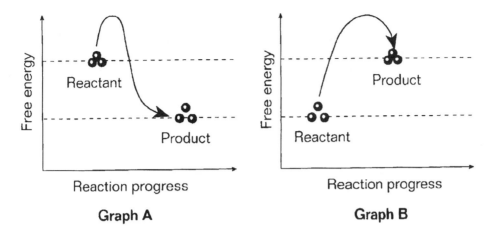

Graph A   **Graph B**

22. Refer to the graphs above. Which graph illustrates what happens during an exergonic reaction?
    a. Graph "A"
    b. Graph "B"
    c. Both graphs; they each show a different stage of an exergonic reaction
    d. Neither graph shows an exergonic reaction

    ANS: A   DIF: I   OBJ: 2-2.2

23. Refer to the graphs above. Which graph illustrates a reaction during which reaction energy is released into the environment?
    a. Graph "A"
    b. Graph "B"
    c. Both graphs,since all chemical reactions release energy into the environment
    d. Neither graph, since chemical reactions do not involve energy

    ANS: A   DIF: I   OBJ: 2-2.2

24. Changing the course or pathway of a chemical reaction so that it requires less activation energy
    a. is a violation of the laws of nature.
    b. requires higher temperatures than those found within cells.
    c. occurs only when reactants are quickly added to the reaction mixture.
    d. is accomplished by the action of catalysts on reactants.

    ANS: D   DIF: I   OBJ: 2-2.2

25. Enzymes
    a. are able to heat up molecules so that they can react.
    b. provide CO_2 for chemical reactions.
    c. are biological catalysts.
    d. absorb excess heat so that reactions occur at low temperatures.

    ANS: C   DIF: I   OBJ: 2-2.3

26. A cell contains
    a. thousands of different kinds of enzymes, each promoting a different chemical reaction.
    b. one kind of enzyme that promotes thousands of different chemical reactions.
    c. approximately 100 kinds of enzymes, each promoting a different chemical reaction.
    d. one enzyme that promotes photosynthesis and one enzyme that promotes cellular respiration.

    ANS: A   DIF: I   OBJ: 2-2.3

27. When a molecule gains an electron and an accompanying hydrogen atom, it has been
    a. oxidized.   c. digested.
    b. reduced.   d. inactivated.

    ANS: B   DIF: I   OBJ: 2-2.4

28. Oxidation-reduction reactions are important in organisms because they
    a. allow the passage of energy from molecule to molecule.
    b. prevent nuclear reactions from occurring.
    c. allow the creation and destruction of energy.
    d. None of the above; oxidation-reduction reactions do not occur in living organisms.

    ANS: A   DIF: I   OBJ: 2-2.4

29. The concentration of a solution is
    a. the number of particles of a substance in a solution.
    b. the amount of a solvent that is dissolved in a fixed amount of a solution.
    c. the amount of a solute that is dissolved in a fixed amount of a solution.
    d. the ratio of solute to solvent in a solution.

    ANS: A   DIF: II   OBJ: 2-3.1

30. A neutral solution has an equal number of
    a. hydrogen and hydronium ions.   c. hydrogen and hydroxide ions.
    b. hydroxide and hydronium ions.   d. oxygen and hydrogen ions.

    ANS: B   DIF: II   OBJ: 2-3.2

31. The terms *base* and *alkaline* refer to solutions that
    a. contain dissolved sodium hydroxide.
    b. contain more hydronium ions than hydroxide ions.
    c. contain more hydroxide ions than hydronium ions.
    d. contain more hydroxide ions than hydrogen ions.

    ANS: C   DIF: II   OBJ: 2-3.3

32. A solution with a pH of 11 is
    a. acidic.   c. neutral.
    b. basic.   d. a buffer.

    ANS: B   DIF: I   OBJ: 2-3.4

33. Acidic solutions have a pH that is
   a. less than 7.
   b. between 0 and 14.
   c. a negative number.
   d. more than 7.

   ANS: A   DIF: I   OBJ: 2-3.4

34. Buffers
   a. are of relatively little importance in living things.
   b. are formed when a large number of hydroxide ions are released in a solution.
   c. are formed when a large number of hydronium ions are released in a solution.
   d. tend to prevent great fluctuations in pH.

   ANS: D   DIF: II   OBJ: 2-3.5

COMPLETION

1. _____ is defined as the ability to cause change or to do work.

   ANS: Energy   DIF: I   OBJ: 2-2.2

2. Substances that are changed when they become involved in chemical reactions are called _____, while the new substances that are formed are called _____.

   ANS: reactants, products   DIF: I   OBJ: 2-2.2

3. The energy needed to break existing chemical bonds during the initiation of a chemical reaction is called _____.

   ANS: activation energy   DIF: I   OBJ: 2-2.2

4. Chemical reactions can be sped up by adding a(n) _____, which lowers the amount of activation energy required to start the reaction.

   ANS: enzyme   DIF: I   OBJ: 2-2.3

5. The loss of electrons from a molecule is called _____, while the gain of electrons by a molecule is called _____.

   ANS: oxidation; reduction   DIF: I   OBJ: 2-2.4

6. A substance that dissolves in another is called a(n) _____.

   ANS: solute   DIF: I   OBJ: 2-3.1

7. _____ is the most common solvent in cells.

   ANS: Water   DIF: I   OBJ: 2-3.1

8. _____ and _____ ions form when water dissociates.

   ANS: Hydroxide; hydrogen   DIF: I   OBJ: 2-3.2

9. An acidic solution is one that has more _____ than
_____ ions.

ANS: hydronium; hydroxide   DIF: I   OBJ: 2-3.3

10. A solution with a pH of 3 has _____ times more hydronium ions than
a solution with a pH of 6.

ANS: 1,000   DIF: II   OBJ: 2-3.4

11. Buffers are important because body fluids must be maintained within a relatively narrow
range of _____.

ANS: pH   DIF: I   OBJ: 2-3.5

PROBLEM

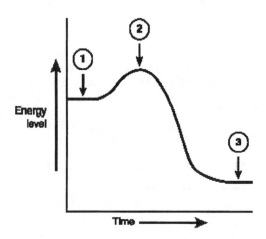

1. Refer to the illustration above. The graph depicts the relative energy levels of the
products and reactants for the following chemical reaction: A + B ↔ C + D. Write your
answers to the following in the spaces below.
   a. Which substances, A, B, C, and/or D, are present at point "1" on the graph?
   b. Which substances, A, B, C, and/or D, are present at point "3" on the graph?
   c. Why is point "2" at a higher energy level than point "1"?
   d. Why is point "3" at a lower energy level than point "1"?
   e. Draw a dashed line on the graph indicating how the energy level of this reaction over
      time would be different if the enzyme that catalyzes the reaction were not present.

ANS:
   a. A and B
   b. C and D
   c. An input of energy, called the activation energy, is required in order to get the
      reaction going.
   d. This is an exergonic reaction. The products contain less energy than the reactants
      and energy is given off in the reaction.
   e. The graph should be the same except that the energy level at point "2" should be
      higher.

DIF: III   OBJ: 2-2.2

ESSAY

1. Plant growers often use sprinkler irrigation to protect crops they are growing from frost damage. The water that lands on the leaves turns to ice. How does this protect the plants from frost damage? Write your answer in the space below.

   ANS:
   Water, as well as any other form of matter, requires an input of thermal energy to change from a solid to a liquid state. It therefore must also give off thermal energy when it changes from a liquid to a solid state. When liquid water turns to ice on plant leaves, it gives off thermal energy that warms the leaves.

   DIF: III   OBJ: 2-2.1

2. Describe how an enzyme can function in speeding up a chemical reaction within a cell. Write your answer in the space below.

   ANS:
   Enzymes are biological catalysts. They are proteins with specific three-dimensional shapes that allow them to bind to particular substrate molecules. Once attached, the enzymes allow substrates to interact, lowering the activation energy that would otherwise be required for this reaction to occur.

   DIF: II   OBJ: 2-2.3

TRUE/FALSE

1. Because water is a polar molecule, it tends to cause ionic compounds mixed in water to dissociate into ions.

    ANS: T   DIF: I   OBJ: 3-1.2

2. Capillarity is apparent when you put a straw in water and the water level inside the straw rises higher than the level in the surrounding container.

    ANS: T   DIF: II   OBJ: 3-1.3

3. Organic compounds are substances produced and found in living things.

    ANS: T   DIF: II   OBJ: 3-2.1

4. Functional groups are side groups of carbon compounds that confer specific properties to these compounds.

    ANS: T   DIF: I   OBJ: 3-2.3

MULTIPLE CHOICE

1. Nonpolar molecules have
    a. no negative or positive poles.
    b. both negative and positive poles.
    c. only a negative pole.
    d. only a positive pole.

    ANS: A   DIF: I   OBJ: 3-1.1

2. A molecule that has a partial positive charge on one side and a partial negative charge on the other side is called a
    a. nonpolar molecule.
    b. polar molecule.
    c. charged molecule.
    d. bipolar molecule.

    ANS: B   DIF: I   OBJ: 3-1.1

3. Water is important to life because it
    a. surrounds all cells.
    b. is found inside cells.
    c. influences the shape of a cell membrane.
    d. All of the above

    ANS: D   DIF: I   OBJ: 3-1.1

4. Water is a polar molecule because
    a. it contains two hydrogen atoms for each oxygen atom.
    b. it has a charge.
    c. different parts of the molecule have slightly different charges.
    d. it does not have a charge.

    ANS: C   DIF: I   OBJ: 3-1.1

5. Water molecules break up other polar substances,
   a. such as sugars.
   b. because of the uneven charge distribution that exists in water molecules.
   c. thus freeing ions in these substances for use by the body.
   d. All of the above

   ANS: D   DIF: II   OBJ: 3-1.2

6. Which of the following characteristics of water is *not* a result of hydrogen bonding?
   a. adhesive strength
   b. capillarity
   c. cohesive strength
   d. All of the above are a result of hydrogen bonding.

   ANS: D   DIF: I   OBJ: 3-1.3

7. All organic compounds contain the element
   a. C.   c. Ca.
   b. N.   d. Na.

   ANS: A   DIF: I   OBJ: 3-2.1

8. Which three elements are often found in organic compounds?
   a. carbon, hydrogen, and oxygen   c. nitrogen, hydrogen, and oxygen
   b. carbon, hydrogen, and neon   d. nitrogen, chlorine, and phosphorus

   ANS: A   DIF: I   OBJ: 3-2.1

9. Carbon is different from most other elements in that
   a. it has four electrons in its outermost energy level.
   b. it readily bonds with other carbon atoms.
   c. it can form single, double, or triple bonds with other atoms.
   d. it shares two electrons with another atom when it forms a covalent bond.

   ANS: B   DIF: II   OBJ: 3-2.2

10. Which of the following is *not* true of alcohols?
    a. They contain a hydroxyl group (–OH).
    b. They are polar molecules.
    c. They can affect processes in living things, either positively or negatively.
    d. They are the only kind of functional group in organic molecules that contain oxygen.

    ANS: D   DIF: II   OBJ: 3-2.3

11. The formation of ADP and inorganic phosphate from ATP and water is an example of which kind of reaction?
    a. condensation   c. hydrolysis
    b. polymerization   d. endergonic

    ANS: C   DIF: II   OBJ: 3-2.4

12. Which of the following is a carbohydrate?
    a. DNA
    b. insulin
    c. wax
    d. sucrose

    ANS: D   DIF: I   OBJ: 3-3.1

13. Which organic molecule below is classified as a carbohydrate?
    a. amino acids
    b. CH$_2$ chains
    c. nucleotides
    d. sugars

    ANS: D   DIF: I   OBJ: 3-3.1

14. Animals store glucose-containing fragments in the form of
    a. cellulose.
    b. glycogen.
    c. wax.
    d. lipids.

    ANS: B   DIF: I   OBJ: 3-3.1

15. Polysaccharides are
    a. carbohydrates.
    b. lipids.
    c. proteins.
    d. unsaturated fats.

    ANS: A   DIF: I   OBJ: 3-3.1

16. All of the following are examples of carbohydrates *except*
    a. sugar.
    b. cellulose.
    c. steroids.
    d. glycogen.

    ANS: C   DIF: I   OBJ: 3-3.1

17. Amino acids are monomers of
    a. disaccharides.
    b. proteins.
    c. nucleotides.
    d. steroids.

    ANS: B   DIF: I   OBJ: 3-3.2

18. Which organic molecule below is most closely related to proteins?
    a. amino acids
    b. CH$_2$ chains
    c. nucleotides
    d. sugars

    ANS: A   DIF: I   OBJ: 3-3.2

19. Long chains of amino acids are found in
    a. carbohydrates.
    b. lipids.
    c. proteins.
    d. sugars.

    ANS: C   DIF: I   OBJ: 3-3.2

20. Amino acids are monomers of
    a. disaccharides.
    b. proteins.
    c. nucleotides.
    d. steroids.

    ANS: B   DIF: I   OBJ: 3-3.2

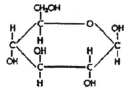

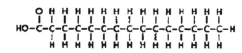

Molecule A   Molecule B

21. Refer to the illustration above. Molecules like Molecule "B" are found in
    a. carbohydrates.   c. nucleic acids.
    b. lipids.   d. proteins.

    ANS: B   DIF: II   OBJ: 3-3.3

22. Lipids are
    a. polar molecules.   c. protein molecules.
    b. similar to water molecules.   d. nonpolar molecules.

    ANS: D   DIF: I   OBJ: 3-3.3

23. All of the following are examples of lipids *except*
    a. saturated fats.   c. cholesterol.
    b. starch.   d. earwax.

    ANS: B   DIF: I   OBJ: 3-3.3

24. Liquid fats called oils contain
    a. long CH_2 chains linked by double covalent bonds.
    b. fat molecules lined up side-by-side.
    c. many glucose molecules.
    d. more hydrogen atoms than hard fats.

    ANS: A   DIF: I   OBJ: 3-3.3

25. Lipids are soluble in
    a. water.   c. oil.
    b. salt water.   d. All of the above

    ANS: C   DIF: I   OBJ: 3-3.3

26. Which organic molecule below is most closely related to lipids?
    a. amino acids   c. nucleotides
    b. CH_2 chains   d. sugars

    ANS: B   DIF: I   OBJ: 3-3.3

27. Which of the following is *not* an organic macromolecule?
    a. carbohydrate   c. lipid
    b. ice   d. nucleic acid

    ANS: B   DIF: I   OBJ: 3-3.4

28. Which organic molecule below is most closely related to nucleic acids?
    a. amino acids
    b. CH$_2$ chains
    c. nucleotides
    d. sugars

    ANS: C   DIF: I   OBJ: 3-3.4

29. Nucleic acids include
    a. chlorophyll and retinal.
    b. DNA and RNA.
    c. lipids and sugars.
    d. glucose and glycogen.

    ANS: B   DIF: I   OBJ: 3-3.4

COMPLETION

1. Water is very effective at dissolving other polar substances because of its
   _____.

   ANS: polarity   DIF: I   OBJ: 3-1.2

2. Breaking of _____ bonds is the first thing that happens when water is
   heated, which means that it takes a great deal of thermal energy to raise the temperature
   of water.

   ANS: hydrogen   DIF: I   OBJ: 3-1.3

3. Because carbon atoms have four electrons in their outermost energy level, they tend to
   form _____ covalent bonds with other atoms.

   ANS: four   DIF: I   OBJ: 3-2.2

4. In the molecule that has the chemical formula C$_2$H$_4$, the carbon atoms are bonded
   together with a _____ bond.

   ANS: double   DIF: III   OBJ: 3-2.2

5. Because oxygen atoms tend to attract positively charged atoms, organic compounds that
   contain oxygen atoms tend to form _____ bonds.

   ANS: hydrogen   DIF: II   OBJ: 3-2.3

6. In a condensation reaction, two molecules become linked together and a molecule of
   _____ is produced.

   ANS: water   DIF: I   OBJ: 3-2.4

7. The formation of polymers from monomers occurs as a result of
   _____ reactions, and the breakdown of polymers into monomers
   occurs as a result of _____ reactions.

   ANS: condensation; hydrolysis   DIF: I   OBJ: 3-2.4

8. Lipids are _____ molecules because they have no negative and positive poles.

    ANS: nonpolar   DIF: I   OBJ: 3-3.3

9. A phospholipid is a molecule with a(n) _____ head.

    ANS: polar   DIF: I   OBJ: 3-3.3

10. Lipids are _____ molecules because they have no negative and positive poles.

    ANS: nonpolar   DIF: I   OBJ: 3-3.3

11. A phospholipid is a molecule with a(n) _____ head.

    ANS: polar   DIF: I   OBJ: 3-3.3

PROBLEM

1. You are given four test tubes containing purified biological macromolecules. The test tubes are unlabeled except for a number between 1 and 4. You are told that one test tube contains a protein, one contains a lipid, one contains a carbohydrate, and one contains a nucleic acid. You then perform some tests on the macromolecules and collect the following information:

    1) Test tubes #2 and #4 contain nitrogen, but the other tubes do not.
    2) The contents of test tube #3 are not soluble in water, but the contents of the other test tubes are soluble in water.
    3) The contents of test tube #1 can be broken down into subunits that are all exactly identical to each other.
    4) The macromolecule in test tube #2 is found to have a globular shape.

What are the identities of the macromolecules present in the four test tubes? Write your answer in the space below.

ANS:
Test tube #1 contains a carbohydrate.
Test tube #2 contains a protein.
Test tube #3 contains a lipid.
Test tube #4 contains a nucleic acid.

DIF: II   OBJ: 3-3.4

TRUE/FALSE

1. Robert Hooke observed cork cells under a microscope.

    ANS: T   DIF: I   OBJ: 4-1.1

2. Anton van Leeuwenhoek concluded that all plants are composed of cells.

    ANS: F   DIF: I   OBJ: 4-1.1

3. All living things are composed of many cells.

    ANS: F   DIF: I   OBJ: 4-1.2

4. A cell is the smallest unit that can carry on all the processes of life.

    ANS: T   DIF: I   OBJ: 4-1.2

5. As a cell gets larger, its volume increases at a faster rate than its surface area.

    ANS: T   DIF: I   OBJ: 4-1.3

6. Inside smaller cells, materials and information can be transported more quickly.

    ANS: T   DIF: I   OBJ: 4-1.3

7. The long extensions on nerve cells enable them to form a rigid scaffolding that gives brain tissue its structure.

    ANS: F   DIF: I   OBJ: 4-1.4

8. Most living prokaryotes are multicellular protists.

    ANS: F   DIF: I   OBJ: 4-1.5

9. The cells of animals are prokaryotes.

    ANS: F   DIF: I   OBJ: 4-1.5

10. All living things that are not bacteria are eukaryotes.

    ANS: T   DIF: I   OBJ: 4-1.5

11. Cell surface proteins float on top of phospholipid bilayers.

    ANS: F   DIF: I   OBJ: 4-2.1

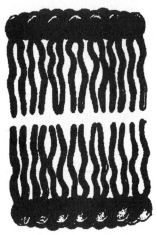

12. Refer to the illustration above. The diagram shows the lipid bilayer that forms the framework of the cell membrane.

    ANS: T   DIF: II   OBJ: 4-2.1

13. Membranes are selectively permeable if they allow only certain substances to diffuse across them.

    ANS: T   DIF: I   OBJ: 4-2.1

14. Organelles enable eukaryotic cells to specialize.

    ANS: T   DIF: I   OBJ: 4-2.2

15. Lysosomes carry on cellular respiration.

    ANS: F   DIF: I   OBJ: 4-2.2

16. DNA stores information that directs the activities of a cell.

    ANS: T   DIF: I   OBJ: 4-2.2

17. Microtubules and microfilaments form the cytoskeleton of cells.

    ANS: T   DIF: I   OBJ: 4-2.2

18. The only difference between a plant cell and an animal cell is that plant cells have chloroplasts.

    ANS: F   DIF: I   OBJ: 4-2.4

19. Colonial organisms differ from single-celled organisms in that each cell cannot support its own existence.

    ANS: F   DIF: I   OBJ: 4-3.2

MULTIPLE CHOICE

1. Hooke's discovery of cells was made observing
   a. living algal cells.
   b. living human blood cells.
   c. dead plant cells.
   d. dead protist cells.

   ANS: C   DIF: I   OBJ: 4-1.1

2. The smallest units of life in all living things are
   a. cells.
   b. mitochondria.
   c. cytoplasm.
   d. Golgi apparatus.

   ANS: A   DIF: I   OBJ: 4-1.2

3. When the volume of a cell increases, its surface area
   a. increases at the same rate.
   b. remains the same.
   c. increases at a faster rate.
   d. increases at a slower rate.

   ANS: D   DIF: I   OBJ: 4-1.3

4. Surface area is an important factor in limiting cell growth because
   a. the cell can burst if the membrane becomes too large.
   b. materials cannot enter the cell if it is too large.
   c. the cell may become too large to take in enough food and to remove enough wastes.
   d. waste products cannot leave the cell if it is too small.

   ANS: C   DIF: I   OBJ: 4-1.3

5. The size to which a cell can grow is limited by its
   a. location.
   b. structure.
   c. function.
   d. surface area.

   ANS: D   DIF: I   OBJ: 4-1.3

6. A cell that can change its shape would be well suited for
   a. receiving and transmitting nerve impulses.
   b. covering the body surface.
   c. moving to different tissues through narrow openings.
   d. All of the above

   ANS: C   DIF: II   OBJ: 4-1.4

7. One difference between prokaryotes and eukaryotes is that
   a. nucleic acids are found only in prokaryotes.
   b. mitochondria are found in larger quantities in eukaryotes.
   c. Golgi vesicles are found only in prokaryotes.
   d. prokaryotes have no nuclear membrane.

   ANS: D   DIF: I   OBJ: 4-1.5

8. Which of the following is characteristic of prokaryotes?
   a. They have a nucleus.
   b. They were found on Earth before eukaryotes.
   c. The organelles in their cytoplasm are surrounded by membranes.
   d. None of the above

   ANS: B   DIF: I   OBJ: 4-1.5

9. Which of the following is an example of a prokaryotic cell?
   a. amoeba   c. bacterium
   b. virus   d. liver cell

   ANS: C   DIF: I   OBJ: 4-1.5

10. Only eukaryotic cells have
    a. DNA.   c. ribosomes.
    b. membrane-bound organelles.   d. cytoplasm.

    ANS: B   DIF: I   OBJ: 4-1.5

11. Studying a picture of a cell taken with an electron microscope, you find that the cell has
    no nucleus and no mitochondria, but it does have a cell membrane and a cell wall. You
    conclude that the cell is probably from a(n)
    a. animal.   c. prokaryote.
    b. plant.   d. now extinct organism.

    ANS: C   DIF: I   OBJ: 4-1.5

12. Cell membranes
    a. are only found on a small number of cells.
    b. contain genes.
    c. are made of DNA.
    d. are thin coverings that surround cells.

    ANS: D   DIF: I   OBJ: 4-2.1

13. The structure that regulates what enters and leaves the cell is called
    a. the nucleus.   c. the nuclear membrane.
    b. the cell wall.   d. the cell membrane.

    ANS: D   DIF: I   OBJ: 4-2.1

14. A protein that fits into the cell membrane
    a. has two polar end sections that bond with water.
    b. floats in the cell membrane.
    c. has a nonpolar middle section.
    d. All of the above

    ANS: D   DIF: I   OBJ: 4-2.1

15. Cell membranes
    a. are only found on a small number of cells.
    b. contain genes.
    c. are made of DNA.
    d. are thin coverings that surround cells.

    ANS: D   DIF: I   OBJ: 4-2.1

16. The cell membrane
    a. encloses the contents of a cell.
    b. allows material to enter and leave the cell.
    c. is selectively permeable.
    d. All of the above

    ANS: D   DIF: I   OBJ: 4-2.1

17. The shape of a protein is determined by
    a. the type and order of its amino acids.   c. its cell location.
    b. its size.   d. None of the above

    ANS: A   DIF: I   OBJ: 4-2.1

18. A structure within a cell that performs a specific function is called a(n)
    a. organelle.   c. tissue.
    b. organ tissue.   d. biocenter.

    ANS: A   DIF: I   OBJ: 4-2.2

19. A particularly active cell might contain large numbers of
    a. chromosomes.   c. mitochondria.
    b. vacuoles.   d. walls.

    ANS: C   DIF: I   OBJ: 4-2.2

20. Golgi apparatus are organelles that
    a. receive proteins and lipids from the endoplasmic reticulum.
    b. label the molecules made in the endoplasmic reticulum with tags that specify their
       destination.
    c. release molecules in vesicles.
    d. All of the above

    ANS: D   DIF: I   OBJ: 4-2.2

21. One important organelle that helps maintain homeostasis by moving supplies from one
    part of the cell to the other is the
    a. endoplasmic reticulum.   c. Golgi apparatus.
    b. mitochondrion.   d. cytoplasm.

    ANS: A   DIF: I   OBJ: 4-2.2

22. In which of the following organelles is a cell's ATP produced?
    a. mitochondrion   c. Golgi apparatus
    b. endoplasmic reticulum   d. lysosome

    ANS: A   DIF: I   OBJ: 4-2.2

23. Numerous threadlike organelles that protrude from the surface of a cell and are packed in
    tight rows are called
    a. flagella.   c. actin filaments.
    b. microtubules.   d. cilia.

    ANS: D   DIF: I   OBJ: 4-2.2

24. Proteins are made in cells on the
    a. mitochondria.   c. nucleus.
    b. ribosomes.   d. cell membrane.

    ANS: B   DIF: I   OBJ: 4-2.2

25. The packaging and distribution center of the cell is the
    a. nucleus.   c. central vacuole.
    b. Golgi apparatus.   d. nuclear envelope.

    ANS: B   DIF: I   OBJ: 4-2.2

26. The double membrane surrounding the nucleus is called the
    a. nucleolus.   c. nucleoplasm.
    b. nuclear wall.   d. nuclear envelope.

    ANS: D   DIF: I   OBJ: 4-2.3

27. All cells have
    a. a covering called a membrane that surrounds the cell and controls what information
        and materials enter and leave it.
    b. an internal fluid that gives shape to the cell and supports the other things within it.
    c. a central zone or nucleus that contains the cell's genes.
    d. All of the above

    ANS: D   DIF: I   OBJ: 4-2.3

28. cell : cell membrane ::
    a. nucleus : chromosome   c. chromosome : DNA
    b. nucleus : nuclear envelope   d. cell : DNA

    ANS: B   DIF: II   OBJ: 4-2.3

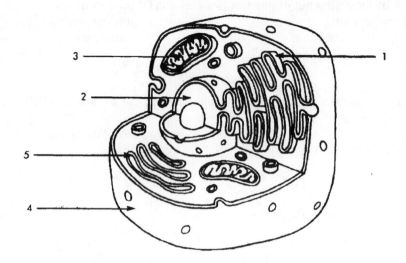

29. Refer to the illustration above. Which structure immediately identifies this cell as a eukaryote?
    a. structure "1"
    b. structure "2"
    c. structure "3"
    d. structure "4"

    ANS: B   DIF: II   OBJ: 4-1.5

30. Refer to the illustration above. The cell uses structure "3"
    a. to transport material from one part of the cell to the other.
    b. to package proteins so they can be stored by the cell.
    c. as a receptor.
    d. to produce energy.

    ANS: D   DIF: II   OBJ: 4-2.2

31. Refer to the illustration above. Structure "1" is
    a. the endoplasmic reticulum.
    b. a Golgi apparatus.
    c. a mitochondrion.
    d. the nucleus.

    ANS: A   DIF: II   OBJ: 4-2.2

32. Refer to the illustration above. In eukaryotic cells, chromosomes are found in
    a. structure "1."
    b. structure "2."
    c. structure "3."
    d. structure "5."

    ANS: B   DIF: II   OBJ: 4-2.3

33. Refer to the illustration above. The cell shown is probably an animal cell because
    a. it has mitochondria.
    b. it does not have a cell wall.
    c. it has a cell membrane.
    d. it does not have a nucleus.

    ANS: B   DIF: II   OBJ: 4-2.4

34. All the following are found in both plant and animal cells, *except*
   a. a cell wall.
   b. a cell membrane.
   c. mitochondria.
   d. the endoplasmic reticulum.

ANS: A   DIF: I   OBJ: 4-2.4

35. How are chloroplasts like mitochondria?
   a. They can both use energy from sunlight.
   b. They look alike.
   c. They both manufacture food and release energy.
   d. They are both found in animal cells.

ANS: C   DIF: I   OBJ: 4-2.4

36. The organelles associated with photosynthesis are the
   a. mitochondria.
   b. chloroplasts.
   c. Golgi apparatus.
   d. vacuoles.

ANS: B   DIF: I   OBJ: 4-2.4

37. The organelles in plant cells that contain a green pigment are the
   a. mitochondria.
   b. bilayer lipids.
   c. chloroplasts.
   d. Golgi apparatus.

ANS: C   DIF: I   OBJ: 4-2.4

38. Plant cells have large membrane-bound spaces in which water, waste products, and nutrients are stored. These places are known as
   a. mitochondria.
   b. chloroplasts.
   c. Golgi apparatus.
   d. vacuoles.

ANS: D   DIF: I   OBJ: 4-2.4

39. Which of the following pairs contains unrelated items?
   a. eukaryote–amoeba
   b. ribosomes–protein
   c. cell wall–animal cell
   d. mitochondria–energy

ANS: C   DIF: I   OBJ: 4-2.4

40. Plant cells
   a. do not contain mitochondria.
   b. have a cell wall instead of a cell membrane.
   c. have a large vacuole instead of a Golgi apparatus.
   d. have chloroplasts and a cell wall.

ANS: D   DIF: I   OBJ: 4-2.4

41. Which of the following is the correct order of organization of structures in living things, from simplest to most complex?
   a. organ systems, organs, tissues, cells
   b. tissues, cells, organs, organ systems
   c. cells, tissues, organ systems, organs
   d. cells, tissues, organs, organ systems

ANS: D   DIF: I   OBJ: 4-3.1

42. Which of the following associations between a type of animal tissue and its primary function is *incorrect*?
   a. connective tissue—transport of substances around the body
   b. epithelial tissue—protective surface coverings
   c. muscle tissue—contraction
   d. nervous tissue—receiving and transmitting messages

   ANS: A   DIF: I   OBJ: 4-3.1

43. Which of the following is *not* a specialized activity found in cells of *Volvox* colonies?
   a. photosynthesis   c. movement
   b. transmission of messages   d. reproduction

   ANS: B   DIF: II   OBJ: 4-3.2

COMPLETION

1. The statement that "cells are produced only from existing cells" is part of the
   _____.

   ANS: cell theory   DIF: I   OBJ: 4-1.2

2. The ratio of surface area to volume puts limitations on a cell's
   _____.

   ANS: size   DIF: I   OBJ: 4-1.3

3. Eukaryotic cells are much larger and have more specialized functions than prokaryotic cells because they contain _____ which take up space and carry out specialized activities.

   ANS: organelles   DIF: II   OBJ: 4-1.4

4. A cell with a well-defined nucleus surrounded by a nuclear membrane is called a(n) _____ cell.

   ANS: eukaryotic   DIF: I   OBJ: 4-1.5

5. A cell membrane is said to be _____ permeable because it allows the passage of some solutes and not others.

   ANS: selectively   DIF: I   OBJ: 4-2.1

6. _____ molecules have "heads" and "tails" and are found in the cell membrane.

   ANS: Lipid   DIF: I   OBJ: 4-2.1

7. Scientists have discovered that cells contain smaller specialized structures known as
   _____.

   ANS: organelles   DIF: I   OBJ: 4-2.2

8. The spherical organelles that are the site of protein synthesis in a cell are the

   _____.

   ANS: ribosomes DIF: I OBJ: 4-2.2

9. The meshlike network of protein fibers that supports the shape of the cell is called the

   _____.

   ANS: cytoskeleton DIF: I OBJ: 4-2.2

10. The fluid portion of the cytoplasm is called the _____.

    ANS: cytosol DIF: I OBJ: 4-2.2

11. Photosynthesis takes place in the _____ of plant cells.

    ANS: chloroplasts DIF: I OBJ: 4-2.4

12. Both plant and animal cells have cell membranes. In addition, plant cells are surrounded by a(n) _____.

    ANS: cell wall DIF: I OBJ: 4-2.4

13. Colonial organisms are like multicellular organisms in that they have

    _____.

    ANS: cell specialization DIF: I OBJ: 4-3.2

PROBLEM

1. A living cell has certain characteristics in common with a working factory. In a factory, products are assembled according to specified plans, energy is used in the assembly process, products are packaged and taken out of the factory, and a supervisor directs and oversees all of the activities occurring in the factory. Draw a model of a factory, labeling areas where the following important activities would occur: main office where supervisor keeps the plans and oversees activities, assembly line, electricity generator, packaging center, and factory doors. Next to each of your labels, write the name of the cellular organelle or structure that has a similar function. Choose the cellular organelles and structures from the list that follows: nucleus, cytoplasm, cell membrane, mitochondrion, endoplasmic reticulum, Golgi apparatus, vacuole. Write your answer in the space below.

   ANS:
   main office—nucleus
   assembly line—endoplasmic reticulum
   electricity generator—mitochondrion
   packaging center—Golgi apparatus
   factory doors—cell membrane

   DIF: III OBJ: 4-2.3

ESSAY

1. How are the organs of a multicellular organism like the organelles of a single cell? Write your answer in the space below.

ANS:
The organs of a multicellular organism each carry out specialized tasks that enable the whole organism to survive. Similarly, organelles of a single cell each carry out specialized tasks that enable the whole cell to survive.

DIF: III   OBJ: 4-3.1

TRUE/FALSE

1. Diffusion is an active process that requires a cell to expend a great deal of energy.

    ANS: F   DIF: I   OBJ: 5-1.1

2. During diffusion, molecules diffuse from a region where their concentration is low to a region where their concentration is higher until they are evenly dispersed.

    ANS: F   DIF: I   OBJ: 5-1.1

3. A cell placed in a strong salt solution would probably burst because of an increase in osmotic pressure.

    ANS: F   DIF: I   OBJ: 5-1.2

4. When the concentration of solutes outside the cell is equal to the concentration of solutes inside the cell, the cell solution is isotonic relative to its environment.

    ANS: T   DIF: I   OBJ: 5-1.2

5. Diffusion occurs only in living systems.

    ANS: F   DIF: I   OBJ: 5-1.2

6. The transport of specific particles through a membrane by carrier proteins is known as facilitated diffusion.

    ANS: T   DIF: I   OBJ: 5-1.3

7. Ion channels are usually able to transport only one type of ion.

    ANS: T   DIF: I   OBJ: 5-1.4

8. Facilitated diffusion moves molecules and ions in one direction only, while active transport moves them in two directions.

    ANS: F   DIF: I   OBJ: 5-2.1

9. In active transport, energy is required to move a substance across a cell membrane.

    ANS: T   DIF: I   OBJ: 5-2.1

10. Both the sodium-potassium pump and the proton pump require energy to move particles across the cell membrane.

    ANS: T   DIF: I   OBJ: 5-2.2

11. The sodium-potassium pump moves sodium and potassium ions against the concentration gradient.

ANS: T   DIF: I   OBJ: 5-2.2

12. Exocytosis helps the cell rid itself of wastes.

ANS: T   DIF: I   OBJ: 5-2.3

13. During the process of exocytosis, the cell membrane extends to engulf substances that are too big to pass through the cell membrane.

ANS: F   DIF: I   OBJ: 5-2.3

MULTIPLE CHOICE

1. As a result of diffusion, the concentration of many types of substances
   a. always remains greater inside a membrane.
   b. eventually becomes balanced on both sides of a membrane.
   c. always remains greater on the outside of a membrane.
   d. becomes imbalanced on both sides of a membrane.

ANS: B   DIF: I   OBJ: 5-1.1

2. Diffusion takes place
   a. only through a lipid bilayer membrane.
   b. from an area of low concentration to an area of high concentration.
   c. only in liquids.
   d. from an area of high concentration to an area of low concentration.

ANS: D   DIF: I   OBJ: 5-1.1

Concentration of Water and Solutes in Four Adjacent Cells

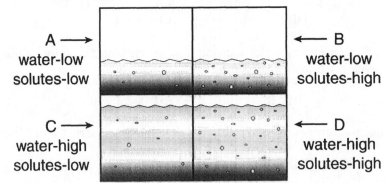

3. Refer to the illustration above. Which cell is most likely to lose both water molecules and solute molecules as the system approaches equilibrium?
   a. cell "A"   c. cell "C"
   b. cell "B"   d. cell "D"

ANS: D   DIF: II   OBJ: 5-1.2

4. Refer to the illustration above. In this system, solute molecules in cell "B" are most likely to
   a. remain in cell "B."
   b. adhere to cell "B's" membrane.
   c. diffuse into cell "A."
   d. diffuse into cell "D."

   ANS: C   DIF: II   OBJ: 5-1.2

5. Refer to the illustration above. In this system, water molecules are most likely to diffuse in which direction?
   a. from "A" to "B"
   b. from "B" to "D"
   c. from "D" to "C"
   d. from "C" to "A"

   ANS: D   DIF: II   OBJ: 5-1.2

6. The dispersal of ink in a beaker of water is an example of
   a. diffusion.
   b. osmosis.
   c. active transport.
   d. endocytosis.

   ANS: A   DIF: I   OBJ: 5-1.2

7. heavy rains : flooding ::
   a. osmosis : proton pumping
   b. high solute concentration : isotonic solution
   c. active transport : ATP
   d. concentration difference : osmosis

   ANS: D   DIF: II   OBJ: 5-1.2

8. Sugar molecules can enter cells through the process of
   a. exocytosis.
   b. facilitated diffusion.
   c. osmosis.
   d. ion pumps.

   ANS: B   DIF: I   OBJ: 5-1.3

9. Channels utilizing facilitated diffusion
   a. work in two directions.
   b. require an electrical signal to function.
   c. Both a and b
   d. None of the above

   ANS: A   DIF: I   OBJ: 5-1.3

10. Which of the following is *not* characteristic of facilitated diffusion?
    a. It requires a carrier protein.
    b. It moves substances against a concentration gradient.
    c. It requires no energy input.
    d. It involves a change in the shape of its carrier.

    ANS: B   DIF: I   OBJ: 5-1.3

11. Which of the following is true of ions and their transport across cell membranes?
    a. The "gates" for ion channels are always open.
    b. Ions are very small and thus can cross cell membranes readily.
    c. Electrical or chemical signals may control the movement of ions across cell membranes.
    d. Because they are charged particles, the movement of ions across cell membranes requires energy input.

    ANS: C   DIF: II   OBJ: 5-1.4

12. Which of the following does *not* expend energy?
    a. diffusion   c. active transport
    b. chemiosmosis   d. a sodium-potassium pump

    ANS: A   DIF: I   OBJ: 5-2.1

13. Which of the following enters a cell by active transport?
    a. glucose   c. sodium ion
    b. water   d. potassium ion

    ANS: D   DIF: I   OBJ: 5-2.1

14. The process by which water passes into or out of a cell is called
    a. solubility.   c. selective transport.
    b. osmosis.   d. endocytosis.

    ANS: B   DIF: I   OBJ: 5-2.2

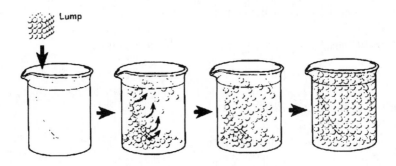

15. Refer to the illustration above. The process shown is called
    a. osmosis.   c. active transport.
    b. facilitated diffusion.   d. diffusion.

    ANS: D   DIF: II   OBJ: 5-2.2

16. The sodium-potassium pump usually pumps
    a. potassium out of the cell.
    b. sodium into the cell.
    c. potassium into the cell.
    d. only a potassium and sugar molecule together.

    ANS: C   DIF: I   OBJ: 5-2.2

Modern Biology Assessment Item Listing
40

17. proton pump : protons ::
    a. ATP : protons
    b. channel : protons
    c. sodium-potassium pump : ATP
    d. sodium-potassium pump : sodium

    ANS: D   DIF: II   OBJ: 5-2.2

18. Ridding the cell of material by discharging it from sacs at the cell surface is called
    a. chemiosmosis.
    b. exorcism.
    c. exocytosis.
    d. endocytosis.

    ANS: C   DIF: I   OBJ: 5-2.3

19. Molecules that are too large to be moved across a cell membrane can be removed from the cell by
    a. diffusion.
    b. exocytosis.
    c. lipid carriers.
    d. osmosis.

    ANS: B   DIF: I   OBJ: 5-2.3

20. Molecules that are too large to be moved through the membrane can be transported into the cell by
    a. osmosis.
    b. endocytosis.
    c. lipid carriers.
    d. diffusion.

    ANS: B   DIF: I   OBJ: 5-2.3

21. endocytosis : exocytosis ::
    a. phagocytosis : bacteria
    b. secrete : exocytosis
    c. cold : hot
    d. white blood cell : bacteria

    ANS: C   DIF: II   OBJ: 5-2.3

COMPLETION

1. Active transport systems are a form of cell transport that requires energy from molecules of _____.

    ANS: ATP   DIF: I   OBJ: 5-2.1

2. _____ allows a cell to stockpile substances in far greater concentrations than they occur outside the cell.

    ANS: Active transport DIF: I   OBJ: 5-2.1

3. The transport of food into cells involves the action of the sodium-potassium pump and _____ channels.

    ANS: coupled   DIF: I   OBJ: 5-2.2

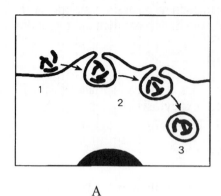

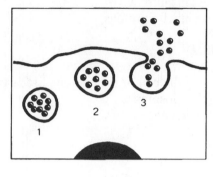

A   B

4. Refer to the illustration above. The process shown in figure "B" is called

_____.

   ANS: exocytosis   DIF: II   OBJ: 5-2.3

5. Refer to the illustration above. Cells often trap extracellular particles and fluid. This is shown in figure _____.

   ANS: "A"   DIF: II   OBJ: 5-2.3

6. The process in which an amoeba engulfs its prey and takes it in is known as

_____.

   ANS: phagocytosis   DIF: I   OBJ: 5-2.3

PROBLEM

Organisms in the genus *Paramecium* are unicellular protists. They have a number of characteristics also found in animals, such as the need to ingest food in order to obtain energy (they are heterotrophs) and they are surrounded by a cell membrane but not by a rigid cell wall. They have organelles found in animal cells, including nuclei, mitochondria, ribosomes, and cilia. In addition, they have star-shaped organelles, called contractile vacuoles, that collect excess water from inside the *Paramecium* and expel it periodically to the outside of the organism. The picture below depicts a *Paramecium*.

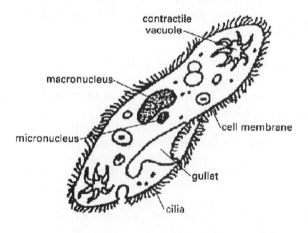

The data presented in the table below were obtained in an experiment in which paramecia were placed in different salt concentrations and the rate at which the contractile vacuole contracted to pump out excess water was recorded.

Salt concentration	Rate of contractile vacuole contractions / minute
Very high	2
High	8
Medium	15
Low	22
Very low	30

1. Refer to the illustration and the table above.
   a. How can you explain the observed relationship between salt concentration and rate of contractile vacuole contraction? Write your answer in the space below.
   b. If something happened to a paramecium that caused its contractile vacuole to stop contracting, what would you expect to happen? Would this result occur more quickly if the paramecium was in water with a high salt concentration or in water with a low salt concentration? Why? Write your answer in the space below.

   ANS:
   a. The contractile vacuole maintains water balance by pumping water outside of the cell. When the salt concentration outside of the cell is very high, water will move from inside to outside the cell—little or no pumping action is required. When the salt concentration outside of the cell is low, the tendency is for water to move from outside to inside the cell, necessitating increased pumping action by the vacuole to move excess water out of the cell.
   b. If the contractile vacuole were to stop contracting, the organism would burst open because water would collect in excess inside of it and the cell membrane would not be strong enough to resist rupturing. This result would be expected to occur more quickly if the organism were placed in water with a low salt concentration than it would if the organism were placed in water with a high salt concentration. This is because water accumulates inside the paramecium more rapidly when it is placed in a low salt environment.

   DIF: III   OBJ: 5-1.2

2. A biologist conducts an experiment designed to determine whether a particular type of molecule is transported into cells by simple diffusion, facilitated diffusion, or active transport. He collects the following information:

1) The molecule is very small.
2) The molecule is polar.
3) The molecule can accumulate inside cells even when its concentration inside the cell initially is higher than it is outside the cell.
4) Cells use up more energy when the molecule is present in the environment around the cells than when it is not present.

The biologist concludes that the molecule moves across cell membranes by facilitated diffusion. Do you agree with his conclusion? Why or why not? Write your answer in the space below.

ANS:
Disagree. The information that cells can accumulate the molecule against a concentration gradient is compelling evidence that active transport is the mechanism of transport. This is the only mechanism among those named that allows movement against a concentration gradient. Active transport also requires energy consumption, which was also found to be a property of transport of this molecule.

DIF: III   OBJ: 5-2.1

ESSAY

1. Why does the addition of a solute with polar molecules to one side of a membrane result in the diffusion of water? Write your answer in the space below.

ANS:
The addition of solutes to one side of a membrane reduces the number of water molecules that can move freely on that side. The water molecules become bound to the polar molecules in the solute. Water then moves by osmosis from the side where water molecule concentration is greatest to the side where concentration is least.

DIF: II   OBJ: 5-1.1

2. Why is it dangerous for humans to drink ocean water? Write your answer in the space below.

ANS:
The concentration of salt in ocean water is higher than the concentration of salt in the fluids that surround the cells in the human body. Drinking ocean water increases the concentration of salt in the body's fluids. This causes water to leave the cells by osmosis, and without the proper amount of water the cells will be harmed or will die.

DIF: II   OBJ: 5-1.2

3. Distinguish facilitated diffusion from active transport. Write your answer in the space below.

ANS:
 Protein channels that assist the diffusion of substances through the cell membrane do so by facilitated diffusion. Facilitated diffusion works in two directions. As long as a molecule or ion fits into the channel, it is free to pass through in either direction. Each kind of molecule or ion diffuses toward the side where it is least concentrated, eventually balancing the concentrations.
 Active transport, on the other hand, allows ions to move through the cell membrane in one direction only, like a turnstile at a subway station. Active transport enables a cell to stockpile certain substances in far greater concentrations than they occur outside the cell. Almost all active transport in cells is carried out by the sodium-potassium pump and the proton pump.

DIF: II   OBJ: 5-2.1

4. Describe the meaning of homeostasis. Write your answer in the space below.

ANS:
To remain alive and function optimally, cells, tissues, organs, and organisms must maintain a biological balance. Cells maintain this balance, or homeostasis, by controlling and regulating cell biology in response to their immediate environment.

DIF: II   OBJ: 5-2.1

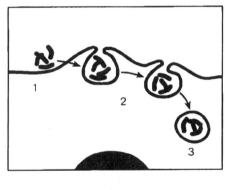

A

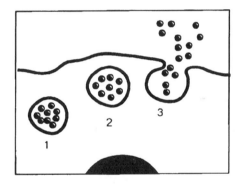

B

5. Refer to the illustration above. Identify and explain the processes taking place in Figure "A" and Figure "B." Write your answer in the space below.

ANS:
Endocytosis is the process taking place in Figure "A." Endocytosis is the process by which cells engulf substances that are too large to enter the cell by passing through the cell membrane. Exocytosis is the process taking place in Figure "B." Exocytosis is the process by which cellular wastes are discharged from sacs at the cell's surface.

DIF: II   OBJ: 5-2.3

CHAPTER 6—PHOTOSYNTHESIS

TRUE/FALSE

1. All organisms require energy to carry out life processes.

    ANS: T   DIF: I   OBJ: 6-1.1

2. Animals that live exclusively on a diet of other animals are unable to use carbohydrates to fuel their life processes.

    ANS: F   DIF: I   OBJ: 6-1.1

3. When light hits a plant, all of the wavelengths are absorbed and used to make sugar.

    ANS: F   DIF: I   OBJ: 6-1.1

4. Photosystems are clusters of light-absorbing pigments located on the thylakoids of a chloroplast.

    ANS: T   DIF: I   OBJ: 6-1.1

5. Most plants are heterotrophic.

    ANS: F   DIF: I   OBJ: 6-1.2

6. Photosynthesis is a process that takes place in autotrophs.

    ANS: T   DIF: I   OBJ: 6-1.2

7. A series of linked chemical reactions in which the product of one chemical reaction serves as the reactant in the next reaction is called a biochemical pathway.

    ANS: T   DIF: I   OBJ: 6-1.2

8. An autotroph is able to make its own organic molecules from inorganic materials and energy.

    ANS: T   DIF: I   OBJ: 6-1.2

9. The major light-absorbing pigment in plants is chlorophyll.

    ANS: T   DIF: I   OBJ: 6-1.2

10. In organisms, when electrons are transferred from one molecule to another, they are usually carried by hydrogen atoms.

    ANS: T   DIF: I   OBJ: 6-1.3

11. Carbon dioxide and water, in the presence of sunlight, will react to form sugars and oxygen gas.

    ANS: T   DIF: I   OBJ: 6-1.4

12. Plant cells use light to make ATP and NADPH.

ANS: T   DIF: I   OBJ: 6-1.5

13. The "light reactions" of photosynthesis can occur only under light conditions, and the "dark reactions" occur only during the dark hours.

ANS: F   DIF: I   OBJ: 6-2.1

14. The final product of photosynthesis is not actually glucose.

ANS: T   DIF: I   OBJ: 6-2.2

15. C_4 and CAM plants use less water to produce the same amount of carbohydrate as C_3 plants.

ANS: T   DIF: I   OBJ: 6-2.3

16. While the rate of photosynthesis is independent of temperature, it has been shown to be markedly affected by changes in light intensity.

ANS: F   DIF: I   OBJ: 6-2.4

MULTIPLE CHOICE

1. Energy is required for a variety of life processes including
   a. growth and reproduction.
   b. movement.
   c. transport of certain materials across cell membranes.
   d. All of the above

ANS: D   DIF: I   OBJ: 6-1.1

2. Heterotrophs are organisms that can
   a. produce food from inorganic molecules and sunlight.
   b. survive without energy.
   c. consume other organisms for energy.
   d. carry out either photosynthesis or chemosynthesis.

ANS: C   DIF: I   OBJ: 6-1.1

3. Based on the cycle of photosynthesis and cellular respiration, one can say that the ultimate original source of energy for all living things on Earth is
   a. carbohydrates.   c. the sun.
   b. water.   d. carbon dioxide.

ANS: C   DIF: I   OBJ: 6-1.1

4. The process whereby plants capture energy and make complex molecules is known as
   a. homeostasis.   c. photosynthesis.
   b. evolution.   d. development.

ANS: C   DIF: I   OBJ: 6-1.1

5. Suspended in the fluid stroma of chloroplasts are
   a. organelles called eukaryotes.
   b. numerous mitochondrial membranes.
   c. small coins that provide energy.
   d. stacks of thylakoids called grana.

   ANS: D   DIF: I   OBJ: 6-1.1

6. electrons : chemical bonds ::
   a. heterotrophs : autotrophs
   b. sunlight : plants
   c. chemical energy : sun
   d. nuclei : atoms

   ANS: B   DIF: II   OBJ: 6-1.1

7. biochemical pathway : energy ::
   a. barrier : reaction
   b. match : burn
   c. carrier : protein
   d. assembly line : workers

   ANS: D   DIF: II   OBJ: 6-1.1

8. light reactions : thylakoids ::
   a. grana : thylakoids
   b. grana : ATP
   c. dark reactions : stroma
   d. stroma : grana of chloroplast

   ANS: C   DIF: II   OBJ: 6-1.1

9. The sun is considered the ultimate source of energy for life on Earth because
   a. all organisms carry out photosynthesis.
   b. all organisms carry out cellular respiration.
   c. either photosynthetic organisms or organisms that have eaten them provide energy
   for all other organisms on Earth.
   d. the sun heats the Earth's atmosphere.

   ANS: C   DIF: I   OBJ: 6-1.2

10. The energy stored in food molecules in living cells is gradually released in a series of
    linked chemical reactions called a
    a. reactant.
    b. ATP generator.
    c. chemical equation.
    d. biochemical pathway.

    ANS: D   DIF: I   OBJ: 6-1.2

11. While energy absorbed by one type of chlorophyll molecule is used to form molecules of
    ATP, electrons from a second kind of chlorophyll molecule are used
    a. in forming molecules of NADPH.
    b. to migrate to another proton pump.
    c. in the second kind of thylakoid.
    d. as a fuel for forming another chlorophyll molecule.

    ANS: A   DIF: I   OBJ: 6-1.2

12. Tiny packets of radiant energy are called
    a. photons.
    b. protons.
    c. eons.
    d. electrons.

    ANS: A   DIF: I   OBJ: 6-1.2

13. When photons of light strike an object, the light may be
    a. reflected.
    b. absorbed.
    c. transmitted.
    d. All of the above

    ANS: D   DIF: I   OBJ: 6-1.2

14. Chlorophyll is green because
    a. it absorbs green wavelengths of light.
    b. it absorbs blue and yellow wavelengths, which make green.
    c. photons of green wavelengths are reflected.
    d. of an optical illusion caused by transmitted light.

    ANS: C   DIF: I   OBJ: 6-1.2

15. What happens when a chlorophyll molecule absorbs a photon of light?
    a. Some of its electrons are raised to a higher energy level.
    b. It disintegrates, giving off huge amounts of heat.
    c. It glows, radiating green light and giving the plant a green appearance.
    d. Red and blue wavelengths are emitted.

    ANS: A   DIF: I   OBJ: 6-1.2

16. Flower petals have a variety of colors other than green because they possess
    a. chlorophyll.
    b. carotenoids.
    c. pigments that reflect green.
    d. chloroplasts.

    ANS: B   DIF: I   OBJ: 6-1.2

17. chloroplast : grana ::
    a. photosystem : pigment molecules
    b. chlorophyll : pigment
    c. thylakoids : grana
    d. chlorophyll : green

    ANS: A   DIF: II   OBJ: 6-1.2

18. When electrons of a chlorophyll molecule are raised to a higher energy level,
    a. they become a photon of light.
    b. they form a glucose bond.
    c. they enter an electron transport chain.
    d. carotenoids are converted to chlorophyll.

    ANS: C   DIF: I   OBJ: 6-1.3

19. NADP⁺ is important in photosynthesis because it
    a. becomes oxidized to form NADP.
    b. is needed to form chlorophyll.
    c. provides additional oxygen atoms.
    d. carries hydrogen atoms and energy for producing organic molecules.

    ANS: D   DIF: I   OBJ: 6-1.3

20. The electrons of photosystem I
    a. are eventually replaced by electrons from photosystem II.
    b. attach to water molecules during the light reaction.
    c. produce molecules of oxygen that enter the atmosphere.
    d. are absorbed by oxygen molecules to form water.

    ANS: A   DIF: I   OBJ: 6-1.3

21. The source of oxygen produced during photosynthesis is
    a. carbon dioxide.   c. the air.
    b. water.   d. glucose.

    ANS: B   DIF: I   OBJ: 6-1.4

22. As a result of photosynthesis,
    a. our atmosphere is now rich in oxygen gas.
    b. animals can get energy directly from the sun.
    c. plants convert chlorophyll into protein channels.
    d. abundant quantities of carbon dioxide are available to fuel the Calvin cycle.

    ANS: A   DIF: I   OBJ: 6-1.4

23. The major atmospheric byproduct of photosynthesis is
    a. nitrogen.   c. water.
    b. carbon dioxide.   d. oxygen.

    ANS: D   DIF: I   OBJ: 6-1.4

24. During the third stage of photosynthesis, carbon-containing molecules are produced from
    a. ADP.
    b. carbon atoms, hydrogen atoms, and oxygen atoms from glucose.
    c. carbon atoms from carbon dioxide in the air and hydrogen atoms from water.
    d. carbon atoms from carbon dioxide in the air and hydrogen atoms from NADPH.

    ANS: D   DIF: I   OBJ: 6-1.5

25. Which of the following enables green plants to convert light energy to chemical energy?
    a. the sodium-potassium pump   c. sugar channels
    b. coupled channels   d. the proton pump

    ANS: D   DIF: I   OBJ: 6-1.5

Modern Biology Assessment Item Listing
50

26. Proton pumps found in the thylakoid membranes are directly responsible for
    a. moving hydrogen nuclei out of the grana.
    b. providing the energy to produce ATP molecules.
    c. producing ATP-synthetase.
    d. generating glucose molecules.

    ANS: B   DIF: I   OBJ: 6-1.5

27. At a proton pump of the thylakoid membrane,
    a. electrons return to their original energy levels.
    b. electrons are pushed out of the thylakoid.
    c. energy from electrons is used to make ATP.
    d. the thylakoid bursts, releasing energy.

    ANS: A   DIF: I   OBJ: 6-1.5

28. Products of the light reactions of photosynthesis that are required by the dark reactions
    are
    a. oxygen and ATP.   c. ATP and NADPH.
    b. water and oxygen.   d. oxygen and NADPH.

    ANS: C   DIF: I   OBJ: 6-1.5

29. The dark reactions of photosynthesis
    a. require ATP and NADPH.
    b. can occur in both light and dark conditions.
    c. generate glucose.
    d. All of the above

    ANS: D   DIF: I   OBJ: 6-2.1

30. The energy used in the Calvin cycle for the production of carbohydrate molecules comes
    from
    a. ATP made during cellular respiration.
    b. the Krebs cycle.
    c. ATP made in the second stage of photosynthesis.
    d. CO_2 absorbed during the last stage of photosynthesis.

    ANS: C   DIF: I   OBJ: 6-2.1

31. During photosynthesis, the series of reactions that create the complex carbohydrates
    needed for energy and growth is called
    a. the Calvin cycle.   c. the energy flow.
    b. the Krebs cycle.   d. carbohydrate loading.

    ANS: A   DIF: I   OBJ: 6-2.1

32. All organic molecules contain carbon atoms that ultimately can be traced back in the
    food chain to
    a. the bodies of heterotrophs.   c. water absorbed by plants.
    b. carbon dioxide from the atmosphere. d. the carbon that comes from the sun.

    ANS: B   DIF: I   OBJ: 6-2.2

33. Which of the following cannot be produced from the products of the Calvin cycle?
    a. carbohydrates
    b. lipids
    c. proteins
    d. All of the above can be produced from Calvin cycle products.

ANS: D   DIF: I   OBJ: 6-2.2

34. C_3, C_4, and CAM plants differ from each other in
    a. that C_3 plants use the Calvin cycle for carbon fixation and C_4 and CAM plants use different pathways for carbon fixation.
    b. that C_3 plants have their stomata open during the day and C_4 and CAM plants have their stomata open at night.
    c. the initial product of carbon fixation.
    d. that C_3 plants use CO_2 to form organic compounds and C_4 and CAM plants use other sources of carbon.

ANS: C   DIF: II   OBJ: 6-2.3

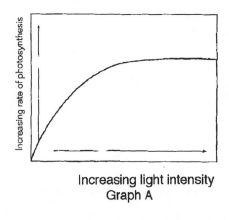

Increasing light intensity
Graph A

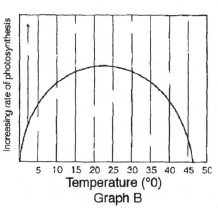

Temperature (°0)
Graph B

35. Refer to the illustration above. Graph "A" demonstrates that the rate of photosynthesis
    a. decreases in response to increasing light intensity.
    b. increases indefinitely in response to increasing light intensity.
    c. increases in response to increasing light intensity, but only to a certain point.
    d. is unaffected by changes in light intensity.

ANS: C   DIF: II   OBJ: 6-2.4

36. Refer to the illustration above. Taken together, these graphs demonstrate that
    a. photosynthesis is independent of environmental influences.
    b. increases in light intensity cause increases in temperature.
    c. as the rate of photosynthesis increases, the temperature of the plant eventually decreases.
    d. the rate of photosynthesis is affected by changes in the plant's environment.

ANS: D   DIF: II   OBJ: 6-2.4

COMPLETION

1. Stacks of thylakoids, called _____, are found suspended in the stroma of chloroplasts.

   ANS: grana   DIF: I   6-1.1

2. A pigment that absorbs primarily red and blue photons of light for photosynthesis is called _____, while pigments that absorb other wavelengths and appear yellow and orange are called _____.

   ANS: chlorophyll, carotenoids   DIF: I   6-1.2

3. Organisms that harvest energy from either sunlight or chemicals in order to make food molecules are called _____.

   ANS: autotrophs   DIF: I   6-1.2

4. The main pigment associated with the two photosystems is _____.

   ANS: chlorophyll   DIF: I   6-1.2

5. In the electron transport chain of photosynthesis, electrons travel from molecule to molecule as part of a(n) _____ atom.

   ANS: hydrogen   DIF: I   6-1.3

6. The abundance of oxygen in Earth's atmosphere is a result of _____.

   ANS: photosynthesis   DIF: I   6-1.4

7. Chemiosmosis results in the release of _____.

   ANS: energy   DIF: I   6-1.5

8. The third stage of photosynthesis, in which glucose is manufactured, is called the

   _____.

   ANS: Calvin cycle   DIF: I   6-2.1

9. The scientist who determined the sequence of steps in the light-independent reactions was

   _____.

   ANS: Melvin Calvin   DIF: I   6-2.1

10. The _____ plants have an enzyme that is more efficient at fixing CO_2 than is the enzyme that accomplishes this in _____.

   ANS: C_4; C_3 DIF: I   6-2.3

PROBLEM

1. Scientists have been able to induce chloroplasts to produce ATP in the dark. First, they remove intact chloroplasts from plants. Next, they soak the chloroplasts in a solution with a low pH (about 4) and keep them in the dark. After a period of time, the chloroplasts are removed from the low pH solution and placed in a higher pH solution (about 8), again in the dark. ATP is soon found to be present in the higher pH solution. Write your answers to the following in the spaces below.
   a. Evaluate the results of this experiment. Include an explanation of what apparently happened to the chloroplasts while they were in the low pH solution and how this enabled them to produce ATP when they were placed in the higher pH solution.
   b. What occurs in chloroplasts exposed to light that was simulated in this experiment?

ANS:
   a. In the low pH solution, the chloroplasts apparently take up hydrogen ions from the solution. The hydrogen ions move inside the thylakoid compartments of the chloroplasts and accumulate there. When the chloroplasts are placed in the higher pH solution, a pH gradient exists between the inside of the thylakoid compartments and the stroma of the chloroplasts. This drives the movement of hydrogen ions from the thylakoid compartments to the stroma. As the hydrogen ions move into the stroma, they pass through the protein ATP synthetase. This enzyme is thereby induced to produce ATP from ADP.
   b. Chloroplasts exposed to light will have electrons passed along an electron transport chain. As they pass along this chain, they give off energy. Some of this energy is used to pump hydrogen ions into the thylakoid compartments. The resulting pH gradient between the thylakoid compartments and the stroma drives the movement of hydrogen ions from the thylakoid compartments to the stroma. As the hydrogen ions move into the stroma they pass through the protein ATP synthetase. This enzyme is thereby induced to produce ATP from ADP.

DIF: III   OBJ: 6-1.1

2. The following statements are about the molecule ATP (adenosine triphosphate). For each statement, indicate first whether it is true or false. Then, if it is false, rewrite the statement so that it is correct. Write your answers in the space below.
   a. ATP is an unstable molecule.
   b. Energy is released when the nitrogen-containing base in ATP is removed.
   c. ATP is a form of kinetic energy.
   d. ATP is the primary source of energy for chemical reactions occurring in all cells of all living organisms.
   e. Energy released when ATP is hydrolyzed to ADP is used in cells by coupling this endergonic reaction to other reactions in the cell that are exergonic.

ANS:
   a. True.
   b. False. Energy is released when one or two of the phosphate groups in ATP is removed.
   c. False. ATP is a form of potential energy.
   d. True.
   e. False. Energy released when ATP is hydrolyzed to ADP is used in cells by coupling this exergonic reaction to other reactions in the cell that are endergonic.

DIF: III   OBJ: 6-1.5

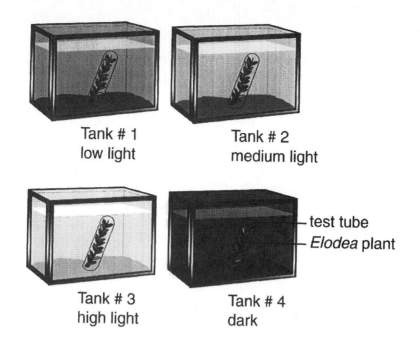

Tank # 1
low light

Tank # 2
medium light

Tank # 3
high light

Tank # 4
dark

— test tube
— *Elodea* plant

3. Refer to the illustration above. Amy wants to test the hypothesis that the rate of photosynthesis is directly related to the light level to which plants are exposed. She has chosen the aquatic plant *Elodea* as her study organism. In her experimental design, she has four different tanks in which she will place *Elodea* plants. Each *Elodea* plant will be placed inside an inverted test tube. She plans to estimate the relative rate of photosynthesis by measuring the amount of oxygen produced by plants placed under different light levels. She plans on comparing the amount of oxygen gas that collects in the top of each of the test tubes. Her experimental set-up looks like this:

Amy plans to place tank #3 next to a window in the classroom. She plans to place tank #2 ten feet away from the window. She plans to place tank #1 twenty feet away from the window. She plans to place tank #4 in the classroom's refrigerator, because it is the only place she can find that is dark. Write your answers to the following in the spaces below.
a. What is wrong with the design of Amy's experiment?
b. What could Amy change in her experimental design to make it a better experiment?

ANS:
a. By placing tank #4 in the refrigerator, Amy would be introducing a second variable, temperature, into her experiment. A true controlled experiment tests only one variable.
b. Amy should find some location for tank #4 that is at least as close to the same temperature as the locations where tanks #1, 2, and 3 are to be placed. It would be better to have tank #4 located in a different room than to have it in the same room at a different temperature.

DIF: II   OBJ: 6-2.4

ESSAY

1. Why do the cells of plant roots generally lack chloroplasts?

   ANS:
   Chloroplasts contain chlorophyll, the pigment that absorbs sunlight. Since most roots are underground, they have no need for chlorophyll or chloroplasts.

   DIF: II   OBJ: 6-1.1

2. What are autotrophs and heterotrophs?

   ANS:
   Organisms that acquire energy by making their own food are called autotrophs. Plants and certain unicellular organisms are autotrophs. Organisms that gain energy by eating other organisms are called heterotrophs. Some unicellular organisms, as well as all animals and fungi, are heterotrophs.

   DIF: II   OBJ: 6-1.1

3. Explain why the leaves of plants appear green to the human eye.

   ANS:
   When photons of visible light strike the leaves of a plant, red and blue wavelengths are absorbed by chlorophyll. Green wavelengths, however, are reflected. These reflected photons enter the eyes of the observer, stimulating receptor cells in the eye that can respond to these wavelengths. The observer perceives the leaves as being green.

   DIF: II   OBJ: 6-1.2

CHAPTER 7—CELLULAR RESPIRATION

TRUE/FALSE

1. Plants carry out cellular respiration.

   ANS: T   DIF: I   OBJ: 7-1.1

2. Oxidative respiration must follow glycolysis if a cell is to maximize its ATP production.

   ANS: T   DIF: I   OBJ: 7-1.2

3. Fermentation and oxidative respiration both take place in the absence of oxygen.

   ANS: F   DIF: I   OBJ: 7-1.3

4. Lactic acid fermentation is a type of anaerobic respiration.

   ANS: T   DIF: I   OBJ: 7-1.3

5. Glycolysis is an efficient pathway for extracting energy from glucose.

   ANS: F   DIF: I   OBJ: 7-1.4

MULTIPLE CHOICE

1. When cells break down food molecules, energy
   a. is released all at once.
   b. is released entirely as body heat into the environment.
   c. is temporarily stored in ATP molecules.
   d. causes excitation of electrons in chlorophyll molecules.

   ANS: C   DIF: I   OBJ: 7-1.1

2. ATP
   a. contains five phosphate groups.
   b. is essential for a cell to perform all the tasks necessary for life.
   c. is found only in bacteria.
   d. All of the above

   ANS: B   DIF: I   OBJ: 7-1.1

3. A substance, produced during the process of photosynthesis, that is used for completion of cellular respiration is
   a. water.   c. NADPH.
   b. ATP.   d. oxygen.

   ANS: D   DIF: I   OBJ: 7-1.1

4. The process of cellular respiration
   a. is performed only by organisms that are incapable of photosynthesis.
   b. breaks down food molecules to release stored energy.
   c. occurs before plants are able to carry out photosynthesis.
   d. occurs only in animals.

   ANS: B   DIF: I   OBJ: 7-1.1

5. photosynthesis : light ::
   a. light bulb : glass   c. automobile : gasoline
   b. trunk : clothing   d. country : nation

   ANS: C   DIF: II   OBJ: 7-1.1

6. When glycolysis occurs,
   a. a molecule of glucose is split.   c. some ATP is produced.
   b. two molecules of pyruvate are made.   d. All of the above

   ANS: D   DIF: I   OBJ: 7-1.2

7. The name of the process that takes place when organic compounds are broken down in
   the absence of oxygen is
   a. respiration.   c. fermentation.
   b. oxidation.   d. All of the above

   ANS: C   DIF: I   OBJ: 7-1.3

8. When muscles are exercised extensively in the absence of sufficient oxygen,
   a. a large amount of ATP is formed.
   b. NADH molecules split.
   c. lactic acid is produced.
   d. oxidative respiration ceases.

   ANS: C   DIF: I   OBJ: 7-1.3

9. You have been growing some animal cells in culture. The cells grow well for several
   weeks, and then don't seem to grow as well. You conduct some tests and determine that
   there is a lot of lactic acid in the culture fluid. Which of the following is the most likely
   explanation for the poor condition of the cells?
   a. There is too much glucose in the culture fluid.
   b. There is not enough glucose in the culture fluid.
   c. There is too much oxygen in the culture fluid.
   d. There is not enough oxygen in the culture fluid.

   ANS: D   DIF: III   OBJ: 7-1.3

10. If the formation of a standard amount of ATP requires 12 kcal of energy and the
    complete oxidation of glucose yields 686 kcal of energy, how efficient is glycolysis at
    extracting energy from glucose?
    a. 1.7%   c. 7.0%
    b. 3.5%   d. 35%

    ANS: B   DIF: I   OBJ: 7-1.4

11. Cellular respiration takes place in two stages:
    a. glycolysis and fermentation.
    b. Stage 1 and Stage 2 of photosynthesis.
    c. glycolysis, then oxidative respiration.
    d. oxidative respiration, then reductive respiration.

    ANS: C   DIF: I   OBJ: 7-2.1

12. In cellular respiration, a two-carbon molecule combines with a four-carbon molecule to form citric acid as part of
    a. glycolysis.   c. the Krebs cycle.
    b. carbon fixation.   d. the electron transport chain.

    ANS: C   DIF: I   OBJ: 7-2.1

13. Acetyl-coenzyme A
    a. is formed from the breakdown of pyruvate.
    b. enters the Krebs cycle.
    c. can be used in fat synthesis.
    d. All of the above

    ANS: D   DIF: I   OBJ: 7-2.1

14. Glycolysis and oxidative respiration are different in that
    a. glycolysis occurs on the cell membrane, while oxidative respiration occurs in mitochondria.
    b. glycolysis occurs only in photosynthesis, while oxidative respiration is part of cellular respiration.
    c. glycolysis occurs in the absence of oxygen, while oxidative respiration requires oxygen.
    d. Both of these terms are different names for the same process.

    ANS: C   DIF: I   OBJ: 7-2.1

15. Which of the following is *not* formed during the Krebs cycle?
    a. CO_2 c. NADH
    b. $FADH_2$ d. NADPH

    ANS: D   DIF: I   OBJ: 7-2.1

16. Which of the following is *not* part of cellular respiration?
    a. electron transport   c. Krebs cycle
    b. glycolysis   d. Calvin cycle

    ANS: D   DIF: I   OBJ: 7-2.1

17. With oxygen present, the Krebs cycle and the electron transport chain
    a. provide organisms an alternative to glycolysis.
    b. produce most of the ATP needed for life.
    c. break down glucose to produce carbon dioxide, water, and ATP.
    d. All of the above

    ANS: D   DIF: I   OBJ: 7-2.2

18. Water is an end product in
    a. lactic acid formation.
    b. fermentation.
    c. the Krebs cycle.
    d. the electron transport system.

    ANS: D   DIF: I   OBJ: 7-2.2

19. Krebs Cycle : CO_2 ::
    a. glycolysis : glucose
    b. acetyl-CoA formation : O_2
    c. cellular respiration : O_2
    d electron transport chain : ATP

    ANS: D   DIF: II   OBJ: 7-2.2

20. ATP molecules produced during aerobic cellular respiration
    a. remain in the mitochondria in which they are formed.
    b. are stored in chloroplasts of the same cell in which they are formed.
    c. enter the cell's cytoplasm through the membranes of the mitochondria in which they
       are formed.
    d. are distributed by the bloodstream to all cells in the body.

    ANS: C   DIF: I   OBJ: 7-2.3

21. After proton pumps in mitochondria have depleted electrons of their energy during ATP
    production,
    a. the electrons carried as part of hydrogen atoms are used in the formation of water.
    b. the electrons carried as part of hydrogen atoms are used in the formation of ethyl
       alcohol.
    c. the electrons build up inside the mitochondria and diffuse back to a thylakoid.
    d. None of the above

    ANS: A   DIF: I   OBJ: 7-2.3

$$C_6H_{12}O_6 + 6O_2 + ADP + P \rightarrow 6CO_2 + 6 H_2O + \text{MOLECULE A}$$

22. The process shown in the equation above begins in the cytoplasm of a cell and ends in the
    a. cytoplasm.
    b. mitochondria.
    c. endoplasmic reticulum.
    d. lysosome.

    ANS: B   DIF: II   OBJ: 7-2.3

23. The equation above summarizes the process known as
    a. photosynthesis.
    b. fermentation.
    c. oxidative respiration.
    d. protein breakdown.

    ANS: C   DIF: II   OBJ: 7-2.4

24. The molecule referred to as Molecule "A" in the equation above is
    a. NADPH.
    b. ATP.
    c. NADH.
    d. ADP.

    ANS: B   DIF: II   OBJ: 7-2.4

25. When living cells break down molecules, energy is
    a. stored as ADP.
    b. stored as ATP.
    c. released as heat.
    d. Both b and c

ANS: D   DIF: I   OBJ: 7-2.4

26. Which of the following is the best explanation for the presence of both chloroplasts and mitochondria in plant cells?
    a. In the light, plants are photosynthetic autotrophs. In the dark, they are heterotrophs.
    b. If plants cannot produce enough ATP in the process of photosynthesis to meet their energy needs, they can produce it in aerobic respiration.
    c. Sugars are produced in chloroplasts. These sugars can be stored in the plant for later use, converted to other chemicals, or broken down in aerobic respiration to yield ATP for the plant to use to meet its energy needs.
    d. The leaves and sometimes the stems of plants contain chloroplasts which produce ATP to meet the energy needs of these plant parts. The roots of plants contain mitochondria which produce ATP to meet the energy needs of these plant parts.

ANS: C   DIF: III   OBJ: 7-2.3

COMPLETION

1. _____ is a biochemical pathway of cellular respiration that is anaerobic.

ANS: Glycolysis   DIF: I   OBJ: 7-1.2

2. Glucose is split into smaller molecules during a biochemical pathway called
   _____.

ANS: glycolysis   DIF: I   OBJ: 7-1.2

3. In the absence of oxygen, instead of oxidative respiration following glycolysis, glycolysis is followed by _____.

ANS: fermentation   DIF: I   OBJ: 7-1.3

4. During fermentation, either ethyl alcohol and carbon dioxide or _____ is formed.

ANS: lactic acid   DIF: I   OBJ: 7-1.3

5. Of the maximum possible of 38 molecules of ATP produced by the complete oxidation of one glucose molecule, _____ molecules of ATP are produced during glycolysis.

ANS: 2   DIF: II   OBJ: 7-1.4

ESSAY

1. The relationship between photosynthesis and cellular respiration is usually described as a cycle. Briefly explain. Write your answer in the space below.

ANS:

The relationship between photosynthesis and cellular respiration is often described as cyclic because the products of one process are used as the reactants for the other. Photosynthesis produces carbohydrates from carbon dioxide and water, incorporating light energy into the bonds of glucose. Cellular respiration, on the other hand, releases energy from the bonds of glucose for use by the cell, and in the process produces carbon dioxide and water.

DIF: II   OBJ: 7-1.1

TRUE/FALSE

1. The information needed by a cell to direct its activities and to determine its characteristics is contained in molecules of deoxyribonucleic acid (DNA).

   ANS: T   DIF: I   OBJ: 8-1.1

2. Eukaryotic chromosomes are contained within a nucleus, while prokaryotic chomosomes are not.

   ANS: T   DIF: I   OBJ: 8-1.2

3. Each human somatic cell contains two copies of each chromosome for a total of 23 homologous chromosomes.

   ANS: F   DIF: I   OBJ: 8-1.3

4. Human sperm and egg cells have 23 chromosomes.

   ANS: T   DIF: I   OBJ: 8-1.3

5. Gametes are diploid so that when fertilization occurs, the resulting zygote will have the characteristic number of chromosomes for that species.

   ANS: F   DIF: I   OBJ: 8-1.3

6. A karyotype is a type of gene.

   ANS: F   DIF: I   OBJ: 8-1.3

7. Cell division in bacteria and eukaryotes takes place in precisely the same manner.

   ANS: F   DIF: I   OBJ: 8-2.2

8. Cells spend most of their lifetime in interphase.

   ANS: T   DIF: I   OBJ: 8-2.2

9. After the replication of a cell's chromatids, there are twice as many centromeres as there are chromosomes.

   ANS: F   DIF: I   OBJ: 8-2.3

10. Asexual reproduction occurs by mitosis.

    ANS: T   DIF: I   OBJ: 8-2.3

11. During telophase, a nuclear envelope surrounds each new set of chromosomes.

    ANS: T   DIF: I   OBJ: 8-2.3

12. Chromatids separate from each other during telophase.

    ANS: F   DIF: I   OBJ: 8-2.3

13. After mitosis and cytokinesis, each new cell has a complete set of the original cell's chromosomes.

    ANS: T   DIF: I   OBJ: 8-2.4

14. Plant cells cannot undergo cell division because of their strong cell walls.

    ANS: F   DIF: I   OBJ: 8-2.4

15. Cytokinesis only occurs during metaphase II.

    ANS: F   DIF: I   OBJ: 8-2.4

16. Meiosis results in the formation of haploid cells from diploid cells.

    ANS: T   DIF: I   OBJ: 8-3.2

17. Meiosis produces four nuclei that have a different chromosome number from the original cell's nucleus.

    ANS: T   DIF: I   OBJ: 8-3.2

18. While paired together during the second division of meiosis, two chromosomes may exchange segments of DNA.

    ANS: F   DIF: I   OBJ: 8-3.3

19. Crossing-over is the exchange of reciprocal segments of DNA between homologous chromosomes.

    ANS: T   DIF: I   OBJ: 8-3.3

MULTIPLE CHOICE

1. In order to fit within a cell, DNA becomes more compact by
   a. breaking apart into separate genes.
   b. extending to form very long, thin molecules.
   c. wrapping tightly around associated proteins.
   d. being enzymatically changed into a protein.

   ANS: C   DIF: I   OBJ: 8-1.1

2. Chromatids are
   a. dense patches within the nucleus.
   b. bacterial chromosomes.
   c. joined strands of duplicated genetic material.
   d. prokaryotic nuclei.

   ANS: C   DIF: I   OBJ: 8-1.1

3. A protein disk that attaches two chromatids to each other in a chromosome is called a(n)
   a. chloroplast.
   b. centromere.
   c. gamete.
   d. centriole.

ANS: B   DIF: I   OBJ: 8-1.1

4. Which of the following is *not* a true difference between the chromosomes of eukaryotes and those of prokaryotes?
   a. Eukaryotic chromosomes are linear, while those of prokaryotes are circular.
   b. Eukaryotic chromosomes are associated with histones, while those of prokaryotes are not.
   c. Eukaryotes usually have more than one chromosome, while prokaryotes have only one chromosome.
   d. Eukaryotic chromosomes contain DNA, while prokaryotic chromosomes contain a different form of genetic material.

ANS: D   DIF: II   OBJ: 8-1.2

5. The chromosomes in your body
   a. exist in 23 pairs.
   b. each contain thousands of genes.
   c. are about 40 percent DNA and 60 percent protein.
   d. All of the above

ANS: D   DIF: I   OBJ: 8-1.3

6. A student can study a karyotype to learn about the
   a. molecular structure of a chromosome.
   b. genes that are present in a particular strand of DNA.
   c. medical history of an individual.
   d. chromosomes present in a somatic cell.

ANS: D   DIF: I   OBJ: 8-1.3

7. A diploid cell is one that
   a. has two homologues of each chromosome.
   b. is designated by the symbol $2n$.
   c. has chromosomes found in pairs.
   d. All of the above

ANS: D   DIF: I   OBJ: 8-1.4

8. diploid : somatic cell :: haploid :
   a. body cell.
   b. chromosome.
   c. gamete.
   b. zygote.

ANS: C   DIF: I   OBJ: 8-1.4

9. The diploid number of chromosomes in a human skin cell is 46. The number of chromosomes found in a human ovum is
a. 46.
b. 92.
c. 23.
d. 12.5.

ANS: C   DIF: I   OBJ: 8-1.4

10. How many chromosomes are in the body cells of an organism that has a haploid number of 8?
a. 4
b. 8
c. 12
d. 16

ANS: D   DIF: I   OBJ: 8-1.4

11. Binary fission
a. occurs when two cells collide with each other.
b. produces excess energy.
c. creates new species.
d. is the process by which bacteria reproduce.

ANS: D   DIF: I   OBJ: 8-2.1

12. The chromosome of a bacterium
a. is wrapped around proteins.
b. has a circular shape.
c. occurs in multiple pairs within the cell.
d. is found within the nucleus.

ANS: B   DIF: I   OBJ: 8-2.1

13. In a bacterium, cell division takes place when
a. its nucleus divides.
b. the cell splits into two cells, one of which receives all of the DNA.
c. the DNA is copied, a new cell wall forms between the DNA copies, and the cell splits into two cells.
d. None of the above

ANS: C   DIF: I   OBJ: 8-2.1

14. The stage of the cell cycle that occupies most of the cell's life is
a. G_1.
b. M.
c. G_2.
d. S.

ANS: A   DIF: I   OBJ: 8-2.2

15. Which of the following shows the correct sequence of the cell cycle?
a. $C \rightarrow M \rightarrow G_1 \rightarrow S \rightarrow G_2$
b. $S \rightarrow G_1 \rightarrow G_2 \rightarrow M \rightarrow C$
c. $G_1 \rightarrow S \rightarrow G_2 \rightarrow M \rightarrow C$
d. None of the above

ANS: C   DIF: I   OBJ: 8-2.2

16. growth : G$_1$ ::
    a. mitosis : meiosis
    b. mitochondria replication : S
    c. cytokinesis : M
    d. DNA copying : S

    ANS: D   DIF: II   OBJ: 8-2.2

17. metaphase : prophase ::
    a. photon : light particle
    b. G$_2$: S
    c. thylakoid : grana
    d. carbon fixation process : Calvin cycle

    ANS: B   DIF: II   OBJ: 8-2.2

18. The phase of mitosis that is characterized by the arrangement of all chromosomes along the equator of the cell is called
    a. telophase.
    b. metaphase.
    c. anaphase.
    d. prophase.

    ANS: B   DIF: I   OBJ: 8-2.3

19. A spindle fiber is a specialized form of
    a. microtubule.
    b. flagellum.
    c. cilium.
    d. chromosome.

    ANS: A   DIF: I   OBJ: 8-2.3

1   2   3   4   5

20. Refer to the illustration above. The cell in diagram "1" is in
    a. metaphase.
    b. telophase.
    c. anaphase.
    d. prophase.

    ANS: C   DIF: II   OBJ: 8-2.3

21. Refer to the illustration above. Mitosis begins with the stage shown in diagram
    a. "1."
    b. "2."
    c. "3."
    d. "4."

    ANS: C   DIF: II   OBJ: 8-2.3

22. Refer to the illustration above. The cell shown in diagram "5" is in
    a. metaphase.
    b. telophase.
    c. anaphase.
    d. prophase.

    ANS: B   DIF: II   OBJ: 8-2.3

23. A typical human cell contains 46 chromosomes. After mitosis and cell division, each of the two new cells formed from the original cell
    a. gets 23 chromosomes.
    b. grows new chromosomes from existing DNA.
    c. gets a complete set of 46 chromosomes.
    d. None of the above

    ANS: C   DIF: I   OBJ: 8-2.3

24. As a result of mitosis, each of the two new cells produced from the original cell during cytokinesis
    a. receives a few chromosomes from the original cell.
    b. receives an exact copy of all the chromosomes present in the original cell.
    c. donates a chromosome to the original cell.
    d. receives exactly half the chromosomes from the original cell.

    ANS: B   DIF: I   OBJ: 8-2.3

   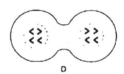

25. Refer to the illustration above. Which of the following correctly indicates the order in which these events occur?
    a. "A," "B," "C," "D"   c. "B," "A," "C," "D"
    b. "C," "B," "A," "D"   d. "A," "C," "B," "D"

    ANS: C   DIF: II   OBJ: 8-2.3

26. Refer to the illustration above. During which stage do the centromeres divide?
    a. "A"   c. "C"
    b. "B"   d. "D"

    ANS: A   DIF: II   OBJ: 8-2.3

27. 5 : cell cycle ::
    a. 6 : prophase   c. 3 : meiosis
    b. 9 : cytokinesis   d. 4 : mitosis

    ANS: D   DIF: II   OBJ: 8-2.3

28. In plant cells, cytokinesis occurs when
    a. the chromosomes make exact copies of themselves.
    b. spindle fibers are formed.
    c. a new cell wall forms.
    d. osmotic pressure is too low.

    ANS: C   DIF: I   OBJ: 8-2.4

29. Mitosis is a process by which
    a. DNA is replicated.
    b. cytokinesis occurs.
    c. cells grow in size.
    d. a cell's nucleus divides.

    ANS: D   DIF: I   OBJ: 8-2.4

30. Which of the following statements is *true*?
    a. Prokaryotes divide by mitosis.
    b. Eukaryotes have circular chromosomes.
    c. Animal cells form new cell walls when they divide.
    d. Cytokinesis differs in plant cells and animal cells.

    ANS: D   DIF: I   OBJ: 8-2.4

31. Separation of homologues occurs during
    a. mitosis.
    b. meiosis I.
    c. meiosis II.
    d. fertilization.

    ANS: B   DIF: I   OBJ: 8-3.1

32. The difference between anaphase of mitosis and anaphase I of meiosis is that
    a. the chromosomes line up at the equator in anaphase I.
    b. centromeres do not exist in anaphase I.
    c. chromatids do not separate at the centromere in anaphase I.
    d. crossing-over occurs only in anaphase of mitosis.

    ANS: C   DIF: I   OBJ: 8-3.1

Diagrams A and B show cells from an organism with a diploid chromosome number of 4.

 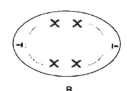

A   B

33. Refer to the illustration above. Which of the cells will be a diploid cell at the completion of division?
    a. "A"
    b. "B"
    c. Both
    d. Neither

    ANS: A   DIF: II   OBJ: 8-3.2

34. Refer to the illustration above. Which of these cells is in the process of dividing to form gametes?
    a. "A"
    b. "B"
    c. Both
    d. Neither

    ANS: B   DIF: II   OBJ: 8-3.4

35. When crossing-over takes place, chromosomes
    a. mutate in the first division.
    b. produce new genes.
    c. decrease in number.
    d. exchange corresponding segments of DNA.

    ANS: D   DIF: I   OBJ: 8-3.3

36. The exchange of segments of DNA between the members of a pair of chromosomes
    a. ensures that variations within a species never occur.
    b. acts as a source of variations within a species.
    c. always produces genetic disorders.
    d. is called *crossing*.

    ANS: B   DIF: I   OBJ: 8-3.3

COMPLETION

1. Following replication of its DNA, each chromosome contains two
   _____, which are attached to each other by a centromere.

   ANS: chromatids   DIF: I   OBJ: 8-1.1

2. Chromosomes that are not involved in sex determination are called

   _____.

   ANS: autosomes   DIF: I   OBJ: 8-1.3

3. A picture of a cell's chromosomes is called a _____.

   ANS: karyotype   DIF: I   OBJ: 8-1.3

4. _____ is the process by which bacteria split asexually into two
   identical organisms.

   ANS: Binary fission   DIF: I   OBJ: 8-2.1

5. In bacteria, cell division takes place in two stages. First the _____ is
   copied, and then the cell splits.

   ANS: DNA   DIF: I   OBJ: 8-2.1

6. The sequence of events that occurs in a cell from one mitotic division to the next is
   called the _____.

   ANS: cell cycle   DIF: I   OBJ: 8-2.2

7. Collectively, the time spent in $G_1 + S + G_2$ is called _____.

   ANS: interphase   DIF: I   OBJ: 8-2.3

8. "Cables" made of microtubules that extend from the poles of a cell to the centromeres during cell division are called _____.

ANS: spindle fibers   DIF: I   OBJ: 8-2.3

9. In mitosis, anaphase follows _____.

ANS: metaphase   DIF: I   OBJ: 8-2.3

10. Chromosomes coil up into short, fat rods during _____.

ANS: prophase   DIF: I   OBJ: 8-2.3

11. During cell division, plant cells form a new _____ in the center of the cell.

ANS: cell wall   DIF: I   OBJ: 8-2.4

12. In eukaryotic cells, _____ takes place after the nucleus divides.

ANS: cytokinesis   DIF: I   OBJ: 8-2.4

13. The stage of meiosis during which homologues line up along the equator of the cell is called _____.

ANS: metaphase I   DIF: I   OBJ: 8-3.1

14. After a new nuclear membrane forms during telophase of mitosis or meiosis, the _____ divides, resulting in two cells.

ANS: cytoplasm   DIF: I   OBJ: 8-3.2

15. The process called _____ guarantees that the number of chromosomes in gametes is half the number of chromosomes in body cells.

ANS: meiosis   DIF: I   OBJ: 8-3.2

16. A reciprocal exchange of corresponding segments of DNA is called _____.

ANS: crossing-over   DIF: I   OBJ: 8-3.3

17. The cells resulting from meiosis in either males or females are called _____.

ANS: gametes   DIF: I   OBJ: 8-3.4

18. As a result of spermatogenesis, _____ cells are produced that can all develop into sperm cells. As a result of oogenesis, only _____ cell(s) develop(s) into (an) egg cell(s).

ANS: 4; 1   DIF: I   OBJ: 8-3.4

ESSAY

1. Refer to the illustration above. Identify the structure in the diagram and discuss its importance during eukaryotic cell division. Write your answer in the space below.

   ANS:
   This is a chromosome, which is made of DNA. During mitosis, the process that precedes eukaryotic cell division, the nucleus of a cell divides into two nuclei, each containing a complete set of the cell's chromosomes. Thus, each new cell formed during cell division contains identical DNA.

   DIF: II   OBJ: 8-1.2

2. What would happen if the chromosome number were not reduced before sexual reproduction? Write your answer in the space below.

   ANS:
   The number of chromosomes in the offspring would be double the number in the parents. The number and characteristics of chromosomes in cells determine the traits of the organism. The organism would almost certainly not survive the doubling of its chromosomes, and even if it did survive and reproduce, then the number of chromosomes would become unmanageably large after only a few generations.

   DIF: II   OBJ: 8-1.3

3. Briefly describe the five stages of the cell cycle. Write your answer in the space below.

   ANS:
   The G_1 stage of the cell cycle is the phase of cell growth. This is followed by the S stage, during which DNA is copied. G_2 involves the cell preparing for cell division. The M phase is when mitosis occurs. The cell cycle concludes with the C stage, during which cytokinesis takes place. The newly formed cells then enter into a new cell cycle, repeating these stages again.

   DIF: II   OBJ: 8-2.2

4. Compare the features of mitotic metaphase, meiotic metaphase I, and meiotic metaphase II. Write your answer in the space below.

ANS:
During metaphase of mitosis, the diploid number of chromosomes of the cell line up single file across the equator of the cell. Meiotic metaphase I is characterized by the homologous chromosomes lining up as pairs (double file) along the equator. Metaphase II of meiosis appears similar to mitotic metaphase, except that the number of chromosomes is the haploid number rather than the diploid number. These chromosomes line up single file across the cell equator.

DIF: II   OBJ: 8-3.2

5. Identify three ways in which genetic recombination results during meiosis. Write your answer in the space below.

ANS:
Genetic recombination results when crossing-over occurs between homologues or between chromatids, when homologous pairs separate independently in meiosis I, or when sister chromatids separate independently in meiosis II.

DIF: II   OBJ: 8-3.3

CHAPTER 9—FUNDAMENTALS OF GENETICS

TRUE/FALSE

1. Genetics is the branch of biology that involves the study of how different traits are transmitted from one generation to the next.

   ANS: T   DIF: I   OBJ: 9-1.1

2. Mendel discovered predictable patterns in the inheritance of traits.

   ANS: T   DIF: I   OBJ: 9-1.1

3. Plants in Mendel's P generation were all heterozygous.

   ANS: F   DIF: II   OBJ: 9-1.1

4. Mendel based his principles on his observations of pea plants.

   ANS: T   DIF: I   OBJ: 9-1.1

5. The scientific study of heredity is called genetics.

   ANS: T   DIF: I   OBJ: 9-1.1

6. In Mendel's experiments with the flower color of pea plants, only the parental generation produced white flowers.

   ANS: F   DIF: I   OBJ: 9-1.1

7. A dominant allele masks the effect of a recessive allele.

   ANS: T   DIF: I   OBJ: 9-1.2

8. Mendel concluded that the patterns of inheritance are determined entirely by the environment.

   ANS: F   DIF: I   OBJ: 9-1.3

9. The law of independent assortment was proposed by Mendel to explain his observations of inheritance patterns.

   ANS: T   DIF: I   OBJ: 9-1.3

10. Genes on chromosomes are the units of inheritance.

   ANS: T   DIF: I   OBJ: 9-1.4

11. The allele for a recessive trait is usually represented by a capital letter.

   ANS: F   DIF: I   OBJ: 9-1.4

12. A Mendelian factor is equivalent to an allele.

   ANS: T   DIF: I   OBJ: 9-1.4

13. Current scientific knowledge supports Mendel's principles.

   ANS: T   DIF: I   OBJ: 9-1.5

14. Heterozygous individuals have two of the same alleles for a particular gene.

   ANS: F   DIF: I   OBJ: 9-2.1

15. In heterozygous individuals, only the recessive allele achieves expression.

   ANS: F   DIF: I   OBJ: 9-2.1

16. A Punnett square represents the phenotype of an organism.

   ANS: F   DIF: I   OBJ: 9-2.1

17. Probability is the likelihood that a certain event will occur.

   ANS: T   DIF: I   OBJ: 9-2.1

18. A probability of 1/4 is equal to a probability of 75 percent.

   ANS: F   DIF: II   OBJ: 9-2.1

19. The physical appearance of an individual organism, as determined by the genes it has inherited from its parents, is called its genotype.

   ANS: F   DIF: I   OBJ: 9-2.2

20. The dominant allele for tallness in pea plants is represented by the letter *t*.

   ANS: F   DIF: I   OBJ: 9-2.2

21. Individuals must exhibit a trait in order for it to appear in their offspring.

   ANS: F   DIF: I   OBJ: 9-2.3

22. In codominance, two alleles are expressed at the same time.

   ANS: T   DIF: I   OBJ: 9-2.3

23. All genes have only two alleles.

   ANS: F   DIF: I   OBJ: 9-2.3

24. A dihybrid cross involves two pairs of contrasting traits.

   ANS: T   DIF: I   OBJ: 9-2.4

25. Crosses involving a study of one gene are called monohybrid crosses.

ANS: T   DIF: I   OBJ: 9-2.4

MULTIPLE CHOICE

1. The scientific study of heredity is called
   a. meiosis.
   b. crossing-over.
   c. genetics.
   d. pollination.

   ANS: C   DIF: I   OBJ: 9-1.1

2. The "father" of genetics was
   a. T. A. Knight.
   b. Hans Krebs.
   c. Gregor Mendel.
   d. None of the above

   ANS: C   DIF: I   OBJ: 9-1.1

3. Mendel obtained his P generation by allowing the plants to
   a. self-pollinate.
   b. cross-pollinate.
   c. assort independently.
   d. segregate.

   ANS: A   DIF: I   OBJ: 9-1.1

4. What is the probability that the offspring of a homozygous dominant individual and a homozygous recessive individual will exhibit the dominant phenotype?
   a. 0.25
   b. 0.5
   c. 0.66
   d. 1.0

   ANS: D   DIF: I   OBJ: 9-1.1

5. True-breeding pea plants always
   a. are pollinated by hand.
   b. produce offspring with either form of a trait.
   c. produce offspring with only one form of a trait.
   d. are heterozygous.

   ANS: C   DIF: I   OBJ: 9-1.1

6. The first filial (F_1) generation is the result of
   a. cross-pollination among parents and the next generation.
   b. crosses between individuals of the parental generation.
   c. crosses between the offspring of a parental cross.
   d. self-fertilization between parental stock.

   ANS: B   DIF: I   OBJ: 9-1.1

7. Which of the following is the designation for Mendel's original pure strains of plants?
   a. P
   b. P_1
   c. F_1
   d. F_2

   ANS: A   DIF: I   OBJ: 9-1.1

8. F_2 : F_1 ::
   a. P : F_1
   b. F_1 : F_2
   c. F_1 : P
   d. dominant trait : recessive trait

ANS: C　　　　　DIF: II　　　　　OBJ: 9-1.1

9. The passing of traits from parents to offspring is called
   a. genetics.
   b. heredity.
   c. development.
   d. maturation.

ANS: B　　　　　DIF: I　　　　　OBJ: 9-1.2

10. A genetic trait that appears in every generation of offspring is called
    a. dominant.
    b. phenotypic.
    c. recessive.
    d. superior.

ANS: A　　　　　DIF: I　　　　　OBJ: 9-1.2

11. homozygous : heterozygous ::
    a. heterozygous : Bb
    b. probability : predicting chances
    c. dominant : recessive
    d. homozygous : BB

ANS: C　　　　　DIF: II　　　　　OBJ: 9-1.2

12. Mendel's finding that the inheritance of one trait had no effect on the inheritance of another became known as the
    a. law of dominance.
    b. law of universal inheritance.
    c. law of separate convenience.
    d. law of independent assortment.

ANS: D　　　　　DIF: I　　　　　OBJ: 9-1.3

13. To describe how traits can disappear and reappear in a certain pattern from generation to generation, Mendel proposed
    a. the law of independent assortment.
    b. the law of segregation.
    c. the law of genotypes.
    d. that the F_2 generation will only produce purple flowers.

ANS: B　　　　　DIF: I　　　　　OBJ: 9-1.3

14. The law of segregation states that
    a. alleles of a gene separate from each other during meiosis.
    b. different alleles of a gene can never be found in the same organism.
    c. each gene of an organism ends up in a different gamete.
    d. each gene is found on a different molecule of DNA.

ANS: A　　　　　DIF: I　　　　　OBJ: 9-1.3

15. When Mendel crossed pea plants with two contrasting traits, such as flower color and plant height,
    a. these experiments led to his law of segregation.
    b. he found that the inheritance of one trait did not influence the inheritance of the other trait.
    c. he found that the inheritance of one trait influenced the inheritance of the other trait.
    d. these experiments were considered failures because the importance of his work was not recognized.

    ANS: B   DIF: I   OBJ: 9-1.3

16. The phenotype of an organism
    a. represents its genetic composition.
    b. reflects all the traits that are actually expressed.
    c. occurs only in dominant pure organisms.
    d. cannot be seen.

    ANS: B   DIF: I   OBJ: 9-2.1

17. If an individual has two recessive alleles for the same trait, the individual is said to be
    a. homozygous for the trait.   c. heterozygous for the trait.
    b. haploid for the trait.   d. mutated.

    ANS: A   DIF: I   OBJ: 9-2.1

18. An individual heterozygous for a trait and an individual homozygous recessive for the trait are crossed and produce many offspring that are
    a. all the same genotype.   c. of three different phenotypes.
    b. of two different phenotypes.   d. all the same phenotype.

    ANS: B   DIF: II   OBJ: 9-2.1

19. Tallness (T) is dominant to shortness (t) in pea plants. Which of the following represents a genotype of a pea plant that is heterozygous for tallness?
    a. T   c. T t
    b. T T   d. t t

    ANS: C   DIF: II   OBJ: 9-2.1

In humans, having freckles (F) is dominant to not having freckles (f). The inheritance of these traits can be studied using a Punnett square similar to the one shown below.

20. Refer to the illustration above. The genotype represented in box "1" in the Punnett square would
   a. be homozygous for freckles.
   b. have an extra freckles chromosome.
   c. be heterozygous for freckles.
   d. have freckles chromosomes.

   ANS: A   DIF: II   OBJ: 9-2.1

21. Refer to the illustration above. The genotype in box "3" of the Punnett square is
   a. FF.
   b. Ff.
   c. ff.
   d. None of the above

   ANS: B   DIF: II   OBJ: 9-2.2

22. A trait that occurs in 450 individuals out of a total of 1,800 individuals occurs with a probability of
   a. 0.04.
   b. 0.25.
   c. 0.50.
   d. 0.75.

   ANS: B   DIF: II   OBJ: 9-2.1

23. How many different phenotypes can be produced by a pair of codominant alleles?
   a. 1
   b. 2
   c. 3
   d. 4

   ANS: C   DIF: II   OBJ: 9-2.1

	GI	Gi	gI	gi
GI				**5**
Gi	**2**	**3**	**X**	
gI	**1**		**4**	**6**
gi				

G = green
g = yellow
I = inflated
i = constricted

24. Refer to the illustration above. The phenotype represented by the cell labeled "1" is
    a. green, inflated.
    b. green, constricted.
    c. yellow, inflated.
    d. yellow, constricted.

    ANS: A   DIF: II   OBJ: 9-2.1

25. Refer to the illustration above. The genotype represented by the cell labeled "2" is
    a. Ggli.
    b. GGli.
    c. GI.
    d. Gi.

    ANS: B   DIF: II   OBJ: 9-2.1

26. 2,000 yellow seeds : 8,000 total seeds ::
    a. 1 : 6
    b. 1 : 8
    c. 1 : 3
    d. 1 : 4

    ANS: D   DIF: II   OBJ: 9-2.1

In rabbits, black fur (B) is dominant to brown fur (b). Consider the following cross between two rabbits.

Bb x Bb

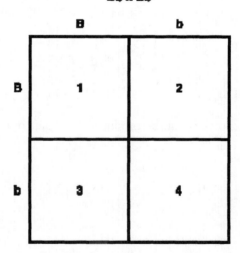

27. Refer to the illustration above. The device shown, which is used to determine the probable outcome of genetic crosses, is called a
   a. Mendelian box.
   c. Genetic graph.
   b. Punnett square.
   d. Phenotypic paradox.

   ANS: B   DIF: I   OBJ: 9-2.2

28. Refer to the illustration above. Both of the parents in the cross are
   a. black.
   c. homozygous dominant.
   b. brown.
   d. homozygous recessive.

   ANS: A   DIF: II   OBJ: 9-2.2

29. Refer to the illustration above. The phenotype of the offspring indicated by box "3" would be
   a. brown.
   c. a mixture of brown and black.
   b. black.
   d. The phenotype cannot be determined.

   ANS: B   DIF: II   OBJ: 9-2.2

30. Refer to the illustration above. The genotypic ratio of the F_1 generation would be
   a. 1:1.
   c. 1:3.
   b. 3:1.
   d. 1:2:1.

   ANS: D   DIF: II   OBJ: 9-2.2

31. What is the expected genotypic ratio resulting from a homozygous dominant × heterozygous monohybrid cross?
   a. 1:0
   c. 1:2:1
   b. 1:1
   d. 1:3:1

   ANS: B   DIF: II   OBJ: 9-2.2

32. What fraction of the offspring resulting from a heterozygous × heterozygous dihybrid cross are homozygous recessive for both traits?
   a. 9/16
   c. 3/16
   b. 1/4
   d. 1/16

   ANS: D   DIF: II   OBJ: 9-2.2

33. What is the expected genotypic ratio resulting from a heterozygous × heterozygous monohybrid cross?
   a. 1:2:1
   c. 1:2
   b. 1:3:1
   d. 1:0

   ANS: A   DIF: II   OBJ: 9-2.2

34. What is the expected phenotypic ratio resulting from a homozygous dominant × heterozygous monohybrid cross?
    a. 1:3:1
    b. 1:2:1
    c. 2:1
    d. 1:0

    ANS: D   DIF: II   OBJ: 9-2.2

	RY	Ry	rY	ry
RY	X		6	
Ry			1	3
rY		2	5	4
ry				

R = round
r = wrinkled
Y = yellow
y = green

35. Refer to the illustration above. The phenotype represented by the cell labeled "1" is
    a. round, yellow.
    b. round, green.
    c. wrinkled, yellow.
    d. wrinkled, green.

    ANS: A   DIF: II   OBJ: 9-2.2

36. Refer to the illustration above. The genotype represented by the cell labeled "2" is
    a. RRYY.
    b. RrYY.
    c. RrYy.
    d. rrYy.

    ANS: C   DIF: II   OBJ: 9-2.2

37. Refer to the illustration above. Which of the following cells represents the same phenotype as the cell labeled "X"?
    a. "3"
    b. "4"
    c. "5"
    d. "6"

    ANS: D   DIF: II   OBJ: 9-2.2

38. An organism that has inherited two of the same alleles of a gene from its parents is called
    a. hereditary.
    b. heterozygous.
    c. homozygous.
    d. a mutation.

    ANS: C   DIF: I   OBJ: 9-2.2

39. In pea plants, yellow seeds are dominant over green seeds. What would be the expected genotype ratio in a cross between a plant with green seeds and a plant that is heterozygous for seed color?
    a. 1:3
    b. 1:2:1
    c. 4:1
    d. 1:1

    ANS: D   DIF: II   OBJ: 9-2.2

40. codominance : both traits are displayed ::
   a. probability : crosses
   b. heterozygous : alleles are the same
   c. homozygous : alleles are the same
   d. Punnett square : chromosomes combine

   ANS: C   DIF: II   OBJ: 9-2.2

41. The difference between a monohybrid cross and a dihybrid cross is that
   a. monohybrid crosses involve traits for which only one allele exists, while dihybrid traits involve two alleles.
   b. monohybrid crosses involve self-pollination, while dihybrid crosses involve cross-pollination.
   c. monohybrid crosses involve one gene; dihybrid crosses involve two genes.
   d. dihybrid crosses require two Punnett squares; monohybrid crosses need only one.

   ANS: C   DIF: I   OBJ: 9-2.4

42. What fraction of the offspring resulting from a heterozygous × heterozygous dihybrid cross are heterozygous for both traits?
   a. 9/16
   b. 1/4
   c. 3/16
   d. 1/16

   ANS: B   DIF: II   OBJ: 9-2.4

43. A cross of two individuals for a single contrasting trait is called
   a. monohybrid.
   b. dihybrid.
   c. dominant.
   d. codominant.

   ANS: A   DIF: I   OBJ: 9-2.4

COMPLETION

1. A reproductive process in which fertilization occurs within a single plant is
   _____.

   ANS: self-pollination   DIF: I   OBJ: 9-1.1

2. The transferring of pollen between plants is called _____.

   ANS: cross-pollination   DIF: I   OBJ: 9-1.1

3. Mendel produced strains of pea plants through the process of _____.

   ANS: self-pollination   DIF: I   OBJ: 9-1.1

4. When two members of the F_1 generation are allowed to breed with each other, the offspring are referred to as the _____ generation.

   ANS: F_2 DIF: I   OBJ: 9-1.1

5. Mendel called the offspring of the P generation the first filial generation, or
_____.

ANS: F_1 generation   DIF: I   OBJ: 9-1.1

6. _____ refers to the transmission of traits from parent to offspring in sexually reproducing organisms.

ANS: Heredity   DIF: I   OBJ: 9-1.1

7. In heterozygous individuals, only the _____ allele achieves expression.

ANS: dominant   DIF: I   OBJ: 9-1.2

8. A trait that is not expressed in the F_1 generation resulting from the crossbreeding of two genetically different, true-breeding organisms is called _____.

ANS: recessive   DIF: I   OBJ: 9-1.2

9. The principle that states that one factor may mask the effect of another factor is the principle of _____.

ANS: dominance   DIF: I   OBJ: 9-1.2

10. In Mendel's experiments, a trait that disappeared in the F_1 generation but reappeared in the F_2 generation was always a _____.

ANS: recessive trait   DIF: II   OBJ: 9-1.2

11. The statement that the members of each pair of alleles separate when gametes are formed is known as the _____.

ANS: law of segregation   DIF: I   OBJ: 9-1.3

12. Different forms of a particular gene are called _____.

ANS: alleles   DIF: I   OBJ: 9-1.3

13. The cellular process that results in the segregation of Mendel's factors is
_____.

ANS: meiosis   DIF: I   OBJ: 9-1.3

14. Mendel formulated two principles known as the laws of _____.

ANS: heredity   DIF: I   OBJ: 9-1.3

15. Different forms of a particular gene are called _____.

ANS: alleles   DIF: I   OBJ: 9-1.4

16. The portion of a DNA molecule containing the coded instructions that result in an individual characteristic of an organism is called a(n) _____.

    ANS: gene   DIF: I   OBJ: 9-1.5

17. An organism that has two identical alleles for a trait is called _____.

    ANS: homozygous   DIF: I   OBJ: 9-2.1

18. An organism's _____ refers to the set of alleles it has inherited.

    ANS: genotype   DIF: I   OBJ: 9-2.1

19. The appearance of an organism as a result of its genotype is its _____.

    ANS: phenotype   DIF: I   OBJ: 9-2.1

20. The likelihood that a specific event will occur is called _____.

    ANS: probability   DIF: I   OBJ: 9-2.1

RRYy X RrYy

	RY	Ry	RY	Ry
RY				
Ry	X			
xx				
ry				

Pea Plants
R = round seed
r = wrinkled seed
Y = yellow seed
y = green seed

21. Refer to the illustration above. The cell of the Punnett square labeled "X" represents the phenotype _____.

    ANS: round, yellow seeds   DIF: I   OBJ: 9-2.1

22. A fractional probability of 1/2 is the same as a decimal probability of _____.

    ANS: 0.5   DIF: II   OBJ: 9-2.1

In pea plants, tallness (T) is dominant to shortness (t). Crosses between plants with these traits can be analyzed using a Punnett square similar to the one shown below.

	T	t
T	1	2
t	3	4

23. Refer to the illustration above. The parents shown in the Punnett square could have offspring with a genotype ratio of _____.

ANS: 1:2:1   DIF: II   OBJ: 9-2.2

24. Refer to the illustration above. Box "2" and box _____ in the Punnett square represent plants that would be heterozygous for the trait for tallness.

ANS: "3"   DIF: II   OBJ: 9-2.2

25. Refer to the illustration above. The phenotype of the plant that would be represented in box "4" of the Punnett square would be _____.

ANS: short   DIF: II   OBJ: 9-2.2

26. Refer to the illustration above. The genotype of both parents shown in the Punnett square above is _____.

ANS: Tt   DIF: II   OBJ: 9-2.2

27. A situation in which two or more alleles influence a phenotype is called

_____.

ANS: codominance   DIF: I   OBJ: 9-2.2

28. A trait controlled by three or more alleles is said to have _____.

ANS: multiple alleles   DIF: I   OBJ: 9-2.2

29. A phenomenon in which a heterozygous individual has a phenotype that is intermediate between the phenotypes of its two homozygous parents is called

_____.

ANS: incomplete dominance   DIF: I   OBJ: 9-2.2

30. A table used to determine and diagram the results of a genetic cross is called a

_____.

ANS: Punnett square   DIF: I   OBJ: 9-2.2

31. In genetics, lowercase letters are usually used to indicate _____.

ANS: recessive traits   DIF: I   OBJ: 9-2.2

32. A cross involving two pairs of contrasting traits is a(n) _____ cross.

ANS: dihybrid   DIF: I   OBJ: 9-2.4

PROBLEM

1. In tomato plants, tallness is dominant over dwarfness and hairy stems are dominant over hairless stems. True-breeding (homozygous) plants that are tall and have hairy stems are available. True-breeding (homozygous) plants that are dwarf and have hairless stems are also available. Design an experiment to determine whether the genes for height and hairiness of the stem are on the same or different chromosomes. Explain how you will be able to determine from the results whether the genes are on the same or different chromosomes. Write your answer in the space below.

ANS:
The experiment should be designed to produce F_1 plants that are then allowed to pollinate each others' flowers and produce an F_2 generation of plants. If the F_2 generation has four different phenotypes present in approximate proportions of 9/16 tall and hairy, 3/16 tall and hairless, 3/16 dwarf and hairy, and 1/16 dwarf and hairless then the student can conclude that the genes for height and hairiness are on different chromosomes. If the F_2 generation has only two different phenotypes present in approximate proportions of 3/4 tall and hairy and 1/4 dwarf and hairless then the student can conclude that the genes for height and hairiness are on the same chromosome. He could also conclude that the genes are located very close to each other on the chromosome. If the F_2 generation has four different phenotypes with the tall and hairless types composing less than 3/16 of the total number and the dwarf and hairy types composing less than 3/16 of the total number, then the student could conclude that the genes for height and hairiness are on the same chromosome but not located adjacent to each other.

DIF: III   OBJ: 9-1.5

2. A scientist crossed true-breeding tall and hairy-stemmed tomato plants with true-breeding dwarf and hairless-stemmed tomato plants. He found that all of the F_1 plants produced as a result of this cross were tall and hairy-stemmed. He then allowed the F_1 plants to pollinate each other and obtained 1000 F_2 plants. Of these 1000 F_2 plants, he observed the following numbers of four different phenotypes:

557 tall and hairy-stemmed plants	192 dwarf and hairy-stemmed plants
180 tall and hairless-stemmed plants	71 dwarf and hairless-stemmed plants

Write your answers to the following in the space below or on a separate sheet of paper.
a. Which height characteristic is dominant, tallness or dwarfness?
b. Which stem hairiness characteristic is dominant, hairiness or hairlessness?
c. What are the genotypes of the original, true-breeding parents? (Be sure to indicate what the symbols you use stand for.)
d. What are the genotypes of the F_1 hybrid plants? (Be sure to indicate what the symbols you use stand for.)
e. What are the genotypes of the four types of plants found in the F_2 generation? (Be sure to indicate what the symbols you use stand for.)
f. What were the expected numbers of plants of each type in the F_2 generation? (Round off to the nearest whole numbers)
g. Why did the observed numbers of plants of each type in the F_2 generation differ from the expected?
h. How could this experiment have been changed to obtain numbers of plants of each type in the F_2 generation that were closer to the expected numbers?

ANS:
a. tallness is dominant
b. hairiness is dominant
c. Let T stand for tallness, t stand for dwarfness, H stand for hairiness, and h stand for hairlessness. The tall, hairy-stemmed true-breeding parent has the genotype TTHH. The dwarf, hairless-stemmed true-breeding parent has the genotype tthh.
d. Use the same symbols as in question c above. The F_1 plants all have the same genotype, which is TtHh.
e. Use the same symbols as in question c above. The possible genotypes of the F_2 plants are the following:
    tall and hairy-stemmed plants: TTHH, TTHh, TtHh, TTHh, TtHh, TtHH
    tall and hairless-stemmed plants: TThh, Tthh
    dwarf and hairy-stemmed plants: ttHH, ttHh
    dwarf and hairless-stemmed plants: tthh
f. The expected numbers were as follows: 563 tall and hairy-stemmed plants, 188 tall and hairless-stemmed plants, 188 dwarf and hairy-stemmed plants, 63 dwarf and hairless-stemmed plants. (Notice that rounding causes the total to exceed 1000.)
g. The expected numbers are based on probabilities. The actual numbers should be close to the expected, but would not likely be exactly the expected numbers.
h. Increasing the sample size, say to 10,000 plants would likely result in the observed numbers being closer to the expected numbers. Again, this is because of probabilities.

DIF: III   OBJ: 9-2.2

ESSAY

3. Briefly discuss the reasons that Mendel chose the pea plant, *Pisum sativum*, as the organism to study in his experiments. Write your answer in the space below.

ANS:
The pea plant, *Pisum sativum*, is an ideal organism for genetic studies for several reasons. There are a number of traits that are easily identified and tracked from generation to generation. Each of these traits has two forms, one of which regularly disappears and reappears in alternate generations. Also, this species is easy to grow and matures quickly. Finally, gametes of both sexes are found in the same flower, so cross-pollination is easy to accomplish by removing the anthers from some flowers and transferring pollen from others to the remaining pistils.

DIF: I   OBJ: 9-1.1

4. Describe pollination in pea plants. Write your answer in the space below.

ANS:
The reproductive structures of seed plants are located inside the flowers. In pea plants, each flower has both male and female structures. The male reproductive parts, the anthers, produce pollen grains that contain sperm. The female reproductive structure produces the egg. The tip of the female structure is called the stigma. Pollination is the transfer of pollen from anthers to stigma.

DIF: I   OBJ: 9-1.1

5. In what ways did Mendel's methods help ensure his success in unraveling the mechanics of heredity? Write your answer in the space below.

ANS:
Mendel's choice of plants to study was fortunate since pea plants displayed several traits in contrasting forms. His use of large numbers of samples allowed the gathering of statistically significant amounts of data. In addition, he kept very careful records and used logical, orderly methods that minimized the possibility of errors.

DIF: II   OBJ: 9-1.1

6. What conclusions did Gregor Mendel reach based on his observations of pea plants? Write your answer in the space below.

ANS:
Mendel studied the hereditary patterns of pea plants by observing the results of controlled crosses. After studying the results of these crosses, Mendel concluded that patterns of inheritance were governed by three principles: (1) the principle of dominance and recessiveness, (2) the principle of segregation, and (3) the principle of independent assortment.

DIF: I   OBJ: 9-1.3

7. Describe the law of independent assortment. Write your answer in the space below.

ANS:
From his work on pea plants, Mendel concluded that factors for different characteristics are not connected. He stated the principle of independent assortment: Factors for different characteristics are distributed to reproductive cells independently.

DIF: I   OBJ: 9-1.3

8. What are three ways to express the probability of an event that occurs 500 times out of 2,000 total trials? Write your answer in the space below.

ANS:
This may be expressed as a ratio (1:4), as a decimal (0.25), or as a percentage (25 percent).

DIF: II   OBJ: 9-2.1

9. Describe how genotype and phenotype are related. Write your answer in the space below.

ANS:
The genetic makeup of an organism is its genotype. The external appearance of an organism as a result of its genotype is its phenotype. For example, the genotype of a pure tall plant is TT. It consists of two dominant alleles for height—T and T. The plant's phenotype, or appearance, is tall.

DIF: II   OBJ: 9-2.2

10. Explain what is meant by homozygous and heterozygous. Write your answer in the space below.

ANS:
When both alleles of a pair are the same, an organism is said to be homozygous for that characteristic. An organism may be homozygous dominant or homozygous recessive. A pea plant that is homozygous dominant for height will have the genotype TT. A pea plant that is homozygous recessive for height will have the genotype tt. When the two alleles in the pair are not the same—for example, when the genotype is Tt—the organism is heterozygous for that characteristic.

DIF: I   OBJ: 9-2.2

11. All of the offspring resulting from a cross between a red snapdragon and a white snapdragon are pink. What is a possible explanation for this? Write your answer in the space below.

ANS:
Incomplete dominance is the phenomenon that occurs when two or more alleles influence a phenotype. In other words, the offspring displays a trait that is intermediate to a trait exhibited by each parent. In this case, the genotype $A^R A^R$ produces red flowers, $A^W A^W$ produces white flowers, and $A^R A^W$ produces pink flowers.

DIF: II   OBJ: 9-2.2

TRUE/FALSE

1. Despite years of research, the actual structure of the DNA molecule is still unknown.

   ANS: F   DIF: I   OBJ: 10-1.2

2. Franklin's X-ray diffraction images suggested that the DNA molecule resembled a tightly coiled spring, a shape called a helix.

   ANS: T   DIF: I   OBJ: 10-1.2

3. In all living things, DNA replication must occur after cell division.

   ANS: F   DIF: I   OBJ: 10-1.5

4. Multiple DNA polymerases may become attached to more than one portion of a DNA molecule at once, speeding up the rate of replication.

   ANS: T   DIF: I   OBJ: 10-1.5

5. Before a DNA molecule can replicate itself, it must make itself more compact. This is accomplished by the double helix coiling up on itself.

   ANS: F   DIF: I   OBJ: 10-1.5

6. During transcription, the information on a DNA molecule is "rewritten" into an mRNA molecule.

   ANS: T   DIF: I   OBJ: 10-2.4

7. Repressor proteins are bound to the DNA in front of each gene, readily allowing transcription to take place as the RNA polymerase moves along that gene.

   ANS: F   DIF: I   OBJ: 10-2.4

8. It has been discovered that each species of organism has its own unique genetic code for synthesis of its proteins.

   ANS: F   DIF: I   OBJ: 10-3.1

9. The genetic code is different in nearly all organisms.

   ANS: F   DIF: I   OBJ: 10-3.1

10. When a tRNA anticodon binds to an mRNA codon, the amino acid detaches from the tRNA molecule and attaches to the end of a growing protein chain.

    ANS: T   DIF: I   OBJ: 10-3.2

Modern Biology Assessment Item Listing
91

11. A codon signifies either a specific amino acid or a stop signal.

    ANS: T   DIF: I   OBJ: 10-3.3

12. Only ribosomal RNA plays a role in translation.

    ANS: F   DIF: I   OBJ: 10-3.4

MULTIPLE CHOICE

1. Each organism has a unique combination of characteristics encoded in molecules of
   a. protein.   c. carbohydrates.
   b. enzymes.   d. DNA.

    ANS: D   DIF: I   OBJ: 10-1.1

2. The primary function of DNA is to
   a. make proteins.
   b. store and transmit genetic information.
   c. control chemical processes within cells.
   d. prevent mutations.

    ANS: B   DIF: II   OBJ: 10-1.1

3. All of the following are true about the structure of DNA *except*
   a. short strands of DNA are contained in chromosomes inside the nucleus of a cell.
   b. every DNA nucleotide contains a sugar, a phosphate group, and a base.
   c. DNA consists of two strands of nucleotides joined by hydrogen bonds.
   d. the long strands of nucleotides are twisted into a double helix.

    ANS: A   DIF: I   OBJ: 10-1.2

4. Molecules of DNA are composed of long chains of
   a. amino acids.   c. monosaccharides.
   b. fatty acids.   d. nucleotides.

    ANS: D   DIF: I   OBJ: 10-1.2

5. Which of the following is *not* part of a molecule of DNA?
   a. deoxyribose   c. phosphate
   b. nitrogenous base   d. ribose

    ANS: D   DIF: I   OBJ: 10-1.2

6. A nucleotide consists of
   a. a sugar, a protein, and adenine.
   b. a sugar, an amino acid, and starch.
   c. a sugar, a phosphate group, and a nitrogen-containing base.
   d. a starch, a phosphate group, and a nitrogen-containing base.

    ANS: C   DIF: I   OBJ: 10-1.2

7. The part of the molecule for which deoxyribonucleic acid is named is the
   a. phosphate group.
   b. sugar.
   c. nitrogen base.
   d. None of the above; DNA is not named after part of the molecule.

   ANS: B   DIF: I   OBJ: 10-1.2

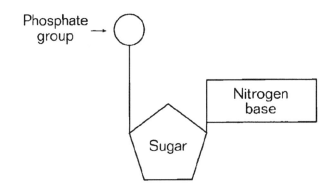

8. Refer to the illustration above. The entire molecule shown in the diagram is called a(n)
   a. amino acid.   c. polysaccharide.
   b. nucleotide.   d. pyrimidine.

   ANS: B   DIF: I   OBJ: 10-1.2

9. Purines and pyrimidines are
   a. bases found in amino acids.
   b. able to replace phosphate groups from defective DNA.
   c. names of specific types of DNA molecules.
   d. bases found in nucleotides.

   ANS: D   DIF: I   OBJ: 10-1.2

10. The scientists credited with establishing the structure of DNA are
    a. Avery and Chargaff.   c. Mendel and Griffith.
    b. Hershey and Chase.   d. Watson and Crick.

    ANS: D   DIF: I   OBJ: 10-1.2

11. X-ray diffraction photographs by Wilkins and Franklin suggested that
    a. DNA and RNA are the same molecules.
    b. DNA is composed of either purines or pyrimidines, but not both.
    c. DNA molecules are arranged as a tightly coiled helix.
    d. DNA and proteins have the same basic structure.

    ANS: C   DIF: I   OBJ: 10-1.2

12. Watson and Crick built models that demonstrated that
    a. DNA and RNA have the same structure.
    b. the DNA helix is held together by hydrogen bonds.
    c. guanine forms hydrogen bonds with adenine.
    d. thymine forms hydrogen bonds with cytosine.

    ANS: B   DIF: I   OBJ: 10-1.2

13. Chargaff's rules, or the base-pairing rules, state that in DNA
    a. the amount of adenine equals the amount of thymine.
    b. the amount of guanine equals the amount of cytosine.
    c. the amount of guanine equals the amount of thymine.
    d. Both a and b

    ANS: D   DIF: I   OBJ: 10-1.3

14. The base-pairing rules state that the following are base pairs in DNA:
    a. adenine—thymine; uracil—cytosine.
    b. adenine—thymine; guanine—cytosine.
    c. adenine—guanine; thymine—cytosine.
    d. uracil—thymine; guanine—cytosine.

    ANS: B   DIF: I   OBJ: 10-1.3

15. ATTG : TAAC ::
    a. AAAT : TTTG   c. GTCC : CAGG
    b. TCGG : AGAT   d. CGAA : TGCG

    ANS: C   DIF: II   OBJ: 10-1.3

16. The attachment of nucleotides to form a complementary strand of DNA
    a. is catalyzed by DNA polymerase.
    b. is accomplished only in the presence of tRNA.
    c. prevents separation of complementary strands of RNA.
    d. is the responsibility of the complementary DNA mutagens.

    ANS: A   DIF: I   OBJ: 10-1.4

17. Which of the following is *not* true about DNA replication?
    a. It must occur before a cell can divide.
    b. Two complementary strands are duplicated.
    c. The double strand unwinds while it is being duplicated.
    d. The process is catalyzed by enzymes called DNA mutagens.

    ANS: D   DIF: I   OBJ: 10-1.4

18. During DNA replication, a complementary strand of DNA is made for each original DNA
    strand. Thus, if a portion of the original strand is CCTAGCT, then the new strand will be
    a. TTGCATG.   c. CCTAGCT.
    b. AAGTATC.   d. GGATCGA.

    ANS: D   DIF: II   OBJ: 10-1.4

19. The enzymes responsible for adding nucleotides to the exposed DNA template bases are
    a. replicases.
    b. DNA polymerases.
    c. helicases.
    d. nucleotidases.

    ANS: B   DIF: I   OBJ: 10-1.5

20. The function of rRNA is to
    a. synthesize DNA.
    b. synthesize mRNA.
    c. form ribosomes.
    d. transfer amino acids to ribosomes.

    ANS: C   DIF: I   OBJ: 10-2.1

21. Which of the following types of RNA carries instructions for making proteins?
    a. mRNA
    b. rRNA
    c. tRNA
    d. All of the above

    ANS: A   DIF: II   OBJ: 10-2.1

22. RNA differs from DNA in that RNA
    a. is sometimes single-stranded.
    b. contains a different sugar molecule.
    c. contains the nitrogen base uracil.
    d. All of the above

    ANS: D   DIF: I   OBJ: 10-2.2

23. Which of the following is *not* found in DNA?
    a. adenine
    b. cytosine
    c. uracil
    d. None of the above

    ANS: C   DIF: I   OBJ: 10-2.2

24. RNA is chemically similar to DNA except that its sugars have an additional oxygen atom, and the base thymine is replaced by a structurally similar base called
    a. uracil.
    b. alanine.
    c. cytosine.
    d. codon.

    ANS: A   DIF: I   OBJ: 10-2.2

25. In RNA molecules, adenine is complementary to
    a. cytosine.
    b. guanine.
    c. thymine.
    d. uracil.

    ANS: D   DIF: I   OBJ: 10-2.2

mRNA: CUCAAGUGCUUC

Genetic Code:

		U	C	A	G	
		Phe	Ser	Tyr	Cys	U
	U	Phe	Ser	Tyr	Cys	C
		Leu	Ser	stop	stop	A
		Leu	Ser	stop	Trp	G
		Leu	Pro	His	Arg	U
	C	Leu	Pro	His	Arg	C
		Leu	Pro	Gln	Arg	A
		Leu	Pro	Gln	Arg	G
		Ile	Thr	Asn	Ser	U
	A	Ile	Thr	Asn	Ser	C
		Ile	Thr	Lys	Arg	A
		Met	Thr	Lys	Arg	G
		Val	Ala	Asp	Gly	U
	G	Val	Ala	Asp	Gly	C
		Val	Ala	Glu	Gly	A
		Val	Ala	Glu	Gly	G

26. Refer to the illustration above. What is the portion of the protein molecule coded for by the piece of mRNA shown in the diagram?
    a. Ser—Tyr—Arg—Gly
    b. Val—Asp—Pro—His
    c. Leu—Lys—Cys—Phe
    d. Pro—Glu—Leu—Val

    ANS: C   DIF: II   OBJ: 10-2.2

27. Which of the following would represent the strand of DNA from which the mRNA strand in the diagram was made?
    a. CUCAAGUGCUUC
    b. GAGUUCACGAAG
    c. GAGTTCACGAAG
    d. AGACCTGTAGGA

    ANS: C   DIF: II   OBJ: 10-2.2

28. Refer to the illustration above. The anticodons for the codons in the mRNA in the diagram are
    a. GAG—UUC—ACG—AAG.
    b. GAG—TTC—ACG—AAG.
    c. CUC—GAA—CGU—CUU.
    d. CUU—CGU—GAA—CUC.

    ANS: A   DIF: II   OBJ: 10-3.2

29. A ribosome has
    a. one binding site for DNA.
    b. three binding sites used during translation.
    c. four binding sites for tRNA.
    d. no binding sites since the proteins must detach.

    ANS: B   DIF: I   OBJ: 10-2.2

30. Suppose that you are given a polypeptide sequence containing the following sequence of amino acids: tyrosine, proline, aspartic acid, isoleucine, and cysteine. Use the portion of the genetic code given in the table below to determine the DNA sequence that codes for this polypeptide sequence.

mRNAs	Amino acid
UAU, UAC	tyrosine
CCU, CCC, CCA, CCG	proline
GAU, GAC	aspartic acid
AUU, AUC, AUA	isoleucine
UGU, UGC	cysteine

  a. AUGGGUCUAUAUACG   c. GCAAACTCGCGCGTA
  b. ATGGGTCTATATACG   d. ATAGGGCTTTAAACA

ANS: B   DIF: III   OBJ: 10-2.2

31. Each of the following is a type of RNA *except*
  a. carrier RNA.   c. ribosomal RNA.
  b. messenger RNA.   d. transfer RNA.

ANS: A   DIF: I   OBJ: 10-2.3

32. Transfer RNA acts as an "interpreter" because it
  a. carries an amino acid to its correct codon.
  b. synthesizes amino acids as they are needed.
  c. produces codons to match the correct anticodons.
  d. converts DNA into mRNA.

ANS: A   DIF: I   OBJ: 10-2.3

33. In order for protein synthesis to occur, mRNA must migrate to the
  a. ribosomes.   c. RNA polymerase.
  b. *lac* operon.   d. heterochromatin.

ANS: A   DIF: I   OBJ: 10-2.3

34. During transcription
  a. proteins are synthesized.   c. RNA is produced.
  b. DNA is replicated.   d. translation occurs.

ANS: C   DIF: I   OBJ: 10-2.4

35. Transcription proceeds when RNA polymerase
  a. attaches to a ribosome.   c. binds to a strand of RNA.
  b. binds to a strand of DNA.   d. attaches to a promoter molecule.

ANS: B   DIF: I   OBJ: 10-2.4

36. Transcription is the process by which genetic information encoded in DNA is transferred to a(n)
    a. RNA molecule.
    b. DNA molecule.
    c. uracil molecule.
    d. transposon.

    ANS: A   DIF: I   OBJ: 10-2.4

37. After the primary structure of a protein has been completed
    a. the codons and anticodons unite.
    b. an enzyme attaches adjacent amino acids to each other to form a chain.
    c. the protein folds into the secondary and tertiary structures.
    d. the tRNA molecules remain attached until the protein is secreted from the cell.

    ANS: C   DIF: I   OBJ: 10-2.4

38. Each nucleotide triplet in mRNA that specifies a particular amino acid is called a
    a. mutagen.
    b. codon.
    c. anticodon.
    d. exon.

    ANS: B   DIF: I   OBJ: 10-3.2

39. codon : nucleotides ::
    a. ribosome : binding sites
    b. ribosome : DNA molecules
    c. RNA : bases
    d. DNA : bases

    ANS: A   DIF: II   OBJ: 10-3.3

40. During translation, the amino acid detaches from the transfer RNA molecule and attaches to the end of a growing protein chain when
    a. the ribosomal RNA anticodon binds to messenger RNA codon.
    b. the transfer RNA anticodon binds to the messenger RNA codon.
    c. a "stop" codon is encountered.
    d. the protein chain sends a signal through the nerve cells to the brain.

    ANS: B   DIF: I   OBJ: 10-3.4

41. During translation in eukaryotes, anticodons
    a. never bind to the mRNA codons.
    b. assist in the assembly of fats.
    c. consist of a five-nucleotide sequence at one end of the transfer RNA molecule.
    d. ensure that each amino acid is delivered to its proper "address" on the mRNA.

    ANS: D   DIF: I   OBJ: 10-3.4

COMPLETION

1. In eukaryotes, gene expression is related to the coiling and uncoiling of
   _____.

   ANS: DNA   DIF: I   OBJ: 10-1.1

2. A DNA subunit composed of a phosphate group, a five-carbon sugar, and a nitrogen-containing base is called a(n) _____.

   ANS: nucleotide   DIF: I   OBJ: 10-1.2

3. The name of the five-carbon sugar that makes up a part of the backbone of molecules of DNA is _____.

   ANS: deoxyribose   DIF: I   OBJ: 10-1.2

4. Watson and Crick determined that DNA molecules have the shape of a(n) _____.

   ANS: double helix   DIF: I   OBJ: 10-1.2

5. Knowing the order of the bases in a gene permits scientists to determine the exact order of the amino acids in the expressed _____.

   ANS: protein   DIF: I   OBJ: 10-1.2

6. Due to the strict pairing of nitrogen base pairs in DNA molecules, the two strands are said to be _____ to each other.

   ANS: complementary   DIF: I   OBJ: 10-1.3

7. According to base-pairing rules, adenine pairs with _____ and guanine pairs with _____.

   ANS: thymine, cytosine   DIF: I   OBJ: 10-1.3

8. The enzyme that is responsible for replicating molecules of DNA by attaching complementary bases in the correct sequence is _____.

   ANS: DNA polymerase   DIF: I   OBJ: 10-1.4

9. Enzymes called _____ are responsible for unwinding the DNA double helix by breaking the hydrogen bonds that hold the complementary strands together.

   ANS: helicases   DIF: I   OBJ: 10-1.5

10. The process by which DNA copies itself is called _____.

    ANS: replication   DIF: I   OBJ: 10-1.5

11. Molecules of _____ carry instructions for protein synthesis from the nucleus to the cytoplasm.

    ANS: RNA   DIF: I   OBJ: 10-2.1

12. The nitrogen-containing base that is found only in RNA is _____.

    ANS: uracil   DIF: I   OBJ: 10-2.2

13. The enzyme responsible for making RNA is called _____.

    ANS: RNA polymerase   DIF: I   OBJ: 10-2.3

14. The form of ribonucleic acid that carries genetic information from the DNA to the ribosomes is _____.

    ANS: mRNA   DIF: I   OBJ: 10-2.3

15. A _____ is a sequence of DNA at the beginning of a gene that signals RNA polymerase to begin transcription.

    ANS: promoter   DIF: I   OBJ: 10-2.4

16. Messenger RNA is produced during the process of _____.

    ANS: transcription   DIF: I   OBJ: 10-2.4

17. Of the 64 codons of mRNA, 61 code for _____, 3 are _____ signals, and one is a _____ signal.

    ANS: amino acids; stop; start   DIF: I   OBJ: 10-3.1

18. Nucleotide sequences of tRNA that are complementary to codons on mRNA are called _____.

    ANS: anticodons   DIF: I   OBJ: 10-3.2

19. The sequence of three nucleotides that code for specific amino acids or stop signals in the synthesis of protein is called a(n) _____.

    ANS: codon   DIF: I   OBJ: 10-3.3

20. The information contained in a molecule of messenger RNA is used to make protein during the process of _____.

    ANS: translation   DIF: I   OBJ: 10-3.4

21. During translation, amino acids are brought to the ribosomes by molecules of _____.

    ANS: transfer RNA   DIF: I   OBJ: 10-3.4

ESSAY

1. The DNA molecule is described as a double helix. Describe the meaning of this expression and the general structure of a DNA molecule. Write your answer in the space below.

   ANS:
   DNA molecules are composed of two complementary strands of nucleotides arranged in a pattern resembling a spiral staircase. Each nucleotide consists of a sugar molecule, a phosphate group, and one of four possible bases. The double helix arrangement is maintained by the formation of hydrogen bonds between complementary bases.

   DIF: II   OBJ: 10-1.2

2. Describe how a molecule of DNA is replicated. Write your answer in the space below.

   ANS:
   To begin the replication process, enzymes called helicases break the hydrogen bonds that hold the two complementary strands of the DNA double helix together, allowing the helix to unwind. At the replication fork, the point at which the double helix separates, a molecule of DNA polymerase attaches and begins to add nucleotides to the exposed bases according to the base-pairing rules. This continues until the DNA polymerase reaches a nucleotide sequence that signals it to detach, having completed the replication of the DNA strand.

   DIF: II   OBJ: 10-1.5

3. Identify the three types of RNA and briefly describe the function of each. Write your answer in the space below.

   ANS:
   Three types of RNA are: messenger RNA (mRNA), transfer RNA (tRNA), and ribosomal RNA (rRNA). Messenger RNA carries hereditary information from the DNA in the nucleus to the site of translation on the ribosomes; tRNA carries amino acids to the ribosomes for assembly into proteins; rRNA is a structural molecule, becoming part of the ribosomes upon which translation occurs.

   DIF: II   OBJ: 10-2.3

Modern Biology Assessment Item Listing
101

TRUE/FALSE

1. There are four steps in the process of gene expression.

    ANS: F   DIF: I   OBJ: 11-1.1

2. Cells regulate gene expression so that each gene will only be transcribed when it is needed.

    ANS: T   DIF: I   OBJ: 11-1.1

3. Gene expression is prevented when a repressor binds to the regulator gene.

    ANS: F   DIF: I   OBJ: 11-1.1

4. The operator portion of an operon controls RNA polymerase's access to structural genes.

    ANS: T   DIF: I   OBJ: 11-1.2

5. A repressor binds to the operator region when lactose is present.

    ANS: F   DIF: I   OBJ: 11-1.2

6. Introns are inert segments of DNA.

    ANS: T   DIF: II   OBJ: 11-1.3

7. Introns are the portions of a gene that actually get translated into proteins.

    ANS: F   DIF: I   OBJ: 11-1.3

8. When mRNA leaves the nucleus and enters the cytoplasm, it has a complete set of both introns and exons.

    ANS: F   DIF: I   OBJ: 11-1.3

9. Introns are deleted before being transcribed from DNA into mRNA.

    ANS: F   DIF: I   OBJ: 11-1.3

10. The DNA in different types of cells of a mature organism differs, which is why the cells have different forms and functions.

    ANS: F   DIF: I   OBJ: 11-2.1

11. A mutation in a homeotic gene can result in the formation of legs in parts of the *Drosophila* body that normally do not have legs.

    ANS: T   DIF: I   OBJ: 11-2.2

12. Specific homeoboxes control the morphogenesis of specific parts of an adult organism.

ANS: T   DIF: I   OBJ: 11-2.2

13. The cells of a malignant tumor undergo metastasis.

ANS: T   DIF: I   OBJ: 11-2.4

14. The difference between oncogenes and tumor-suppressor genes is that oncogenes are mutant forms of genes that lack the ability to regulate cell division and tumor-suppressor genes are genes that regulate cell division but can lose this ability if they become mutated.

ANS: T   DIF: II   OBJ: 11-2.5

MULTIPLE CHOICE

1. Cells must control gene expression so that
   a. their genes will only be expressed when needed.
   b. their genes will always be expressed.
   c. their genes will never be expressed.
   d. genetic disorders can be corrected.

ANS: A   DIF: I   OBJ: 11-1.1

2. Cells control the expression of their genes
   a. with regulatory sites found on each gene.
   b. with specific regulatory proteins.
   c. by determining when individual genes are to be transcribed.
   d. All of the above

ANS: D   DIF: I   OBJ: 11-1.1

3. In prokaryotic cells, a group of genes that code for functionally related proteins is a(n)
   a. exon.   c. operon.
   b. intron.   d. riboson.

ANS: C   DIF: I   OBJ: 11-1.2

4. The function of an operator is to
   a. regulate access of RNA polymerase to structural genes.
   b. turn on and off the molecules of tRNA.
   c. control the process of transcription within the nucleus.
   d. generate amino acids for protein synthesis.

ANS: A   DIF: I   OBJ: 11-1.2

5. A repressor protein
   a. prevents DNA synthesis.
   b. blocks movement of RNA polymerase.
   c. attaches to ribosomes during translation.
   d. destroys amino acids before protein synthesis occurs.

ANS: B   DIF: I   OBJ: 11-1.2

6. Inducer molecules allow transcription to proceed by
   a. destroying repressor molecules.
   b. unwinding the cell's DNA molecules.
   c. activating the ribosomes.
   d. changing the shape of repressor molecules.

   ANS: D   DIF: I   OBJ: 11-1.2

7. In order for RNA polymerase to attach to a DNA molecule,
   a. an activator must initiate unwinding of DNA.
   b. an inducer must attach to the RNA polymerase molecule.
   c. transcription must first occur.
   d. translation must be completed.

   ANS: A   DIF: I   OBJ: 11-1.2

8. What type of gene codes for a repressor?
   a. regulator   c. operon
   b. promoter   d. enhancer

   ANS: A   DIF: I   OBJ: 11-1.2

9. The presence of a repressor molecule prevents the action of what enzyme?
   a. DNA polymerase   c. RNA polymerase
   b. lactase   d. permease

   ANS: C   DIF: I   OBJ: 11-1.2

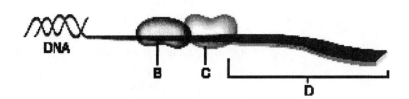

10. Refer to the illustration above. To which portion of the *lac* operon does the repressor
    bind?
    a. regulator   c. "C"
    b. "B"   d. "D"

    ANS: C   DIF: II   OBJ: 11-1.2

11. Refer to the illustration above. Which of the following structures codes for the repressor?
    a. regulator   c. "C"
    b. "B"   d. "D"

    ANS: A   DIF: II   OBJ: 11-1.2

12. Refer to the illustration above. Where on the *lac* operon does transcription take place?
   a. regulator
   b. "B"
   c. "C"
   d. "D"

ANS: D   DIF: II   OBJ: 11-1.2

13. Refer to the illustration above. Which portion of the *lac* operon codes for polypeptides?
   a. regulator
   b. "B"
   c. "C"
   d. "D"

ANS: D   DIF: II   OBJ: 11-1.2

14. Where on the *lac* operon does a repressor molecule bind when lactose is absent?
   a. to the operator
   b. to the promoter
   c. to a structural gene
   d. to the regulator

ANS: A   DIF: I   OBJ: 11-1.2

15. The *lac* operon is shut off when
   a. lactose is present.
   b. lactose is absent.
   c. glucose is present.
   d. glucose is absent.

ANS: B   DIF: I   OBJ: 11-1.2

16. An inducer molecule functions by
   a. causing DNA replication.
   b. binding the rRNA subunits of a ribosome.
   c. removing a repressor molecule from an operator.
   d. digesting lactose molecules in bacterial cells.

ANS: C   DIF: I   OBJ: 11-1.2

17. repressor : operator ::
   a. promoter : RNA polymerase
   b. promoter : DNA
   c. termination signal : RNA polymerase
   d. termination signal : DNA

ANS: C   DIF: II   OBJ: 11-1.2

18. The portions of DNA molecules that actually code for the production of proteins are called
   a. mutons.
   b. exons.
   c. introns.
   d. exposons.

ANS: B   DIF: I   OBJ: 11-1.3

19. The noncoding portions of DNA that are separated from the portions of DNA actually used during transcription are called
   a. mutons.
   b. exons.
   c. introns.
   d. exposons.

ANS: C   DIF: I   OBJ: 11-1.3

20. Many thousands of proteins may have arisen from only a few thousand exons because
    a. an exon may be used by many different genes.
    b. there really is no difference between one protein and another.
    c. an exon does not actually code for any meaningful information.
    d. one gene can code for hundreds of different proteins.

    ANS: A   DIF: I   OBJ: 11-1.3

21. After mRNA has been transcribed,
    a. its introns are cut out.   c. it leaves the nucleus by way of pores.
    b. its exons are joined together.   d. All of the above

    ANS: D   DIF: I   OBJ: 11-1.3

22. What must happen in order for a eukaryotic gene to be expressed?
    a. The enhancer must be activated.   c. The enhancer must be inactivated.
    b. A repressor must be present.   d. A repressor must be absent.

    ANS: A   DIF: I   OBJ: 11-1.4

23. A sequence of nucleotides in a DNA molecule that aids in exposing RNA polymerase
    binding sites of specific genes is called a(n)
    a. repressor.   c. operator.
    b. operon.   d. enhancer.

    ANS: D   DIF: I   OBJ: 11-1.4

24. Which of the following is *not* part of morphogenesis?
    a. the formation of cellular extensions in nerve cells and the functioning of these cells
       in receiving and transmitting signals
    b. the formation of long, thin muscle cells that are able to respond to the proper
       stimulus by contracting
    c. the formation of liver cells that produce enzymes that break down fat
    d. the formation of a zygote

    ANS: D   DIF: II   OBJ: 11-2.1

25. Which of the following is *not* characteristic of homeoboxes?
    a. They are genes.
    b. They produce regulatory proteins that switch on or off groups of developmental
       genes.
    c. They determine what species of organism will develop from a zygote.
    d. Each controls the development of a specific part of the adult organism.

    ANS: C   DIF: II   OBJ: 11-2.3

26. A substance that causes cancer is known as a
    a. tumor.   c. mutation.
    b. carcinogen.   d. metastasis.

    ANS: B   DIF: I   OBJ: 11-2.4

27. Metastasis is characterized by
    a. the growth of a benign tumor.
    b. spread of malignant cells beyond their original site.
    c. localization of a tumor to a particular location.
    d. conversion of a malignant tumor to a benign tumor.

    ANS: B   DIF: I   OBJ: 11-2.4

28. Cells grow and divide at an abnormally high rate in
    a. diabetes.   c. cytokinesis.
    b. cancer.   d. mitosis.

    ANS: B   DIF: I   OBJ: 11-2.4

29. An oncogene
    a. metastasizes to other chromosomes.
    b. prevents a cell from reproducing.
    c. induces numerous mutations of the chromosome on which it is found.
    d. may cause a cell to become a cancer cell.

    ANS: D   DIF: I   OBJ: 11-2.5

COMPLETION

1. Transcription and translation are stages in the process of _____.

    ANS: gene expression   DIF: I   OBJ: 11-1.1

2. Cells must regulate gene expression so that genes will only be _____ when the proteins are needed.

    ANS: transcribed   DIF: I   OBJ: 11-1.1

3. The process of _____ is initiated by an inducer.

    ANS: gene expression   DIF: II   OBJ: 11-1.1

4. The first stage of gene expression is called _____.

    ANS: transcription   DIF: I   OBJ: 11-1.1

5. A(n) _____ is a cluster of genes in a bacterial cell that codes for proteins with related functions.

    ANS: operon   DIF: I   OBJ: 11-1.2

6. A _____ is a molecule that prevents transcription by blocking the path of RNA polymerase along a molecule of DNA.

    ANS: repressor protein   DIF: I   OBJ: 11-1.2

7. In certain bacteria, the gene that codes for the production of the enzyme that digests lactose is switched on in the presence of lactose. In this case, molecules of lactose act as _____.

ANS: inducers   DIF: I   OBJ: 11-1.2

8. Nucleotide segments of a DNA molecule that make up genes and are actually expressed in the phenotype of an organism are called _____.

ANS: exons   DIF: I   OBJ: 11-1.3

9. Portions of genes that actually get translated into proteins are called _____.

ANS: exons   DIF: I   OBJ: 11-1.3

10. Genes may be made more accessible to RNA polymerase by a sequence of nucleotides called _____.

ANS: enhancers   DIF: I   OBJ: 11-1.4

11. As an organism grows from a zygote, certain genes in each cell are allowed to be expressed and others are not. This process is called _____ and results in the development of a characteristic form in an organism.

ANS: differentiation   DIF: I   OBJ: 11-2.1

12. In *Drosophila*, _____ genes contain regions within them called _____, each of which controls the morphogenesis of a particular part of the *Drosophila* larva.

ANS: homeotic; homeoboxes   DIF: I   OBJ: 11-2.2

13. The presence of _____ homeobox genes in *Drosophila* and in mice indicates that all eukaryotic organisms may have similar homeoboxes regulating their development.

ANS: homologous   DIF: II   OBJ: 11-2.3

14. Environmental agents that can cause defects in genetic material are called _____.

ANS: mutagens   DIF: I   OBJ: 11-2.4

15. Diseases characterized by abnormal cell growth in which cells undergo repeated uncontrollable divisions are called _____.

ANS: cancers   DIF: I   OBJ: 11-2.4

16. Cancer occurs as a result of disorders in cell _____.

    ANS: division   DIF: I   OBJ: 11-2.4

17. In general, lives are not threatened by tumors that are _____.

    ANS: benign   DIF: I   OBJ: 11-2.4

18. A gene that, when mutated, can cause a cell to become cancerous is called a(n) _____.

    ANS: proto-oncogene   DIF: I   OBJ: 11-2.5

ESSAY

1. In a particular eukaryotic cell, the chromatin fails to uncoil. What effect will this have on gene expression in this cell? Write your answer in the space below.

    ANS:
The degree to which DNA uncoils is an indication of the degree of gene expression. It is the uncoiled DNA that is the site of transcription of DNA into mRNA. Therefore, failure to uncoil will ultimately inhibit or prevent gene expression.

    DIF: II   OBJ: 11-1.1

2. Genes control cellular activities through a two-step process known as gene expression. Name and discuss the significance of the two steps. Write your answer in the space below.

    ANS:
Information encoded in DNA molecules undergoes *transcription* as RNA polymerase makes an mRNA molecule with nucleotides having a sequence that is complementary to that of one of the original DNA strands. The mRNA molecule leaves the nucleus and associates with a ribosome, where the second step, *translation*, occurs. Translation involves the synthesis of the amino acid sequence of a protein molecule by the combined action of mRNA, tRNA, and rRNA. The sequence of mRNA nucleotides determines the sequence of amino acids in the assembled protein.

    DIF: II   OBJ: 11-1.1

3. Describe the physical structure of the *lac* operon. Write your answer in the space below.

    ANS:
The *lac* operon consists of three segments. These include a promoter, an operator, and three structural genes. In addition, a regulator gene lies close to the *lac* operon.

    DIF: I   OBJ: 11-1.2

4. Generally describe the operon model of gene regulation as proposed by Jacob and Monod. Write your answer in the space below.

ANS:
An operon is a cluster of genes that code for functionally related proteins. A portion of the operon called an operator acts as a switch, controlling access of RNA polymerase to the structural genes of the operon. When the operator does not have a repressor molecule attached to it, the RNA polymerase catalyzes transcription of the structural genes of the operon. However, when a repressor molecule is attached to the operator, RNA polymerase is blocked from accessing the portions of the operon that code for a particular protein or group of proteins. An inducer molecule can remove the repressor molecule, thus allowing the RNA polymerase to attach to the operon, permitting transcription.

DIF: II   OBJ: 11-1.2

5. What is the function of the regulator gene in the *lac* operon? Write your answer in the space below.

ANS:
The regulator gene, which lies close to the *lac* operon, codes for the repressor. The repressor attaches to the operator portion of the operon, preventing the attachment of RNA polymerase and thereby inhibiting the gene from being expressed.

DIF: II   OBJ: 11-1.2

6. In a mutant strain of *Escherichia coli*, lactose fails to bind to the repressor on the operator portion of the *lac* operon. What is likely to be the result of this failure? Write your answer in the space below.

ANS:
The failure of lactose to bind to and remove the repressor will prevent the *lac* operon from functioning. As a result, RNA polymerase will not transcribe the structural genes of the *lac* operon, and the enzymes that normally break down lactose will not be produced.

DIF: II   OBJ: 11-1.2

7. In the *lac* operon, how does RNA polymerase affect the expression of the structural genes, and how is the activity of RNA polymerase controlled? Write your answer in the space below.

ANS:
RNA polymerase is needed to transcribe the DNA code into mRNA. As long as the repressor is attached to the operon, the activity of the RNA polymerase is prevented. When lactose binds to and removes the repressor, the RNA polymerase can move to the structural genes of the *lac* operon, and mRNA can be transcribed.

DIF: II   OBJ: 11-1.2

8. The arrangements of genes on chromosomes of prokaryotes and eukaryotes are known to be different. What are the differences and what evolutionary importance may this have? Write your answer in the space below.

ANS:
The genes of prokaryotic chromosomes are continuous, while those of eukaryotic chromosomes are separated into exons and introns. This arrangement in eukaryotic cells allows exons to be transcribed as part of more than one gene, resulting in different combinations of information. From an evolutionary viewpoint, this may be advantageous since a large number of proteins may be made using a relatively small number of exons. A wide diversity of proteins in eukaryotic cells may be favored by natural selection.

DIF: II   OBJ: 11-1.3

9. Distinguish between benign and malignant tumors. Write your answer in the space below.

ANS:
A *benign* tumor is one that does not invade surrounding tissues. Such tumors can usually be surgically removed and cause relatively few problems. *Malignant* tumors are invasive, spreading into nearby tissues and interfering with organ functions. Cells of this latter type of tumor may break free of the original tumor and metastasize to other locations in the body.

DIF: II   OBJ: 11-2.4

10. A doctor analyzes a patient's tumor and determines that it is benign. Why can the doctor inform the patient that he or she does not have cancer? Write your answer in the space below.

ANS:
The term *cancer* refers to a disorder in which the cells of malignant tumors undergo metastasis. Cells in benign tumors do not undergo metastasis.

DIF: II   OBJ: 11-2.4

11. A great deal of research on the causes of and a possible cure for cancer focuses on mitosis. Why? Write your answer in the space below.

ANS:
Cancer is a disease in which cells grow and undergo mitosis at an abnormally high rate. If mitosis of cancerous cells could be better controlled, perhaps cancer could be slowed or cured.

DIF: II   OBJ: 11-2.4

CHAPTER 12—INHERITANCE PATTERNS AND HUMAN GENETICS

TRUE/FALSE

1. A male can produce sperm that contains either an X or a Y chromosome.

   ANS: T   DIF: I   OBJ: 12-1.1

2. If an inherited disease is recessive and X-linked, then all males with one copy of the disease-causing gene will have the disease.

   ANS: T   DIF: II   OBJ: 12-1.2

3. In a chromosome map, the percentage of crossing-over between two genes is equal to the number of map units separating the genes.

   ANS: T   DIF: I   OBJ: 12-1.4

4. The condition that results from the loss of an entire chromosome is called monosomy.

   ANS: T   DIF: I   OBJ: 12-1.5

5. It is possible that a fragment of DNA may become detached from a chromosome and then reattach in the reverse orientation, resulting in a mutation called inversion.

   ANS: T   DIF: I   OBJ: 12-1.5

6. Mutations that result from the substitution of one nitrogen-containing base for another are called deletions.

   ANS: F   DIF: I   OBJ: 12-1.5

7. Changes in the DNA of an organism are called mutations.

   ANS: T   DIF: I   OBJ: 12-1.5

8. If each parent carries a copy of the sickle cell gene, there is a one-in-four chance that their child will have sickle cell anemia.

   ANS: T   DIF: II   OBJ: 12-1.5

9. Somatic mutations affect an organism's offspring.

   ANS: F   DIF: I   OBJ: 12-1.5

10. Mutations usually introduce new chromosomes into the genome of an organism.

    ANS: F   DIF: I   OBJ: 12-1.5

11. Mutations are always harmful.

    ANS: F   DIF: I   OBJ: 12-1.5

The partial pedigree below is for a family with a genetic disorder.

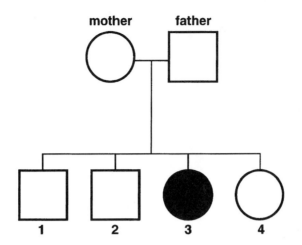

12. Refer to the illustration above. The father listed in the pedigree is most likely heterozygous for the trait.

    ANS: T   DIF: II   OBJ: 12-2.1

13. Refer to the illustration above. Child # 3 probably has a homozygous recessive phenotype.

    ANS: T   DIF: II   OBJ: 12-2.1

14. Refer to the illustration above. The trait indicated in the pedigree is sex-linked.

    ANS: F   DIF: II   OBJ: 12-2.1

15. An individual who expresses a genetic disorder is called a carrier.

    ANS: F   DIF: I   OBJ: 12-2.1

16. A pedigree is a family record that shows how a trait is inherited over several generations.

    ANS: T   DIF: I   OBJ: 12-2.1

17. An autosomal trait will occur with equal frequency in both males and females.

    ANS: T   DIF: I   OBJ: 12-2.3

18. The expression of sex-linked genes is controlled by hormones.

    ANS: F   DIF: I   OBJ: 12-2.4

19. Down syndrome occurs as a result of nondisjunction of chromosome 21 during meiosis.

    ANS: T   DIF: I   OBJ: 12-2.5

20. Trisomy is the addition or removal of a single nitrogen-containing base.

ANS: F   DIF: I   OBJ: 12-2.5

21. Nondisjunction results from the failure of replicated chromosomes to separate during cell division.

ANS: T   DIF: I   OBJ: 12-2.5

MULTIPLE CHOICE

1. The X and Y chromosomes are called the
   a. extra chromosomes.   c. sex chromosomes.
   b. phenotypes.   d. All of the above

   ANS: C   DIF: I   OBJ: 12-1.1

2. Monosomy : nondisjunction ::
   a. chromatids : centromere   c. haploid : mitosis
   b. male : XY chromosomes   d. meiosis : diploid

   ANS: B   DIF: II   OBJ: 12-1.1

3. female : XX ::
   a. female : gametes   c. male : YY
   b. female : eggs   d. male : XY

   ANS: D   DIF: II   OBJ: 12-1.1

4. Which of the following is the best explanation for the observation that females rarely get the disease hemophilia?
   a. Large quantities of male hormones are necessary in order for the gene carrying the disease to be expressed.
   b. Female fetuses that carry the gene for the disease die before birth.
   c. A female could only get the disease by having a mother who is a carrier and a father who has the disease. Since most males with the disease do not survive to reproductive age, this is an extremely unlikely event.
   d. A female could only get the disease by having parents who are both carriers of the disease. Because males cannot be carriers, this is an impossible event.

   ANS: C   DIF: II   OBJ: 12-1.2

5. In a mating between two parental types, one of which is homozygous dominant for two linked traits and one of which is homozygous recessive for the same two linked traits, evidence of crossing-over would be apparent in which of the following generations?
   a. parents   c. F_2
   b. F_1 d. All of the above

   ANS: C   DIF: II   OBJ: 12-1.3

6. Which of the following is *not* true of chromosome maps?
   a. They depict the linear sequence of genes on a chromosome.
   b. They are constructed using crossing-over data from mating experiments.
   c. They depict absolute differences between genes on a chromosome.
   d. They are practical with species having only a few chromosomes.

   ANS: C   DIF: II   OBJ: 12-1.4

7. A mutation caused by a piece of DNA breaking away from its chromosome and becoming attached to a nonhomologous chromosome is called
   a. deletion.   c. inversion.
   b. duplication.   d. translocation.

   ANS: D   DIF: I   OBJ: 12-1.5

8. A change in a gene due to damage or being copied incorrectly is called
   a. evolution.   c. segregation.
   b. meiosis.   d. a mutation.

   ANS: D   DIF: I   OBJ: 12-1.5

9. The effects of a mutation can be
   a. helpful.   c. neutral.
   b. harmful.   d. All of the above

   ANS: D   DIF: II   OBJ: 12-1.5

10. A diagram in which several generations of a family and the occurrence of certain genetic characteristics are shown is called a
    a. Punnett square.   c. pedigree.
    b. monohybrid cross.   d. family karyotype.

    ANS: C   DIF: I   OBJ: 12-2.1

11. A family record that indicates the occurrence of a trait is a
    a. sonogram.   c. pedigree.
    b. karyotype.   d. chromosome map.

    ANS: C   DIF: I   OBJ: 12-2.1

12. Which of the following traits is controlled by multiple alleles in humans?
    a. sickle cell anemia   c. hemophilia
    b. blood type   d. pattern baldness

    ANS: B   DIF: I   OBJ: 12-2.2

13. What would be the blood type of a person who inherited an A allele from one parent and an O allele from the other?
    a. type A   c. type AB
    b. type B   d. type O

    ANS: A   DIF: II   OBJ: 12-2.2

14. Which of the following describes hemophilia?
    a. multiple-allele trait
    b. dominant trait
    c. sex-linked trait
    d. codominant trait

    ANS: C   DIF: I   OBJ: 12-2.3

15. In humans, the risks of passing on a genetic disorder to one's children can be assessed by
    a. analysis of a pedigree.
    b. genetic counseling.
    c. prenatal testing.
    d. All of the above

    ANS: D   DIF: I   OBJ: 12-2.3

16. Genetic counseling is a process that
    a. helps identify parents at risk for having children with genetic defects.
    b. assists parents in deciding whether or not to have children.
    c. uses a family pedigree.
    d. All of the above

    ANS: D   DIF: I   OBJ: 12-2.3

17. While studying several generations of a particular family, a geneticist observed that a certain disease was found equally in males and females and that all children who had the disease had parents who also had the disease. The gene coding for this disease is probably
    a. sex-linked recessive.
    b. sex-linked dominant.
    c. autosomal recessive.
    d. autosomal dominant.

    ANS: D   DIF: II   OBJ: 12-2.3

18. If both parents carry the recessive allele that causes cystic fibrosis, the chance that their child will develop the disease is
    a. one in two.
    b. one in four.
    c. two in five.
    d. 100 percent.

    ANS: B   DIF: II   OBJ: 12-2.3

19. If a characteristic is sex-linked, it
    a. occurs most commonly in males.
    b. occurs only in females.
    c. can never occur in females.
    d. is always fatal.

    ANS: A   DIF: I   OBJ: 12-2.4

20. Since the allele for colorblindness is located on the X chromosome, colorblindness
    a. cannot be inherited.
    b. occurs only in adults.
    c. is sex-linked.
    d. None of the above

    ANS: C   DIF: I   OBJ: 12-2.4

21. People with Down syndrome have
    a. 45 chromosomes.
    b. 46 chromosomes.
    c. 47 chromosomes.
    d. no X chromosomes.

    ANS: C   DIF: I   OBJ: 12-2.5

22. Trisomy is a mutation that results in a cell having an extra
    a. nitrogen base.
    b. codon.
    c. chromosome.
    d. gene.

    ANS: C   DIF: I   OBJ: 12-2.5

23. If nondisjunction occurs,
    a. there will be too many gametes produced.
    b. no gametes will be produced.
    c. a gamete will receive too many or too few homologues of a chromosome.
    d. mitosis cannot take place.

    ANS: C   DIF: I   OBJ: 12-2.5

COMPLETION

1. The X and Y chromosomes are called the _____ chromosomes.

   ANS: sex   DIF: I   OBJ: 12-1.1

2. In humans, the genotype XX results in a _____.

   ANS: female   DIF: I   OBJ: 12-1.1

3. Consider a cross between a homozygous, white-eyed female *Drosophila* and a red-eyed male *Drosophila*. What proportion of the female offspring would be expected to be white-eyed? _____. What proportion of the male offspring would be expected to be white-eyed? _____

   ANS: none; all   DIF: III   OBJ: 12-1.2

4. Linked genes can be separated from each other in meiosis if _____ occurs.

   ANS: crossing-over   DIF: I   OBJ: 12-1.3

5. When traits do not appear according to the expected ratio in offspring, _____ may have occurred.

   ANS: crossing-over   DIF: II   OBJ: 12-1.4

6. When a piece of chromosome attaches itself to a nonhomologous chromosome, the resulting mutation is called a _____.

   ANS: translocation   DIF: I   OBJ: 12-1.5

7. A mutation in which an entire chromosome is lost during meiosis is called a(n) _____.

   ANS: deletion   DIF: I   OBJ: 12-1.5

8. A change in an organism's DNA is called a(n) _____.

ANS: mutation   DIF: I   OBJ: 12-1.5

9. Spontaneous changes in genetic material are called _____.

ANS: mutations   DIF: I   OBJ: 12-1.5

10. Identifying patterns of inheritance within a family over several generations is possible by studying a diagram called a(n) _____.

ANS: pedigree   DIF: I   OBJ: 12-2.1

11. _____ technology is making it possible to cure genetic disorders.

ANS: Gene   DIF: I   OBJ: 12-2.1

12. A person who is heterozygous for a recessive disorder is called a _____.

ANS: carrier   DIF: I   OBJ: 12-2.1

13. By studying a _____, genetic counselors can study how a trait was inherited over several generations.

ANS: pedigree   DIF: I   OBJ: 12-2.1

14. A genetic disorder resulting in defective blood clotting is _____.

ANS: hemophilia   DIF: I   OBJ: 12-2.3

15. A genetic disorder in which an individual lacks an enzyme responsible for converting the amino acid phenylalanine into the amino acid tyrosine is called _____.

ANS: phenylketonuria (PKU)   DIF: I   OBJ: 12-2.3

16. A trait that is determined by a gene that is found only on the X chromosome is said to be _____.

ANS: sex-linked   DIF: I   OBJ: 12-2.4

17. In humans, the genetic disorder caused by an extra chromosome 21 is called _____.

ANS: Down syndrome   DIF: I   OBJ: 12-2.5

18. The failure of replicated chromosomes to separate is called _____.

ANS: nondisjunction   DIF: I   OBJ: 12-2.5

PROBLEM

1. In humans, cystic fibrosis is caused by a recessive gene that is not sex-linked. A man and a woman, neither of whom has cystic fibrosis, have two children with the disease. What is the probability that their third child will have the disease? Write your answer in the space below.

ANS:
25% (The probability that any one child will have the disease is 25%. This probability is entirely independent of the number of children already born with the disease.)

DIF: I   OBJ: 12-2.3

ESSAY

1. Explain the mechanism of sex determination in humans. Write your answer in the space below.

ANS:
Homologous chromosomes segregate during meiosis I. The sex chromosomes pair and segregate in the same manner as other chromosomes. A female parent donates one X chromosome. A male parent donates either an X or a Y chromosome. If an egg is fertilized by a sperm containing an X chromosome, the resulting zygote will be XX, and the new individual will be female. If an egg is fertilized by a sperm containing a Y chromosome, the resulting zygote will be XY, and the new individual will be male.

DIF: II   OBJ: 12-1.1

2. Explain why crossing-over is an important source of genetic variation. Write your answer in the space below.

ANS:
Crossing-over occurs when two homologous chromosomes exchange reciprocal segments of DNA during prophase I of meiosis. This results in chromosomes in which the two chromatids no longer have identical genetic material. When meiosis is completed, the resulting gametes carry new combinations of genes.

DIF: II   OBJ: 12-1.3

3. Discuss the inheritance pattern that would be seen in a pedigree designed to study a recessive sex-linked trait. Write your answer in the space below.

ANS:
Sex-linked traits are carried on the X chromosome. As a result, recessive sex-linked traits are rarely seen in a female, unless she is the offspring of an affected male and a female who is a carrier or is affected. Males born to a female who is either a carrier or affected may inherit the sex-linked allele. If the female is affected, both of her X chromosomes will carry the allele under study and male offspring will inherit it. If she is a carrier, only one of her X chromosomes will carry the sex-linked allele and male offspring will have a 50-50 chance of inheriting this allele. Because males have only one X chromosome, they do not have a dominant allele to counteract the effect of the sex-linked allele.

DIF: II   OBJ: 12-2.1

4. What are the possible genotypes of children born to a man who has the genotype $I^A i$ for blood type and a woman who has the genotype $I^A I^B$? What are the possible phenotypes? Write your answer in the space below.

ANS:
The trait of blood type in humans is determined by multiple alleles. A Punnett square may be used to determine that the possible genotypes are $I^A I^A$, $I^A I^B$, $I^A i$, and $I^B i$. The phenotypes that correspond to these genotypes are blood types A, AB, A, and B, respectively.

DIF: II   OBJ: 12-2.2

5. In humans, colorblindness is a recessive, sex-linked trait. What is the likelihood that the children of a woman heterozygous for colorblindness and a man with normal color vision will be colorblind? Explain your answer. Write your answer in the space below.

ANS:
Since all the female offspring receive the normal allele for vision from the father, all female offspring will have normal color vision, although half of them will receive the recessive allele from the mother and thus be carriers. Since all of the male offspring receive the Y chromosome from the father, it is the X chromosome they receive from the mother that will determine whether or not they are colorblind. Since the mother is heterozygous, male offspring will have a 50 percent chance of being colorblind.

DIF: II   OBJ: 12-2.4

6. Discuss how a karyotype can be used to diagnose Down syndrome. Write your answer in the space below.

ANS:
A karyotype is a photograph that shows the collection of chromosomes found in an individual's cells. Analysis of this collection of chromosomes can reveal abnormalities in chromosome number. Down syndrome is associated with trisomy 21—an extra chromosome 21 in the cells of a person. Such an abnormality can be detected by observing a person's karyotype.

DIF: II   OBJ: 12-2.5

7. Describe Down syndrome and its cause. Write your answer in the space below.

ANS:
Down syndrome is a disorder characterized by mental retardation and weak muscles. This syndrome results from an extra copy of chromosome 21.

DIF: II   OBJ: 12-2.5

TRUE/FALSE

1. Genetic engineering can be used to move genes from the chromosomes of one organism into those of another.

   ANS: T   DIF: I   OBJ: 13-1.1

2. Gene cloning is an efficient way to produce many copies of a specific gene.

   ANS: T   DIF: I   OBJ: 13-1.1

3. In the practice of genetic engineering, scientists directly manipulate genes.

   ANS: T   DIF: I   OBJ: 13-1.1

4. Genetic engineering is the application of molecular genetics for practical purposes.

   ANS: T   DIF: I   OBJ: 13-1.1

5. Genetic engineering can be used to identify genes for specific traits.

   ANS: T   DIF: I   OBJ: 13-1.1

6. Before a donor gene is inserted into a plasmid, the plasmid is opened with a restriction enzyme.

   ANS: T   DIF: I   OBJ: 13-1.2

7. Restriction enzymes make a straight cut through both strands of DNA.

   ANS: F   DIF: I   OBJ: 13-1.2

8. The "sticky ends" of a DNA fragment can combine with any other DNA fragment cut by the same restriction enzyme.

   ANS: T   DIF: I   OBJ: 13-1.2

9. Restriction enzymes are used to cut DNA molecules into pieces.

   ANS: T   DIF: I   OBJ: 13-1.2

10. Gene cloning is an efficient means of producing large numbers of different genes.

    ANS: F   DIF: I   OBJ: 13-1.3

11. A ring of DNA in a bacterium is called a plasmid.

    ANS: T   DIF: I   OBJ: 13-1.3

12. Plasmids are pieces of viral DNA that commonly infect human cells.

    ANS: F   DIF: I   OBJ: 13-1.3

13. The tumor-causing Ti plasmid can be transformed into an effective vector for genetic engineering in plants.

    ANS: T   DIF: I   OBJ: 13-1.3

14. Recombinant DNA is usually composed of DNA segments obtained from two different organisms.

    ANS: T   DIF: I   OBJ: 13-1.4

15. A DNA fingerprint is a pattern of bands made up of specific fragments from an individual's DNA.

    ANS: T   DIF: I   OBJ: 13-2.1

16. The fragments of DNA in a DNA fingerprint appear as fuzzy bands of stain arranged in columns.

    ANS: T   DIF: I   OBJ: 13-2.1

17. The effort to catalog, locate, and sequence all the chromosomes of every living organism is called the Human Genome Project.

    ANS: F   DIF: I   OBJ: 13-2.3

18. Scientists have used genetic engineering to produce bacteria capable of synthesizing human proteins.

    ANS: T   DIF: I   OBJ: 13-3.1

19. Injection of a particular vaccine can cause the body to produce antibodies that protect against the possibility of future infection by a particular pathogen.

    ANS: T   DIF: I   OBJ: 13-3.1

20. If a crop is made herbicide-resistant, treating it with an herbicide will seriously reduce its yield.

    ANS: F   DIF: I   OBJ: 13-3.2

21. Despite the potential environmental benefits, genetic engineers have been unable to develop crop plants that are resistant to weedkillers.

    ANS: F   DIF: I   OBJ: 13-3.2

22. Genetic engineers have developed a method of infecting cows with milk-producing bacteria to increase the amount of milk produced by the cows.

    ANS: F   DIF: I   OBJ: 13-3.2

23. Genetic engineering techniques can be used to make crops resistant to destructive insects.

    ANS: T   DIF: I   OBJ: 13-3.2

24. The FDA requires that manufacturers of all genetically engineered foods provide evidence that the foods are not harmful in any way to humans.

    ANS: F   DIF: I   OBJ: 13-3.3

MULTIPLE CHOICE

1. Restriction enzymes are specific in their identification of
   a. base sequences.
   b. amino acids.
   c. proteins.
   d. chromosomes.

    ANS: A   DIF: I   OBJ: 13-1.2

2. Fragments of DNA having complementary "sticky ends"
   a. are found only in bacterial cells.
   b. can join with each other.
   c. can join only with complementary fragments of the same species.
   d. are immediately digested by enzymes in the cytoplasm of the cell.

    ANS: B   DIF: I   OBJ: 13-1.2

3. Enzymes that cut DNA molecules at specific places
   a. have sticky ends.
   b. are restriction enzymes.
   c. work only on bacterial DNA.
   d. always break the DNA between guanine and adenine.

    ANS: B   DIF: I   OBJ: 13-1.2

4. Plasmids
   a. are circular pieces of bacterial DNA.
   b. can replicate independently of the organism's main chromosome.
   c. are often used as vectors in genetic engineering experiments.
   d. All of the above

    ANS: D   DIF: I   OBJ: 13-1.3

5. Cloning is a process by which
   a. undesirable genes may be eliminated.
   b. many identical DNA fragments are produced.
   c. a virus and a bacterium may be fused into one.
   d. many identical cells may be produced.

    ANS: D   DIF: I   OBJ: 13-1.3

6. Which of the following procedures is *not* a usual step in a gene transfer experiment?
   a. inducing a mutation in a source chromosome
   b. cleaving DNA with a restriction enzyme
   c. recombining pieces of DNA from different organisms
   d. cloning and screening target cells

ANS: A   DIF: I   OBJ: 13-1.4

7. The use of genetic engineering to transfer human genes into bacteria
   a. is impossible with current technology.
   b. causes the human genes to manufacture bacterial proteins.
   c. results in the formation of a new species of organism.
   d. allows the bacteria to produce human proteins.

ANS: D   DIF: I   OBJ: 13-1.4

8. A strand of DNA formed by the splicing of DNA from two different species is called
   a. determinant RNA.   c. plasmid DNA.
   b. recombinant DNA.   d. restriction RNA.

ANS: B   DIF: I   OBJ: 13-1.4

9. Recombinant DNA is formed by joining DNA molecules
   a. from two different sources.
   b. from two chromosomes of the same organism.
   c. with RNA molecules.
   d. with proteins from a different species.

ANS: A   DIF: I   OBJ: 13-1.4

10. donor gene : recombinant DNA ::
    a. heat : ice   c. basketball : basketball court
    b. sugar : salt   d. false tooth : complete set of teeth

ANS: D   DIF: II   OBJ: 13-1.4

11. DNA fingerprinting has been used in criminal investigations because
    a. criminals leave DNA samples behind them when they touch objects at a crime scene.
    b. DNA analysis is believed to allow investigators to distinguish body cells of different individuals, who are unlikely to have the same DNA.
    c. bacterial DNA on the hands of criminals may provide a clue as to where that person was when the crime was committed.
    d. DNA found on murder weapons is easy to identify.

ANS: B   DIF: I   OBJ: 13-2.1

12. Restriction fragment length polymorphism (RFLP) analysis is the procedure used for
    a. making recombinant DNA.
    b. DNA fingerprinting.
    c. creating plasmids in bacterial cells.
    d. cloning cells that might contain specific genes of interest.

ANS: B   DIF: I   OBJ: 13-2.2

13. PCR and DNA replication
    a. are used in genetic engineering to make copies of RNA.
    b. require the same ingredients to make copies of DNA.
    c. are used in genetic engineering to make proteins.
    d. None of the above

    ANS: B   DIF: I   OBJ: 13-2.2

14. PCR : copies of DNA segments ::
    a. genetically engineered bacterium : human proteins
    b. genetic engineering : new genes
    c. RNA polymerase : restriction enzymes
    d. DNA plasmid : gel electrophoresis

    ANS: A   DIF: II   OBJ: 13-2.2

15. A genome is
    a. an organism's collection of genes.
    b. a process used to copy DNA.
    c. the nucleotide sequence that makes up a particular gene.
    d. a fragment of DNA added to a chromosome during a gene transfer experiment.

    ANS: A   DIF: I   OBJ: 13-2.3

16. The goal of the Human Genome Project is to
    a. create maps showing where genes are located on human chromosomes.
    b. create maps showing where chromosomes are located on human genes.
    c. treat patients with genetic diseases.
    d. identify people with genetic diseases.

    ANS: A   DIF: I   OBJ: 13-2.3

17. RFLP : DNA fingerprints ::
    a. screening cells : electrophoresis
    b. Human Genome Project : human genetic maps
    c. DNA fingerprints : fingerprints
    d. recombinant DNA : electrophoresis

    ANS: B   DIF: II   OBJ: 13-2.3

18. Transferring normal human genes into human cells that lack them
    a. is impossible at this time.   c. will cause antibodies to kill those cells.
    b. will cause cancer.   d. is called gene therapy.

    ANS: D   DIF: I   OBJ: 13-2.4

19. The risk associated with vaccines prepared by injecting killed or weakened pathogens is that
    a. a few remaining live or unweakened pathogens could still cause the disease.
    b. the antibodies that result may not work.
    c. the vaccine protects only against other diseases.
    d. None of the above; there is no risk with this type of vaccine.

    ANS: A   DIF: I   OBJ: 13-3.1

20. A gene that codes for resistance to an herbicide has been added to the genome of certain plants. These plants will
    a. produce chemicals that kill weeds growing near them.
    b. die when exposed to the herbicide.
    c. convert the herbicide to fertilizer.
    d. survive when the herbicide is sprayed on the field.

    ANS: D   DIF: II   OBJ: 13-3.2

21. If major cash crops could be genetically engineered to carry out nitrogen fixation,
    a. the need for nitrogen fertilizers would be greatly reduced.
    b. plants would be able to absorb N_2 from the air and convert it to a useful form.
    c. the cost of cultivating the crops would be considerably reduced.
    d. All of the above

    ANS: D   DIF: I   OBJ: 13-3.2

22. Legumes are plants with nodules on their roots containing bacteria that convert N_2 gas into a form of nitrogen that plants can use. To accomplish this conversion, the bacteria carry out a process called
    a. genetic fixation.   c. nitrogen fixation.
    b. nitrogen plasmid formation.   d. nitrogenous decomposition.

    ANS: C   DIF: I   OBJ: 13-3.2

23. Genetic engineering of crop plants to make them resistant to weed killers is important because
    a. it increases erosion of topsoil.
    b. many weed killers remain active for years.
    c. weed killers also kill moth and butterfly larvae.
    d. the cost of producing these crops is less since they do not need to be weeded.

    ANS: D   DIF: I   OBJ: 13-3.2

24. nitrogen-fixing bacteria : air ::
    a. fertilizers : low-nitrogen fertilizer
    b. crops : air
    c. crops : high-nitrogen fertilizer
    d. genetically engineered crops : fertilizer

    ANS: C   DIF: II   OBJ: 13-3.2

25. Which of the following is *not* a concern expressed by some people about genetically engineered crops?
   a. Wild plants could cross-breed with engineered crop plants and become "superweeds."
   b. Genetically engineered crops could produce chemicals that leach into the ground water and poison people who drink the water.
   c. Genetically engineered crops could spread into the wild and wipe out native plant species.
   d. Foods produced by genetically engineered crops could contain substances that cause allergies.

   ANS: B   DIF: I   OBJ: 13-3.3

COMPLETION

1. The process used to isolate a gene from the DNA of one organism and transfer the gene into the DNA of another is called _____.

   ANS: genetic engineering   DIF: I   OBJ: 13-1.1

2. Proteins that cut DNA segments into shorter pieces are called _____.

   ANS: restriction enzymes   DIF: I   OBJ: 13-1.2

3. _____ are used in the laboratory to cut strands of DNA between specific nucleotides into fragments.

   ANS: Restriction enzymes   DIF: I   OBJ: 13-1.2

4. Long segments of DNA can be cut by the use of _____.

   ANS: restriction enzymes   DIF: I   OBJ: 13-1.2

5. Enzymes that cleave DNA at specific sequences, generating a set of small fragments of DNA, are called _____.

   ANS: restriction enzymes   DIF: I   OBJ: 13-1.2

6. A large number of genetically identical cells grown from a single cell are called _____.

   ANS: clones   DIF: I   OBJ: 13-1.3

7. The process of allowing cells to reproduce in order to obtain a large number of identical cells is called _____.

   ANS: cloning   DIF: I   OBJ: 13-1.3

8. The process by which a foreign gene is replicated by insertion into a bacterium is called _____.

   ANS: gene cloning   DIF: I   OBJ: 13-1.3

9. A(n) _____ is an agent that is used to carry a DNA fragment isolated from one cell into another cell.

    ANS: cloning vector   DIF: I   OBJ: 13-1.3

10. A _____ is a carrier that is used to clone a gene and transfer it from one organism to another.

    ANS: cloning vector   DIF: I   OBJ: 13-1.3

11. Splicing DNA from two different organisms produces a new DNA segment called
    _____.

    ANS: recombinant DNA   DIF: I   OBJ: 13-1.4

12. The set of thousands of DNA fragments produced by cutting a genome with restriction enzymes is called a _____.

    ANS: genomic library   DIF: I   OBJ: 13-1.4

13. The combination of DNA from two or more sources is called _____.

    ANS: recombinant DNA   DIF: I   OBJ: 13-1.4

14. A host organism receiving DNA from a foreign source is called a
    _____.

    ANS: transgenic organism   DIF: I   OBJ: 13-1.4

15. A technique known as _____ can be used to separate molecules in a mixture by subjecting them to an electrical field within a gel.

    ANS: gel electrophoresis   DIF: I   OBJ: 13-2.2

16. Unlimited copies of a gene or segment of a DNA molecule can be produced by a process known as _____.

    ANS: polymerase chain reaction (PCR)   DIF: I   OBJ: 13-2.2

17. The name of the scientific program that has the goals of constructing physical maps of human chromosomes and determining the DNA sequences of those chromosomes is the
    _____.

    ANS: Human Genome Project   DIF: I   OBJ: 13-2.3

18. The entire collection of genes within the cells of a human is referred to as the
    _____.

    ANS: human genome   DIF: I   OBJ: 13-2.3

19. Transferring normal human genes into human cells that lack them is called _____.

ANS: gene therapy   DIF: I   OBJ: 13-2.4

20. Treating a genetic disorder by introducing a gene into a cell or by correcting a gene defect in a cell's genome is called _____.

ANS: gene therapy   DIF: I   OBJ: 13-2.4

21. A(n) _____ is a preparation of killed or weakened pathogens that is introduced into the body to produce immunity.

ANS: vaccine   DIF: I   OBJ: 13-3.1

22. A process by which legumes, such as soybeans, peanuts, and clover, convert N_2 gas in the air into chemical forms that plants can use is known as _____.

ANS: nitrogen fixation   DIF: I   OBJ: 13-3.2

23. A major concern about genetically engineered foods is that they might contain substances that cause _____ in people who eat them.

ANS: allergies   DIF: I   OBJ: 13-3.3

ESSAY

1. A scientist has produced a bacterium containing a human gene that codes for a useful protein. How can the scientist use gene cloning to produce large quantities of this protein? Write your answer in the space below.

ANS:
First the scientist should place the bacterium in culture medium to allow the cell to divide. Each new cell produced through division will contain the human gene. As these genes are expressed, the protein will be produced and can be harvested from the culture.

DIF: II   OBJ: 13-1.3

2. A scientist has a long segment of sequenced DNA that contains a gene that he would like to clone. However, the segment of DNA containing the gene is too large to insert into a bacterial plasmid. How might the scientist reduce the size of the fragment containing the gene? Write your answer in the space below.

ANS:
The scientist could use restriction enzymes to cut the DNA into smaller pieces. By choosing the right restriction enzymes, the scientist could create a smaller segment that still contained the gene to be cloned. This smaller fragment could then be spliced into the bacterial plasmid.

DIF: II   OBJ: 13-1.3

3. In order to transfer a gene from a member of one species to another, several steps must be followed. Identify, in the correct order, the steps of a gene transfer experiment. Write your answer in the space below.

ANS:
First, a chromosome from a source organism must be cleaved using a restriction enzyme, resulting in a fragment of DNA containing a desired gene for transfer. Then recombinant DNA is produced by inserting the source DNA fragment into bacterial or viral DNA, creating a vector that is allowed to infect a target cell. Third, the target cell is cloned. Finally, the cloned target cells are screened to select those cells that exhibit the desired gene action.

DIF: II   OBJ: 13-1.4

4. Describe how a gene may be spliced into an *E. coli* plasmid. Write your answer in the space below.

ANS:
First the plasmid is removed from the *E. coli* and cut with a restriction enzyme. Then the gene is inserted into the plasmid. The sticky ends of the gene and plasmid join resulting in recombinant DNA.

DIF: II   OBJ: 13-1.4

5. Discuss the accuracy of using DNA fingerprints to establish relatedness. Write your answer in the space below.

ANS:
DNA fingerprints are considered to be very accurate, when prepared correctly and carefully, because they compare segments of DNA that vary the most from person to person.

DIF: II   OBJ: 13-2.1

6. Describe how a DNA fingerprint is prepared. Write your answer in the space below.

ANS:
(1) Extract DNA from a specimen and cut the DNA into fragments using restriction enzymes. (2) Separate the fragments of DNA using gel electrophoresis. (3) Make visible only the bands that are being compared using probes and photographic film.

DIF: II   OBJ: 13-2.1

7. List three practical uses of PCR. Write your answer in the space below.

ANS:
Answers include that PCR can be used to make DNA fingerprints from small samples found at a crime scene, to diagnose genetic disorders from a few embryonic cells, and to study ancient fragments of DNA found in minute amounts.

DIF: I   OBJ: 13-2.2

8. Genetic engineering has made it possible for pharmaceutical companies to produce medicines such as insulin and human growth hormones. Give at least two reasons why this is important. Write your answer in the space below.

ANS:
The production of genetically engineered medicines is important because (1) large amounts of medicines can be produced, (2) it is safer—the process eliminates risk of contamination from diseases such as AIDS in human blood products, and (3) it is less expensive.

DIF: I   OBJ: 13-3.1

9. Explain how a harmless virus might be used to make a vaccine by using genetic engineering. Write your answer in the space below.

ANS:
A DNA fragment coding for a surface protein of a disease-causing organism is inserted into the genome of a harmless virus. The recombinant virus is allowed to infect the organism that is to be protected. The recipient organism's body will respond by making antibodies that attack the surface protein of the disease-causing organism. If the vaccinated organism is ever exposed to the actual disease-causing organism, the vaccinated organism will immediately produce large amounts of the desired antibody to defend itself.

DIF: II   OBJ: 13-3.1

10. Describe how herbicides work and why farmers use them. Write your answer in the space below.

ANS:
Farmers often apply herbicides (weedkillers) to their crops to get better yields. Herbicides work because they are selective—they kill the weeds but not the crop. Herbicides lower the cost of producing crops since the fields do not have to be weeded and the crop plants grow better. Herbicides also help to prevent soil erosion since the soil does not have to be disturbed to remove weeds.

DIF: I   OBJ: 13-3.2

11. One of the greatest benefits of genetic engineering has been the manipulation of genes in crop plants such as wheat and soybeans. In what ways can genetic engineering affect agriculture? Write your answer in the space below.

ANS:
Gene transfers have already produced crop plants that are more resistant to disease, herbicides, or insects. The bacterial genes for nitrogen fixation have been successfully inserted into plants, but these genes do not seem to function properly in their new hosts. Experiments are under way to overcome this difficulty. Genetic engineering has also been effective in increasing the milk production and growth rate of livestock.

DIF: II   OBJ: 13-3.2

CHAPTER 14—ORIGIN OF LIFE

TRUE/FALSE

1. It is impossible to test any assumptions about the origin of life.

   ANS: F   DIF: I   OBJ: 14-1.2

2. Pasteur's experiments provided conclusive evidence against the presence of a "vital force" in the air because Pasteur allowed air to enter his flasks after the broth had been boiled.

   ANS: T   DIF: II   OBJ: 14-1.3

3. The Earth's age is estimated to be more than 4 billion years.

   ANS: T   DIF: I   OBJ: 14-2.1

4. The term half-life is used to indicate when an organism's life span is half over.

   ANS: F   DIF: I   OBJ: 14-2.2

5. According to Oparin, the energy for the formation of molecules in the early oceans came from photosynthesis.

   ANS: F   DIF: I   OBJ: 14-2.3

6. One of the sources of energy for the origin of life on Earth may have been lightning.

   ANS: T   DIF: I   OBJ: 14-2.3

7. One of the first gases found in the Earth's atmosphere was oxygen.

   ANS: F   DIF: I   OBJ: 14-2.3

8. Miller and Urey succeeded in producing primitive living organisms from simple chemical compounds.

   ANS: F   DIF: I   OBJ: 14-2.3

9. Urey and Miller simulated the conditions that Oparin had proposed existed on early Earth, and were able to generate amino acids and other complex molecules.

   ANS: T   DIF: I   OBJ: 14-2.3

10. Many scientists think that DNA was the first genetic material.

    ANS: F   DIF: I   OBJ: 14-3.1

11. If life exists on another planet, heredity must depend on DNA.

    ANS: F   DIF: I   OBJ: 14-3.1

12. Photosynthetic organisms are all unicellular, but chemosynthetic organisms may be either unicellular or multicellular.

    ANS: F   DIF: I   OBJ: 14-3.3

13. Oxygen is a product of aerobic respiration and is a reactant in photosynthesis.

    ANS: F   DIF: II   OBJ: 14-3.4

14. In endosymbiosis, one organism lives inside of another organism in a relationship that benefits one organism but harms the other organism.

    ANS: F   DIF: I   OBJ: 14-3.5

15. The hypothesis of the origin of mitochondria and chloroplasts by endosymbiosis is supported by the observation that mitochondria and chloroplasts contain some of their own genes and that they replicate independently of the cell that contains them.

    ANS: T   DIF: II   OBJ: 14-3.5

MULTIPLE CHOICE

1. Spontaneous generation has been offered as an explanation for
   a. the birth of live offspring from a mother
   b. the germination of a seed.
   c. the appearance of maggots on rotting meat.
   d. All of the above

    ANS: C   DIF: I   OBJ: 14-1.1

2. How did Redi test the hypothesis of spontaneous generation?
   a. He placed meat in one container and left another container empty; he then observed the containers for the appearance of maggots.
   b. He placed meat in two containers and covered one of them; he then observed the containers for the appearance of maggots.
   c. He placed meat in two containers and fly eggs in one of them; he then observed the containers for the appearance of maggots.
   d. He placed adult flies in two containers, one with meat in it and one without. He then observed the containers for the appearance of maggots.

    ANS: B   DIF: I   OBJ: 14-1.2

3. What did Pasteur do in his experiments on spontaneous generation that other scientists before him had not done?
   a. He boiled the broth in his flasks.
   b. He sealed his flasks.
   c. He used curve-necked flasks and left them open.
   d. He added microorganisms to the broth before he boiled it.

    ANS: C   DIF: I   OBJ: 14-1.3

4. The age of Earth is estimated to be
   a. 2 million years.
   b. 2 billion years.
   c. 2 trillion years.
   d. 4 billion years.

   ANS: D   DIF: I   OBJ: 14-2.1

5. Which of the following is *not* thought to have been a factor in the formation of Earth?
   a. Pieces of debris in space collided with Earth, thereby heating it.
   b. Pieces of debris in space added to the size of Earth.
   c. Earth was formed from debris that circled the sun as it formed.
   d. Earth was formed from the collision of two small stars.

   ANS: D   DIF: II   OBJ: 14-2.1

6. If the half-life of a radioactive isotope is 5,000 years, how much of the radioactive
   isotope in a specimen will be left after 10,000 years?
   a. all of it
   b. one-half of the original amount
   c. one-quarter of the original amount
   d. none of it

   ANS: C   DIF: I   OBJ: 14-2.2

7. The half-life of a radioisotope
   a. does not change.
   b. varies with the seasons.
   c. increases as the radioisotope ages.
   d. fluctuates.

   ANS: A   DIF: I   OBJ: 14-2.2

8. The age of fossils, such as those of bones, can often be determined by
   a. their magnetism.
   b. measuring the amount of a specific radioactive isotope in the fossil bones.
   c. analyzing the DNA in the bones.
   d. their developmental pattern.

   ANS: B   DIF: I   OBJ: 14-2.2

9. The half-life of carbon-14 is 5,730 years. How much of an initial amount of this
   substance would remain after 17,190 years, which is three half-lives?
   a. none
   b. one-half
   c. one-fourth
   d. one-eighth

   ANS: D   DIF: I   OBJ: 14-2.2

10. Isotopes are forms of the same element that differ in
    a. atomic number.
    b. number of electrons.
    c. number of neutrons.
    d. number of protons.

    ANS: C   DIF: I   OBJ: 14-2.2

11. Which of the following gases was thought by Oparin to be part of the Earth's early atmosphere?
    a. oxygen
    b. ozone
    c. ammonia
    d. carbon dioxide

    ANS: C   DIF: I   OBJ: 14-2.3

12. Oparin believed that macromolecules, such as proteins, first appeared
    a. in volcanoes.
    b. in the atmosphere.
    c. in water.
    d. on iron pyrite and clay.

    ANS: C   DIF: I   OBJ: 14-2.3

13. Miller and Urey did not use oxygen gas in their apparatus because oxygen
    a. is not essential to most forms of life.
    b. does not react with ammonia, methane, or hydrogen.
    c. would have led to the formation of microorganisms.
    d. was not believed to have been present in the Earth's early atmosphere.

    ANS: D   DIF: I   OBJ: 14-2.3

14. In their experiment, Miller and Urey produced
    a. energy.
    b. microorganisms.
    c. radioactive isotopes.
    d. amino acids.

    ANS: D   DIF: I   OBJ: 14-2.3

The apparatus shown below was used by scientists in the 1950s to re-create the conditions of early Earth.

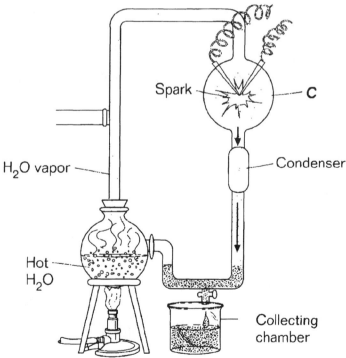

15. Refer to the illustration above. Miller and Urey's apparatus was designed to demonstrate that life on Earth might have originated from
    a. radioactive decay.
    b. simple organic molecules.
    c. extraterrestrial life.
    d. None of the above

    ANS: B   DIF: II   OBJ: 14-2.3

16. Refer to the illustration above. Water vapor in the reaction chamber labeled "C" was mixed with all of the following *except*
    a. ammonia.
    b. hydrogen.
    c. oxygen.
    d. methane.

    ANS: C   DIF: II   OBJ: 14-2.3

17. Refer to the illustration above. Gases were circulated through the apparatus. When the mixture reached the reaction chamber labeled "C," an electric spark was activated so that
    a. they could be removed for analysis.
    b. extra nitrogen could be added.
    c. lightning discharge through the gases could be simulated.
    d. excess carbon monoxide could be removed.

    ANS: C   DIF: II   OBJ: 14-2.3

18. Experiments conducted by Miller and Urey, and by others since them, have demonstrated that molecules important for life could have been produced in Earth's early atmosphere. These molecules include amino acids, carbohydrates, lipids, ATP, and nucleotides of DNA and RNA. Which of the following suggests how the genetic material of cells may have evolved to give instructions for the functioning and replication of cells?
    a. A spark of electricity can catalyze chemical reactions that produce proteins from DNA.
    b. Cells link amino acids together into proteins, using instructions carried in the DNA and enzymes to catalyze the reactions.
    c. RNA, like enzymes, can catalyze chemical reactions, and some RNA molecules could be self-replicating.
    d. Chains of nucleotides form when water evaporates from a solution of nucleotides.

    ANS: C   DIF: III   OBJ: 14-2.3

19. RNA
    a. was probably the first genetic molecule.
    b. can undergo natural selection and thus can evolve.
    c. probably evolved before DNA.
    d. All of the above

    ANS: D   DIF: I   OBJ: 14-3.1

20. RNA
    a. has a three-dimensional structure.
    b. is a nucleic acid.
    c. can act like an enzyme.
    d. All of the above

    ANS: D   DIF: I   OBJ: 14-3.1

21. RNA molecules can
    a. catalyze the synthesis of DNA.
    b. catalyze the synthesis of lipid bilayers.
    c. produce complementary copies of their own nucleotide sequence.
    d. All of the above

    ANS: C   DIF: I   OBJ: 14-3.1

22. Presently, scientists think that DNA
    a. evolved before RNA.
    b. evolved simultaneously with RNA.
    c. was essential for the formation of the first cells.
    d. evolved after RNA.

    ANS: D   DIF: I   OBJ: 14-3.1

23. The first macromolecules on Earth were
    a. probably composed of DNA.   c. probably composed of RNA.
    b. proteins.   d. forms of ATP.

    ANS: C   DIF: I   OBJ: 14-3.2

24. Scientists think that the first cells resembled modern
    a. animal cells.   c. archaebacteria.
    b. mitochondria.   d. chloroplasts.

    ANS: A   DIF: I   OBJ: 14-3.2

25. Scientists have inferred that the first cells were
    a. prokaryotic and autotrophic.   c. eukaryotic and autotrophic.
    b. prokaryotic and heterotrophic.   d. eukaryotic and heterotrophic.

    ANS: B   DIF: I   OBJ: 14-3.2

26. Which of the following is a true difference between photosynthetic organisms and chemosynthetic organisms?
    a. They differ in the source of energy they use to produce organic molecules.
    b. They differ in the source of carbon they use to produce organic molecules.
    c. Photosynthetic organisms are found on Earth today, while chemosynthetic organisms are no longer found on Earth.
    d. Photosynthetic organisms are eukaryotic, while chemosynthetic organisms are prokaryotic.

    ANS: A   DIF: II   OBJ: 14-3.3

27. The surface of the Earth is protected from damaging ultraviolet light by
    a. oxygen.   c. hydrogen.
    b. ozone.   d. nitrogen.

    ANS: B   DIF: I   OBJ: 14-3.4

28. Which of the following is thought to have been an important early function of aerobic respiration?
    a. It enabled some early organisms to live on land.
    b. It consumed oxygen that could destroy chemicals in early organisms.
    c. It protected early organisms from ultraviolet radiation, which damages DNA.
    d. All of the above

ANS: B   DIF: I   OBJ: 14-3.4

29. Many scientists think that early aerobic prokaryotes invaded larger cells and eventually gave rise to
    a. chloroplasts   c. mitochondria
    b. DNA   d. ribosomes

ANS: C   DIF: I   OBJ: 14-3.5

COMPLETION

1. The concept of spontaneous generation states that living things could arise from
   _____.

   ANS: nonliving things   DIF: I   OBJ: 14-1.1

2. Spallanzani demonstrated that _____ would not grow in flasks containing broth that had been boiled and sealed.

   ANS: microorganisms   DIF: I   OBJ: 14-1.2

3. Spallanzani's critics claimed that he had destroyed a _____ present in the air by boiling his flasks too long.

   ANS: vital force   DIF: I   OBJ: 14-1.2

4. The _____ neck of Pasteur's flasks prevented microorganisms from getting into the broth in the flasks.

   ANS: curved   DIF: I   OBJ: 14-1.3

5. The half-life of carbon-14 is 5,730 years. One-fourth of an initial amount of this substance would remain after _____ years.

   ANS: 11,460   DIF: I   OBJ: 14-2.2

6. The period of time it takes for one-half of a radioactive isotope to decay is called its
   _____.

   ANS: half-life   DIF: I   OBJ: 14-2.2

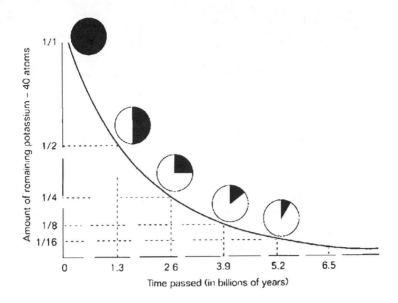

7. The diagram above illustrates the radioactive decay of potassium-40. The half-life of potassium-40 is about _____ billion years.

   ANS: 1.3   DIF: II   OBJ: 14-2.2

8. In 1953, _____ re-created the conditions of early Earth inside a laboratory apparatus.

   ANS: Miller and Urey   DIF: I   OBJ: 14-2.3

9. _____ hypothesis about the origin of life suggests that the Earth's oceans contained simple organic molecules.

   ANS: Oparin's   DIF: I   OBJ: 14-2.3

10. Protein molecules organized as a membrane form tiny structures called _____.

   ANS: microspheres   DIF: I   OBJ: 14-2.4

11. Some scientists think that small, membrane-bound structures composed of organic molecules in water may have been the first stage in the evolution of _____.

   ANS: cells   DIF: I   OBJ: 14-2.4

12. Many scientists now think that _____ was the first information-storing molecule to form on Earth.

   ANS: RNA   DIF: I   OBJ: 14-3.1

13. The two types of autotrophic organisms are _____ organisms and _____ organisms.

ANS: photosynthetic; chemosynthetic   DIF: I   OBJ: 14-3.3

ESSAY

1. Explain how carbon dating is used to determine the absolute age of fossils. Write your answer in the space below.

ANS:
Carbon dating is based on the ratio of carbon-14 to carbon-12 in fossils. During the life of an organism, this ratio is constant. When an organism dies, the carbon-12 is stable but the carbon-14 decays at a constant rate, thereby decreasing the ratio of carbon-14 to carbon-12. By determining this ratio for a fossil, scientists can estimate how long ago the organism died.

DIF: II   OBJ: 14-2.2

2. Describe how the first cells might have evolved. Write your answer in the space below.

ANS:
Tiny spheres of lipids formed and then dispersed in the early oceans. Over millions of years, membrane-bound structures that could survive longer by taking in molecules and energy from their surroundings formed. Once these molecules could pass these survival techniques along to "offspring" coacervates through self-replicating RNA, life had begun.

DIF: II   OBJ: 14-2.4

CHAPTER 15—EVOLUTION: EVIDENCE AND THEORY

TRUE/FALSE

1. The fossil record suggests that species have become less diverse with time.

    ANS: F   DIF: II   OBJ: 15-1.1

2. Mass extinctions are long periods during which few species disappeared.

    ANS: F   DIF: I   OBJ: 15-1.3

3. The theory of evolution states that species change over time.

    ANS: T   DIF: I   OBJ: 15-2.1

4. The inheritance of acquired characteristics was one mechanism of evolution supported by Darwin.

    ANS: F   DIF: I   OBJ: 15-2.2

5. Darwin observed that the plants and animals of the Galapagos Islands were the same as those on islands off the coast of Africa with similar environments.

    ANS: F   DIF: I   OBJ: 15-2.3

6. The book *Principles of Geology* by Charles Lyell described how changes in land formations can cause species to evolve.

    ANS: F   DIF: I   OBJ: 15-2.3

7. Species that have evolved from a common ancestor should have certain characteristics in common.

    ANS: T   DIF: I   OBJ: 15-2.4

8. In his "Essay on the Principle of Population," Malthus said humans were the only population that could continue to grow in size indefinitely.

    ANS: F   DIF: I   OBJ: 15-2.4

9. The two major ideas that Darwin presented in *The Origin of Species* were that evolution occurred and that natural selection was its mechanism.

    ANS: T   DIF: I   OBJ: 15-2.4

10. The environment dictates only the direction and extent of evolution.

    ANS: T   DIF: I   OBJ: 15-2.4

11. Natural selection can cause the spread of an advantageous adaptation in a population.

   ANS: T   DIF: I   OBJ: 15-2.4

12. The environment selects which organisms will survive and reproduce by presenting challenges that only individuals with particular traits can meet.

   ANS: T   DIF: I   OBJ: 15-2.4

13. Evidence for evolution occurs only in the fossil record.

   ANS: F   DIF: I   OBJ: 15-3.1

14. The human forelimb and the bat forelimb are homologous structures.

   ANS: T   DIF: I   OBJ: 15-3.1

15. The theory of evolution predicts that genes will accumulate more alterations in their nucleotide sequences over time.

   ANS: T   DIF: I   OBJ: 15-3.2

16. Early in development, human embryos and the embryos of all other vertebrates are strikingly similar.

   ANS: T   DIF: I   OBJ: 15-3.2

17. The way an embryo develops is not important in determining the evolutionary history of a species.

   ANS: F   DIF: I   OBJ: 15-3.2

18. The accumulation of differences between species or populations is called convergence.

   ANS: F   DIF: I   OBJ: 15-3.3

19. Within populations, divergence leads to new species.

   ANS: T   DIF: I   OBJ: 15-3.3

20. Coevolution occurs when two or more species change in response to one another.

   ANS: T   DIF: I   OBJ: 15-3.3

MULTIPLE CHOICE

1. Which of the following are examples of fossils?
   a. shells or old bones
   b. any traces of dead organisms
   c. footprints of human ancestors, insects trapped in tree sap, and animals buried in tar
   d. All of the above

   ANS: D   DIF: I   OBJ: 15-1.1

2. Animal fossils may form when
   a. an animal is buried by sediment.
   b. burial takes place on the ocean floor, in swamps, in mud, or in tar pits.
   c. the tissue is replaced by harder minerals.
   d. All of the above

   ANS: D   DIF: I   OBJ: 15-1.1

3. Darwin conducted much of his research on
   a. the Samoan Islands.   c. the Hawaiian Islands.
   b. Manhattan Island.   d. the Galapagos Islands.

   ANS: D   DIF: I   OBJ: 15-2.3

4. The finches that Darwin studied differed in the shape of their beaks. According to Darwin, the finches probably
   a. all had a common ancestor.
   b. had been created by design that way.
   c. were descended from similar birds in Africa.
   d. ate the same diet.

   ANS: A   DIF: I   OBJ: 15-2.3

5. Darwin thought that the plants and animals of the Galapagos Islands were similar to those of the nearby coast of South America because
   a. their ancestors had migrated from South America to the Galapagos Islands.
   b. they had all been created by God to match their habitat.
   c. the island organisms had the same nucleotide sequences in their DNA as the mainland organisms.
   d. he found fossils proving that the animals and plants had common ancestors.

   ANS: A   DIF: I   OBJ: 15-2.3

6. The process by which a population becomes better suited to its environment is known as
   a. accommodation.   c. adaptation.
   b. variation.   d. selection.

   ANS: C   DIF: I   OBJ: 15-2.4

7. In order to fit into their habitat, the Galapagos finches had
   a. not changed.   c. evolved.
   b. been created as superior birds. d. All of the above

   ANS: C   DIF: I   OBJ: 15-2.4

8. According to Darwin, evolution occurs
   a. by chance.   c. because of natural selection.
   b. during half-life periods of 5,715 years. d. rapidly.

   ANS: C   DIF: I   OBJ: 15-2.4

9. Organisms well suited to their environment
   a. reproduce more successfully than those less suited to the same environment.
   b. are always larger than organisms less suited to that environment.
   c. always live longer than organisms less suited to that environment.
   d. need less food than organisms less suited to that environment.

   ANS: A   DIF: I   OBJ: 15-2.4

10. When Darwin published his theory of evolution, he included all of the following ideas *except*
    a. the idea that species change slowly over time.
    b. the idea that some organisms reproduce at a greater rate than others.
    c. Mendel's ideas about genetics.
    d. the idea that some organisms become less suited to their environment than others.

    ANS: C   DIF: I   OBJ: 15-2.4

11. The major idea that Darwin presented in his book *The Origin of Species* was that
    a. species changed over time and never competed with each other.
    b. animals changed, but plants remained the same.
    c. giraffes and peppered moths changed constantly.
    d. species changed over time by natural selection.

    ANS: D   DIF: I   OBJ: 15-2.4

12. Natural selection is the process by which
    a. the age of selected fossils is calculated.
    b. organisms with traits well suited to their environment survive and reproduce more successfully than less well-adapted organisms in the same environment.
    c. acquired traits are passed on from one generation to the next.
    d. All of the above

    ANS: B   DIF: I   OBJ: 15-2.4

13. Natural selection could not occur without
    a. genetic variation in species.
    b. environmental changes.
    c. competition for unlimited resources.
    d. gradual warming of the Earth.

    ANS: A   DIF: I   OBJ: 15-2.4

14. Populations of the same species living in different places
    a. do not vary.
    b. always show balancing selection.
    c. have a half-life in relation to the size of the population.
    d. become increasingly different as each becomes adapted to its own environment.

    ANS: D   DIF: I   OBJ: 15-2.4

15. Scarcity of resources and a growing population are most likely to result in
    a. homology.
    b. protective coloration.
    c. competition.
    d. convergent evolution.

    ANS: C   DIF: I   OBJ: 15-2.4

16. Since natural resources are limited, all organisms
    a. must migrate to new habitats.
    b. must compete for resources.
    c. display vestigial structures.
    d. have a species half-life.

    ANS: B   DIF: I   OBJ: 15-2.4

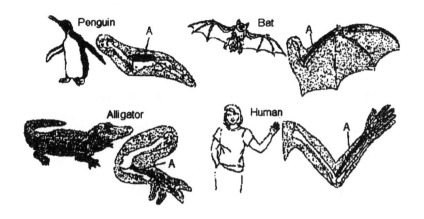

17. Refer to the illustration above. An analysis of DNA from these organisms would indicate that
    a. they have identical DNA.
    b. they all have gill pouches.
    c. their nucleotide sequences show many similarities.
    d. they all have the same number of chromosomes.

    ANS: C   DIF: II   OBJ: 15-3.1

18. Refer to the illustration above. The similarity of these structures suggests that the organisms
    a. share a common ancestor.
    b. all grow at different rates.
    c. evolved slowly.
    d. live for a long time.

    ANS: A   DIF: II   OBJ: 15-3.1

19. Refer to the illustration above. The bones labeled "A" are known as
    a. vestigial structures.
    b. sequential structures.
    c. homologous structures.
    d. fossil structures.

    ANS: C   DIF: II   OBJ: 15-3.1

20. Which of the following is a vestigial structure?
    a. the human tailbone
    b. the bill of a finch
    c. flower color
    d. fossil cast

ANS: A DIF: I OBJ: 15-3.1

21. Homologous structures in organisms suggest that the organisms
    a. share a common ancestor.
    b. must have lived at different times.
    c. have a skeletal structure.
    d. are now extinct.

ANS: A DIF: I OBJ: 15-3.1

22. Structures that no longer serve an important function are called
    a. inorganic.
    b. mutated.
    c. fossilized.
    d. vestigial.

ANS: D DIF: I OBJ: 15-3.1

23. The beak of a bird and the beak of a giant squid evolved independently and serve the same function. The beaks are
    a. convergent structures.
    b. homologous structures.
    c. analogous structures.
    d. hybrid structures.

ANS: C DIF: II OBJ: 15-3.1

24. vestigial structures : macroevolution ::
    a. homologous structures : common ancestry
    b. common ancestry : fossils
    c. common ancestry : rock
    d. homologous structures : unrelated species

ANS: A DIF: II OBJ: 15-3.1

25. The occurrence of the same blood protein in a group of species provides evidence that these species
    a. evolved in the same habitat.
    b. evolved in different habitats.
    c. descended from a common ancestor.
    d. descended from different ancestors.

ANS: C DIF: I OBJ: 15-3.2

26. Evidence for evolution includes all of the following *except*
    a. acquired characteristics.
    b. similarities and differences in proteins and DNA sequences between organisms.
    c. the fossil record.
    d. homologous structures.

ANS: A DIF: I OBJ: 15-3.2

27. The theory of evolution predicts that
   a. closely related species will show similarities in nucleotide sequences.
   b. if species have changed over time, their genes should have changed.
   c. closely related species will show similarities in amino acid sequences.
   d. All of the above

ANS: D   DIF: I   OBJ: 15-3.2

28. Cytochrome c is a protein that is involved in cellular respiration in all eukaryotic organisms. Human cytochrome c contains 104 amino acids. The following table compares cytochrome c from a number of other organisms with human cytochrome c.

Organism	Number of cytochrome c amino acids different from humans
Chimpanzees	0
Chickens	18
Dogs	13
Rattlesnakes	20
Rhesus monkeys	1
Yeasts	56

Which of the following is *not* a valid conclusion that can be drawn from these data?
   a. Chimpanzees are more closely related to humans than rhesus monkeys are.
   b. The cytochrome c of chimpanzees differs from that of rhesus monkeys by only one amino acid.
   c. Dogs are more closely related to humans than chickens are.
   d. The proteins produced by chimpanzees and humans are identical to each other. Therefore these organisms differ in characteristics that aren't determined by proteins.

ANS: D   DIF: II   OBJ: 15-3.2

29. The accumulation of differences between species or populations is called
   a. gradualism.   c. divergent evolution.
   b. adaptation.   d. cumulative differentiation.

ANS: C   DIF: I   OBJ: 15-3.3

30. The process by which two or more species change in response to each other is called
   a. compromise.   c. coevolution.
   b. parasitism.   d. ecology.

ANS: C   DIF: I   OBJ: 15-3.3

31. Over millions of years, plants and their pollinators have
   a. coevolved.   c. become parasites.
   b. crossbred.   d. become competitive.

ANS: A   DIF: I   OBJ: 15-3.3

A Comparison of Dolphins and Sharks

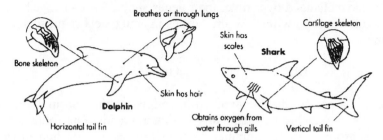

32. Refer to the illustration above. While the shark and dolphin are similar in appearance, they evolved independently. This is an example of
    a. cladistics.
    b. phenetics.
    c. convergent evolution.
    d. divergent evolution.

    ANS: C   DIF: II   OBJ: 15-3.3

33. A biologist analyzes the DNA sequences in three different primates. The biologist finds that primates "A" and "B" have almost exactly the same DNA sequences. The DNA sequences in primate "C" are significantly different from those of primate "A" and primate "B". This information allows the biologist to infer that
    a. primates "A" and "B" are more closely related to each other than either is to primate "C."
    b. all three primates appeared on Earth at about the same time.
    c. either primate "A" or primate "B" must be a direct ancestor of primate "C."
    d. primate "C" must have been the ancestor of both primate "A" and "B."

    ANS: A   DIF: I   OBJ: 15-3.3

COMPLETION

1. When an organism becomes _____, the tissues are replaced by harder minerals.

    ANS: fossilized   DIF: I   OBJ: 15-1.1

2. A species that has disappeared permanently is said to be _____.

    ANS: extinct   DIF: I   OBJ: 15-1.3

3. A change in species over time is called _____.

    ANS: evolution   DIF: I   OBJ: 15-2.1

4. The process by which organisms with traits well suited to an environment survive and reproduce at a greater rate than organisms less suited for that environment is called

    _____.

    ANS: natural selection   DIF: I   OBJ: 15-2.4

5. According to Darwin, the _____ determines the rate at which organisms survive and reproduce.

ANS: environment   DIF: I   OBJ: 15-2.4

6. A(n) _____ consists of all the individuals of a particular species in a particular place.

ANS: population   DIF: I   OBJ: 15-2.4

7. Homologous structures are similar because they originated in a shared _____.

ANS: ancestor   DIF: I   OBJ: 15-3.1

8. _____ structures are similar because they originated in a shared ancestor.

ANS: Homologous   DIF: I   OBJ: 15-3.1

9. Closely related species show more _____ in nucleotide sequences than distantly related species.

ANS: similarities   DIF: I   OBJ: 15-3.2

10. _____ occurs as two or more species change in response to each other.

ANS: Coevolution   DIF: I   OBJ: 15-3.3

PROBLEM

1. For each of the characteristics named below, describe how it might provide a selective advantage for males possessing the characteristic. Write your answers in the space below.
   a. larger than average antlers on a deer
   b. a more elaborate than average nest built by a bower bird
   c. the ability of an insect to remove another insect's sperm packet from the reproductive tract of a female

   ANS:
   a. A male deer with larger than average antlers would be more likely to win battles with other males, sending the other males away or killing them. Thus, a deer with larger antlers would be more likely to mate with a female deer and produce offspring.
   b. A bower bird that builds a more elaborate nest than other bower birds is more likely to attract the attention of a female. Thus, he is also more likely to mate with a female bower bird and produce offspring.
   c. A male insect that could remove another male's sperm packet from a female's body could then mate with the female himself. Thus, this insect would be more likely to produce offspring than males that don't have this ability.

   DIF: III   OBJ: 15-2.4

2. You are a biologist accompanying some other scientists on an expedition in a region that has not been studied intensively. In your explorations, you come across a colony of small vertebrates that do not look familiar to you. After conducting electronic searches of worldwide data bases, you arrive at the tentative conclusion that this organism has never been observed before. Now your job is to determine what kind of vertebrate it is by identifying its closest relatives. Identify three types of data that you would collect and describe how you would use these data to draw your conclusions. Write your answer in the space below.

ANS:
1) Analysis of anatomical structures and comparison of these to similar structures of other vertebrates. For example, the bones composing the forelimb of your organism could be compared to the forelimbs of other vertebrates. Those vertebrates having the greatest number of similar (homologous) anatomical structures to those of your organism could be presumed to be its closest relatives.
2) Analysis of the DNA and/or a protein and comparison of this material to that of other vertebrates. For example, DNA hybridization studies could be conducted with your organism and other vertebrates. Those vertebrates having the fewest differences in sequences of DNA and/or proteins from your organism could be presumed to be its closest relatives.
3) Analysis of embryonic development and comparison of structures present at different stages and the pattern of development with the structures and patterns of other vertebrates. For example, a comparison could be made between the persistence of a particular trait until late in embryonic development and the persistence of the same trait in the embryos of other vertebrates.

DIF: III   OBJ: 15-3.2

ESSAY

1. Why has there been a burst of evolution after each of the great mass extinctions? Write your answer in the space below.

ANS:
The organisms that survive the mass extinctions find themselves in a world of opportunity—an Earth full of food and space that is no longer used by others.

DIF: II   OBJ: 15-1.3

2. Why did Darwin think that the finches he observed and collected in the Galapagos Islands shared a common ancestor? Write your answer in the space below.

ANS:
Although there were differences among these finch species, all the species also had many traits in common. The main similarities among these species led Darwin to conclude that they had a common ancestor.

DIF: II   OBJ: 15-2.3

3. Suppose that you are a zoologist studying birds on a group of islands. You have just discovered four species of birds that have never before been seen. Each species is on a separate island. The birds are identical to each other except for the shape of their beaks. How can you explain their similarities and differences? Write your answer in the space below.

ANS:
It is likely that the four species evolved from a common ancestor, with each species adapting to the conditions on its island. The differences in beak shape may be the result of differences in available food among the islands. Each bird species adapted to the food that was available on its island.

DIF: II   OBJ: 15-2.3

4. Why is competition among individuals of the same species generally so intense? Write your answer in the space below.

ANS:
Individuals of the same species require the same resources for survival. Because resources are generally limited, only those individuals able to secure sufficient amounts of those resources will survive.

DIF: II   OBJ: 15-2.4

5. What role does the environment play in natural selection? Write your answer in the space below.

ANS:
According to Darwin's theory, those organisms that have traits best suited to the environment most successfully survive and reproduce.

DIF: II   OBJ: 15-2.4

6. To control its wild rabbit population, the Australian government introduced the viral disease myxomatosis. At first the virus was very deadly to the rabbits. Explain what happened to the rabbit population and why the virus became less virulent. Write your answer in the space below.

ANS:
At first the virus was very deadly, so rabbits that survived tended to be resistant to the virus. The virus also became less deadly because viral infections that kill their hosts too quickly are not able to spread to as many other rabbits. The rabbits and virus coevolved.

DIF: II   OBJ: 15-3.3

TRUE/FALSE

1. If all different sizes of fish in a population are equally able to reproduce, then the average size will stay the same in successive generations.

   ANS: T   DIF: I   OBJ: 16-1.1

2. Usually both environmental factors and heredity play a role in variation.

   ANS: T   DIF: I   OBJ: 16-1.2

3. Real populations may violate the conditions necessary for genetic equilibrium.

   ANS: T   DIF: I   OBJ: 16-1.4

4. Natural selection acts on phenotypes, not genotypes.

   ANS: T   DIF: I   OBJ: 16-2.1

5. Natural selection always eliminates any genetic disorders from a population, regardless of the frequency of the gene that is responsible for a disorder.

   ANS: F   DIF: I   OBJ: 16-2.1

6. Genetic drift may result in homozygosity for a gene that may make a population susceptible to extinction because it does not confer advantages, and it can also "fix" advantageous genes in a population.

   ANS: T   DIF: III   OBJ: 16-2.3

7. When sexual selection is acting in a species, all males tend to look alike.

   ANS: F   DIF: I   OBJ: 16-2.5

8. One of the limitations of the biological concept of species is that it cannot be used to distinguish species in extinct organisms.

   ANS: T   DIF: I   OBJ: 16-3.1

9. Geographic isolation occurs when individuals who could potentially interbreed are prevented from doing so because they are physically separated from each other.

   ANS: T   DIF: I   OBJ: 16-3.2

10. Punctuated gradualism refers to the hypothesis that evolution occurs only in short periods of time.

    ANS: F   DIF: I   OBJ: 16-3.4

11. Two hypotheses suggested about the rate at which evolution proceeds are gradualism and punctuated equilibrium.

ANS: T   DIF: I   OBJ: 16-3.4

12. Postzygotic isolation can keep species separate even if they do interbreed, as long as the offspring are inviable or sterile.

ANS: T   DIF: I   OBJ: 16-3.4

MULTIPLE CHOICE

1. Which of the following describes a population?
   a. dogs and cats living in Austin, Texas
   b. four species of fish living in a pond
   c. dogwood trees in Middletown, Connecticut
   d. roses and tulips in a garden

ANS: C   DIF: I   OBJ: 16-1.1

2. Variation in genotype is caused by
   a. mutations only.
   b. recombination of genes as a result of sexual reproduction.
   c. phenotypes changing more quickly than genotypes.
   d. None of the above

ANS: B   DIF: I   OBJ: 16-1.2

3. Cystic fibrosis is a disease caused by a recessive allele. The disease occurs in about 1 out of every 2000 North American Caucasians. Approximately how many North American Caucasians out of 1000 will be carriers, heterozygous for the cystic fibrosis allele?
   a. 4.3   c. 43
   b. 8.6   d. 86

ANS: C   DIF: I   OBJ: 16-1.3

4. The number of individuals with a particular phenotype divided by the total number of individuals in the population is the
   a. genotype frequency.   c. Hardy-Weinberg equilibrium.
   b. phenotype frequency.   d. allele frequency.

ANS: B   DIF: I   OBJ: 16-1.3

5. RR : homozygous dominant ::
   a. Rr : heterozygous   c. Yy : homozygous
   b. rr : heterozygous recessive   d. yy : heterozygous dominant

ANS: A   DIF: II   OBJ: 16-1.3

6. recessive allele frequency : 0.02 ::
   a. dominant allele frequency : 0.01
   b. dominant allele frequency : 0.04
   c. dominant allele frequency : 0.98
   d. dominant allele frequency : 1.0

   ANS: C   DIF: II   OBJ: 16-1.3

7. Actual proportions of homozygotes and heterozygotes can differ from Hardy-Weinberg predictions because of
   a. the occurrence of mutations.
   b. nonrandom mating among individuals.
   c. genetic drift within the population.
   d. All of the above

   ANS: D   DIF: I   OBJ: 16-1.4

8. Which of the following conditions is required for Hardy-Weinberg genetic equilibrium?
   a. No mutations occur.
   b. The population is infinitely large.
   c. Individuals neither leave nor enter the population.
   d. All of the above are required.

   ANS: D   DIF: I   OBJ: 16-1.4

9. Natural selection acts
   a. on heterozygous genotypes.
   b. only on recessive alleles.
   c. on phenotypes that are expressed.
   d. on all mutations.

   ANS: C   DIF: I   OBJ: 16-2.1

10. The movement of alleles into or out of a population due to migration is called
    a. mutation.
    b. gene flow.
    c. nonrandom mating.
    d. natural selection.

    ANS: B   DIF: I   OBJ: 16-2.1

11. Which of the following conditions can cause evolution to take place?
    a. genetic drift
    b. migration
    c. nonrandom mating
    d. All of the above

    ANS: D   DIF: I   OBJ: 16-2.1

12. Gene flow describes the
    a. movement of genes from one generation to the next.
    b. movement of genes from one population to another.
    c. exchange of genes during recombination.
    d. movement of genes within a population because of interbreeding.

    ANS: B   DIF: I   OBJ: 16-2.2

13. nonrandom mating : increasing proportion of homozygotes ::
    a. migration of individuals : gene flow
    b. mutation : major change in allele frequencies
    c. Hardy-Weinberg equation : natural selection
    d. inbreeding : frequency of alleles

    ANS: A   DIF: II   OBJ: 16-2.2

14. What type of population is most susceptible to loss of genetic variability as a result of genetic drift?
    a. large populations   c. small populations
    b. medium-sized populations   d. populations that fluctuate in size

    ANS: C   DIF: I   OBJ: 16-2.3

15. A change in the frequency of a particular gene in one direction in a population is called
    a. directional selection.   c. chromosome drift.
    b. acquired variation.   d. stabilizing selection.

    ANS: A   DIF: I   OBJ: 16-2.4

16. The type of selection that may eliminate intermediate phenotypes is
    a. direction selection.   c. polygenic selection.
    b. disruptive selection.   d. stabilizing selection.

    ANS: B   DIF: I   OBJ: 16-2.4

17. Directional selection tends to eliminate
    a. both extremes in a range of phenotypes.
    b. one extreme in a range of phenotypes.
    c. intermediate phenotypes.
    d. None of the above; it causes new phenotypes to form.

    ANS: B   DIF: I   OBJ: 16-2.4

18. The large, brightly colored tail feathers of the male peacock are valuable to him because
    a. they warn off potential predators.
    b. they warn off potential competitors for mates.
    c. they attract potential mates.
    d. they attract people who provide them with food.

    ANS: C   DIF: I   OBJ: 16-2.5

19. The major limitation to the morphological concept of species is that
    a. there may be a great deal of phenotypic variability in a species.
    b. organisms that actually can interbreed may have very different physical characteristics.
    c. it does not consider whether individuals of a species can mate and produce viable offspring.
    d. All of the above

    ANS: D   DIF: II   OBJ: 16-3.1

20. Speciation can occur as a result of geographic isolation because
    a. members of a species can no longer find mates.
    b   populations that live in different environments may be exposed to different selection pressures.
    c. the biological concept of species defines noninterbreeding individuals as members of different species.
    d. All of the above

    ANS: B   DIF: II   OBJ: 16-3.2

21. Which of the following is an example of postzygotic isolation?
    a. A mating call is not recognized by a potential mate.
    b. Mating times of potential mates differ.
    c. Offspring of two individuals of two interbreeding species die early.
    d. None of the above

    ANS: C   DIF: I   OBJ: 16-3.3

22. The hypothesis that evolution occurs at a slow, constant rate is known as
    a. gradualism.   c. natural selection.
    b. slow motion.   d. adaptation.

    ANS: A   DIF: I   OBJ: 16-3.4

23. The hypothesis that evolution occurs at an irregular rate through geologic time is known as
    a. directional evolution.   c. punctuated equilibrium.
    b. directional equilibrium.   d. punctuated evolution.

    ANS: C   DIF: I   OBJ: 16-3.4

24. Which of the following is *not* a form of prezygotic isolation?
    a. different months of flowering of two wildflower species
    b. species-specific recognition proteins on the surfaces of egg and sperm cells
    c. different courtship rituals of different species
    d. the formation of a sterile hybrid between two species

    ANS: D   DIF: II   OBJ: 16-3.4

COMPLETION

1. _____ is the study of evolution from a genetic point of view.

    ANS: Population genetics   DIF: I   OBJ: 16-1.1

2. A _____ shows that most members of a population have similar values for a given measurable trait.

    ANS: bell curve   DIF: I   OBJ: 16-1.1

3. _____ results from flawed copies of individual genes.

ANS: Mutation DIF: I OBJ: 16-1.2

4. Alternative versions of genes are called _____.

ANS: alleles DIF: I OBJ: 16-1.3

5. _____ is determined by dividing the number of a certain allele by the total number of all types in the population.

ANS: Allele frequency DIF: I OBJ: 16-1.3

6. According to _____, allele frequencies in a population tend to remain the same from generation to generation unless acted on by outside influences.

ANS: Hardy-Weinberg genetic equilibrium DIF: I OBJ: 16-1.4

7. The movement of individuals from one population to another is called _____.

ANS: migration DIF: I OBJ: 16-2.2

8. When there are only a few surviving individuals of a species, the species is vulnerable to extinction because there is little if any _____ on which natural selection can act.

ANS: genetic variability DIF: I OBJ: 16-2.3

9. _____ selection causes the range of phenotypes to become narrower, increasing the number of individuals with characteristics near the middle of the range.

ANS: Stabilizing DIF: I OBJ: 16-2.4

10. Differences in physical characteristics between males and females of the same species indicate that _____ selection is important in the species.

ANS: sexual DIF: II OBJ: 16-2.5

11. The key element in the biological concept of species is that individuals within a species can _____.

ANS: interbreed DIF: I OBJ: 16-3.1

12. When geographic isolation occurs, _____ flow between separated individuals ceases, and this can then lead to speciation.

ANS: gene DIF: I OBJ: 16-3.2

13. _____ isolation is a type of reproductive isolation that occurs before fertilization.

ANS: Prezygotic   DIF: I   OBJ: 16-3.3

14. _____ isolation is a type of reproductive isolation that occurs after fertilization.

ANS: Postzygotic   DIF: I   OBJ: 16-3.3

15. _____ is the hypothesis that evolution occurs at a constant rate.

ANS: Gradualism   DIF: I   OBJ: 16-3.4

16. Reproductive isolation differs from geographic isolation in that members of the same species are not _____.

ANS: physically separated   DIF: I   OBJ: 16-3.4

ESSAY

1. In comparing two species that look very different, how could a comparison of the species' genes contribute to an understanding of their evolutionary relationship? Write your answer in the space below.

ANS:
Studying the species' genes would provide much more information than could be obtained by simply observing the physical appearance of the species. If the species had many genes in common, they would likely be more closely related than their physical appearance would suggest. If the species did not have many genes in common, this information would tend to strengthen the argument that the species were not closely related.

DIF: II   OBJ: 16-1.2

2. In a population of birds, 16 of 100 individuals suffer from a recessive genetic disorder that causes the feathers to fall off their wings. What proportion of the bird population are heterozygous carriers of the disorder? Write your answer in the space below.

ANS:
Given that 16 of 100 birds express the disorder, the proportion of the population that is homozygous recessive (q^2) is 0.16. Based on this, $q = 0.4$. Since $p + q = 1$, then $p = 1 - q = 1 - 0.4 = 0.6$. The proportion of birds that are heterozygous carriers of the disorder: $2pq = 2 (0.6) (0.4) = 0.48$ or 48 out of 100.

DIF: II   OBJ: 16-1.3

3. Describe how you would determine the phenotype frequency of a population. Write your answer in the space below.

ANS:
Determine the number of individuals with the phenotype. Then divide by the number of individuals in the population.

DIF: I   OBJ: 16-1.3

4. An agricultural plot of land is sprayed with a very powerful insecticide to destroy harmful insects. Nevertheless, many of the same species of insects are present on the land the following year. How might evolution theory account for this phenomenon? Write your answer in the space below.

ANS:
A part of evolution theory states that genetic variations exist within a species. A small percentage of the insects exposed to the insecticide might have been immune or capable of detoxifying the substance. They survived and produced offspring that were also resistant to the insecticide.

DIF: II   OBJ: 16-2.1

TRUE/FALSE

1. Humans and their closest fossil relatives are known as hominids.

   ANS: T   DIF: I   OBJ: 17-1.1

2. Fossil evidence indicates that most extinct primate species lived in trees.

   ANS: T   DIF: I   OBJ: 17-1.2

3. Movable fingers and toes with flattened nails are typical of primates.

   ANS: T   DIF: I   OBJ: 17-1.2

4. Depth perception is a characteristic of primates.

   ANS: T   DIF: I   OBJ: 17-1.2

5. An opposable thumb is characteristic of anthropoids.

   ANS: T   DIF: I   OBJ: 17-1.3

6. Chimpanzees and humans have very similar DNA.

   ANS: T   DIF: I   OBJ: 17-1.3

7. Apes and humans are classified as hominids.

   ANS: F   DIF: I   OBJ: 17-1.3

8. Anthropoids have larger brains than prosimians.

   ANS: T   DIF: I   OBJ: 17-1.3

9. Based on an examination of fossils, Australopithecines were taller than modern humans.

   ANS: F   DIF: I   OBJ: 17-2.1

10. Lucy's skeleton revealed that she walked on four legs.

    ANS: F   DIF: I   OBJ: 17-2.1

11. All known hominids are direct ancestors of modern humans.

    ANS: F   DIF: I   OBJ: 17-2.2

12. The evolutionary history of hominids is clearly established and agreed upon by scientists.

    ANS: F   DIF: I   OBJ: 17-2.3

13. *Homo habilis* had a larger brain than *Homo erectus*.

ANS: F   DIF: I   OBJ: 17-3.1

14. *Homo habilis* made stone tools.

ANS: T   DIF: I   OBJ: 17-3.1

15. Some scientists think that *Homo habilis* had brain areas essential for speech.

ANS: T   DIF: I   OBJ: 17-3.1

16. *Homo habilis* evolved from australopithecine ancestors.

ANS: T   DIF: I   OBJ: 17-3.1

17. Neanderthals are members of the species *Homo sapiens*.

ANS: T   DIF: I   OBJ: 17-3.2

MULTIPLE CHOICE

1. Examination of some hominid fossils and their surroundings can reveal the fossil organism's
   a. diet.   c. brain size.
   b. age.   d. All of the above

   ANS: D   DIF: I   OBJ: 17-1.1

2. The first primates probably resembled modern
   a. humans.   c. gorillas.
   b. prosimians.   d. chimpanzees.

   ANS: B   DIF: I   OBJ: 17-1.2

3. Two distinctive features of all primates are
   a. depth perception and grasping hands.
   b. grasping hands and feet.
   c. depth perception and S-shaped spines.
   d. opposable thumbs and S-shaped spines.

   ANS: A   DIF: I   OBJ: 17-1.2

4. Anthropoid primates are different from prosimians in that they
   a. have opposable thumbs and large brains.
   b. live in trees.
   c. have binocular vision.
   d. only come out at night.

   ANS: A   DIF: I   OBJ: 17-1.3

5. Because DNA sequences in humans and chimpanzees are very similar,
    a. humans must have evolved from chimpanzees.
    b. chimpanzees must have single-stranded DNA.
    c. humans and chimpanzees probably shared a recent a common ancestor.
    d. humans and chimpanzees are the same species.

    ANS: C   DIF: I   OBJ: 17-1.3

The diagram below illustrates the evolutionary relationship between apes and humans.

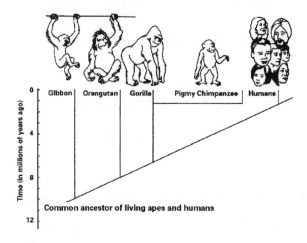

6. Refer to the illustration above. According to the diagram, gorillas evolved
    a. about 7 million years ago.
    b. more than 10 million years ago.
    c. about the same time as orangutans did.
    d. after chimpanzees did.

    ANS: A   DIF: II   OBJ: 17-1.3

7. Refer to the illustration above. According to the diagram,
    a. humans evolved from gibbons.
    b. humans evolved from chimpanzees.
    c. humans and chimpanzees share a common ancestor.
    d. humans evolved long before chimpanzees did.

    ANS: C   DIF: II   OBJ: 17-1.3

Skeletons of two Primates

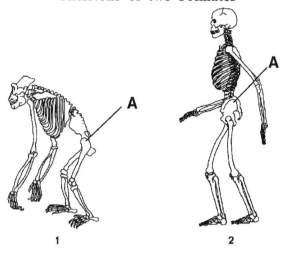

1   2

8. Refer to the illustration above. The bone labeled "A" on both primates is the
   a. pelvis.   c. fibula.
   b. femur.   d. spine.

   ANS: A   DIF: II   OBJ: 17-1.3

9. Refer to the illustration above. Diagram "2" shows the skeleton of a
   a. chimpanzee.   c. prosimian.
   b. gorilla.   d. hominid.

   ANS: D   DIF: II   OBJ: 17-1.4

10. Refer to the illustration above. By examining the skeletons in the diagram, scientists
    would conclude that only the primate labeled "2"
    a. could walk upright on two legs.   c. had opposable big toes.
    b. had opposable thumbs.   d. All of the above

    ANS: A   DIF: II   OBJ: 17-1.4

11. Chimpanzees are different from humans in that they
    a. have long hair and walk on four legs.
    b. have identical skeletons but smaller brains.
    c. have very different DNA from that of humans.
    d. All of the above

    ANS: A   DIF: I   OBJ: 17-1.4

The diagrams below represent jaws from two kinds of primates.

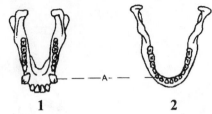

1   2

12. Refer to the illustration above. The teeth labeled "A" in the diagram are
 a. molars.   c. canines.
 b. premolars.   d. incisors.

 ANS: C   DIF: II   OBJ: 17-1.4

13. Refer to the illustration above. Diagram "2" is probably the jaw of a
 a. chimpanzee.   c. prosimian.
 b. gorilla.   d. hominid.

 ANS: D   DIF: II   OBJ: 17-1.4

14. Language
 a. is unique to humans.   c. is typical of the anthropoids.
 b. is not present in monkeys. d. is found in all animals.

 ANS: A   DIF: I   OBJ: 17-1.4

15. Which of the following characteristics is most easily inferred from the measurement of a fossil skull's cranial capacity?
 a. intelligence   c. cultural development
 b. brain size   d. evolutionary position

 ANS: B   DIF: II   OBJ: 17-2.1

16. Lucy's skeleton revealed that she was bipedal. This means that she
 a. walked using all four limbs. c. walked on two legs.
 b. lived in trees.   d. crawled along the jungle floor.

 ANS: C   DIF: I   OBJ: 17-2.1

17. All australopithecine fossils have been found in
 a. South America.   c. Australia.
 b. Africa.   d. Asia.

 ANS: B   DIF: I   OBJ: 17-2.2

18. Which of the following hominids is probably an ancestor of modern humans?
    a. *Australopithecus afarensis*   c. *Australopithecus robustus*
    b. *Australopithecus africanus*   d. All of the above

    ANS: A   DIF: I   OBJ: 17-2.2

19. The human evolutionary tree is best represented by
    a. a single trunk with no side branches.
    b. one major trunk and one side branch.
    c. many parallel branches.
    d. All of the above

    ANS: B   DIF: II   OBJ: 17-2.2

20. An examination of australopithecine fossils indicates that australopithecines
    a. were shorter than modern humans.   c. had relatively small brains.
    b. were bipedal.   d. All of the above

    ANS: D   DIF: I   OBJ: 17-2.2

21. A fossil organism discovered in 1995 which may or may not have been bipedal is
    a. *Australopithecus anamensis.*   c. *Australopithecus africanus.*
    b. *Australopithecus afarensis.*   d. *Ardipithecus ramidus.*

    ANS: D   DIF: I   OBJ: 17-2.3

22. The first member of the genus *Homo* was
    a. *Homo sapiens.*   c. *Homo habilis.*
    b. *Homo erectus.*   d. *Homo hominid.*

    ANS: C   DIF: I   OBJ: 17-3.1

23. *Homo erectus*
    a. had a large brain.   c. was larger than *Homo habilis.*
    b. walked erect.   d. All of the above

    ANS: D   DIF: I   OBJ: 17-3.1

24. Hunting large animals, use of fire, and living in caves are associated with
    a. *H. habilis.*   c. *A. robustus.*
    b. *A. africanus.*   d. *H. erectus.*

    ANS: D   DIF: I   OBJ: 17-3.1

25. When comparing *Homo habilis* and *Homo erectus*, we find that
    a. *Homo habilis* was taller and walked upright.
    b. *Homo habilis* had a larger brain.
    c. *Homo erectus* was taller and walked upright.
    d. *Homo erectus* built houses and grew crops.

    ANS: C   DIF: I   OBJ: 17-3.1

26. orangutan : ape ::
    a. *Homo erectus* : hominid
    b. *Australopithecus* : *Homo*
    c. monkey : ape
    d. hominid : ape

    ANS: A   DIF: II   OBJ: 17-3.1

27. Neanderthals probably evolved from
    a. *H. habilis.*
    b. *A. africanus.*
    c. *H. erectus.*
    d. *A. boisei.*

    ANS: C   DIF: I   OBJ: 17-3.2

28. Modern *Homo sapiens* appeared in Africa about
    a. 10 million years ago.
    b. 1 million years ago.
    c. 100,000 years ago.
    d. 10,000 years ago.

    ANS: C   DIF: I   OBJ: 17-3.2

29. The Neanderthals are noted for
    a. having heavily-built bodies.
    b. using several tools to scrape animal hides.
    c. having a larger brain size than modern humans.
    d. All of the above

    ANS: D   DIF: I   OBJ: 17-3.2

30. Modern humans are most closely related to
    a. *A. boisei.*
    b. Neanderthals.
    c. *A. africanus.*
    d. *Homo habilis.*

    ANS: B   DIF: I   OBJ: 17-3.2

31. The hypothesis that *Homo sapiens* evolved in Africa is supported by the finding that
    a. *Homo sapiens* have different numbers of chromosomes.
    b. most human mitochondria have very similar genes.
    c. only modern Africans have mitochondrial DNA.
    d. human mitochondrial DNA shows millions of years of accumulated mutations.

    ANS: B   DIF: I   OBJ: 17-3.3

COMPLETION

1. Most primate characteristics probably are adaptations to life in

   _____.

   ANS: trees   DIF: I   OBJ: 17-1.2

2. The position of the eyes in primates allows them to perceive _____.

   ANS: binocular   DIF: I   OBJ: 17-1.2

3. A(n) _____ thumb can be bent toward the other fingers.

    ANS: opposable   DIF: I   OBJ: 17-1.3

4. The group of animals known as _____ includes humans, apes, monkeys, and marmosets.

    ANS: primates   DIF: I   OBJ: 17-1.3

5. Humans and apes share a common _____.

    ANS: ancestor   DIF: I   OBJ: 17-1.4

6. The oldest hominid fossils are those of _____.

    ANS: *Australopithecus afarensis*   DIF: I   OBJ: 17-2.1

7. The most complete hominid fossil ever found was that of a female nicknamed _____.

    ANS: Lucy   DIF: I   OBJ: 17-2.1

8. Most researchers think that hominids of the genus _____ are the ancestors of all other hominids.

    ANS: *Australopithecus*   DIF: I   OBJ: 17-2.2

9. The hominid species _____, which was discovered in 1995, is 300,000 years older than the oldest known *Australopithecus afarensis* specimens.

    ANS: *Australopithecus anamensis*   DIF: I   OBJ: 17-2.3

10. Neanderthals are classified as the species _____.

    ANS: *Homo sapiens*   DIF: I   OBJ: 17-3.2

11. The appearance of the species _____ marked the beginnings of an expansion of hominid populations across the globe.

    ANS: *Homo erectus*   DIF: I   OBJ: 17-3.3

12. Modern humans all over Earth belong to the species _____.

    ANS: *Homo sapiens*   DIF: I   OBJ: 17-3.3

13. Analysis of the genes found in _____ indicates that *H. sapiens* probably evolved in Africa.

    ANS: mitochondria   DIF: I   OBJ: 17-3.3

ESSAY

1. If you were looking for early hominid fossils, on what continent would you search? Why? Write your answer in the space below.

   ANS:
   Africa. Because the earliest relatives of humans, the chimpanzees and gorillas, lived in Africa, humans probably evolved there, too.

   DIF: II   OBJ: 17-1.1

2. Describe adaptations of primate vision for living in trees. Write your answer in the space below.

   ANS:
   Good vision is an adaptive trait for tree dwellers. Cones, color-sensitive cells in the eyes, give primates color vision. This allows primates to locate ripe fruit in trees. Front-facing eyes and a reduced snout enable primates to integrate images from both eyes simultaneously and thus perceive depth accurately. Therefore arboreal primates can gauge distances as they leap or swing from branch to branch.

   DIF: II   OBJ: 17-1.2

3. Describe the abilities of humans and apes to communicate. Write your answer in the space below.

   ANS:
   Humans have the unique ability to communicate using verbal language. Apes communicate through sounds and gestures; they can also be taught to use certain forms of sign language. However, apes in the wild have not developed any complex, flexible set of signals that can compare to those of human language.

   DIF: II   OBJ: 17-1.4

4. Describe adaptations of the human skeleton for bipedalism. Write your answer in the space below.

   ANS:
   The cupped-shape of the human pelvis is an adaptation for bipedalism. The pelvis supports the internal organs during upright walking. Another adaptation for bipedalism is the shape of the human foot. The toes are relatively short and are aligned with each other. This causes body weight to be distributed evenly during upright walking.

   DIF: II   OBJ: 17-1.4

5. How were Neanderthals similar to modern humans? Write your answer in the space below.

   ANS:
   The bodies of Neanderthals were similar to the bodies of modern humans, and their brains were larger than those of modern humans. In addition, Neanderthals made complex stone tools and shelters.

   DIF: II   OBJ: 17-3.2

CHAPTER 18—CLASSIFICATION

TRUE/FALSE

1. The identification and classification of organisms is the science of biosystematics.

   ANS: F   DIF: I   OBJ: 18-1.1

2. The Greek philosopher Aristotle grouped animals into land dwellers, water dwellers, and air dwellers.

   ANS: T   DIF: I   OBJ: 18-1.1

3. Linnaeus was the first scientist to give species Latin names.

   ANS: F   DIF: I   OBJ: 18-1.1

4. Linnaeus used a five-kingdom classification system.

   ANS: F   DIF: I   OBJ: 18-1.2

5. Linnaeus classified organisms into groups according to their evolutionary relationships.

   ANS: F   DIF: I   OBJ: 18-1.2

6. The first word of a scientific name identifies the kind of organism within the genus.

   ANS: F   DIF: I   OBJ: 18-1.3

7. To ensure accurate communication of information, biologists assign a unique two-word scientific name to each organism.

   ANS: T   DIF: I   OBJ: 18-1.3

8. Linnaeus's system of classification was based on morphological characteristics. Modern biologists try to classify organisms based on their evolutionary relationships to other organisms, which may or may not be reflected in similar morphological characteristics.

   ANS: T   DIF: II   OBJ: 18-1.4

9. A phylogenetic tree depicts a hypothesis, rather than information known with certainty.

   ANS: T   DIF: I   OBJ: 18-2.1

10. Fossils are the most helpful form of evidence that can be used to construct a phylogenetic tree.

    ANS: F   DIF: I   OBJ: 18-2.2

11. Cells in vertebrate embryos become committed to becoming a particular part of the organism earlier than they do in arthropods.

    ANS: F   DIF: I   OBJ: 18-2.3

12. Cladograms represent direct information about ancestors and descendants, showing who came from whom.

    ANS: F   DIF: I   OBJ: 18-2.4

13. Each of the kingdoms of living things exhibits multicellularity.

    ANS: F   DIF: I   OBJ: 18-3.1

14. Eukaryotic, multicellular, autotrophic organisms belong to the Kingdom Plantae.

    ANS: T   DIF: I   OBJ: 18-3.1

15. Organisms in the Kingdom Animalia are multicellular and obtain nutrition by ingesting food.

    ANS: T   DIF: I   OBJ: 18-3.1

16. Eukaryotes are the most abundant inhabitants of Earth.

    ANS: F   DIF: I   OBJ: 18-3.2

17. The gene translation machinery of eubacteria is different from that of both archaebacteria and eukaryotes.

    ANS: F   DIF: I   OBJ: 18-3.2

18. Mitosis distinguishes prokaryotic organisms from eukaryotes.

    ANS: T   DIF: I   OBJ: 18-3.2

19. The three-domain system of classification assumes that all living things had a common ancestor and that all living things today naturally fall into three groups that have descended from this common ancestor.

    ANS: T   DIF: I   OBJ: 18-3.4

20. The three-domain system of classification has two domains of prokaryotic organisms, while the six-kingdom system of classification has only one kingdom of prokaryotic organisms.

    ANS: F   DIF: I   OBJ: 18-3.5

21. The three-domain system of classification differs from the six-kingdom system in that it is based on a type of evidence that is found in all living things.

    ANS: T   DIF: I   OBJ: 18-3.5

MULTIPLE CHOICE

1. The science of classifying living things is called
   a. identification.
   b. classification.
   c. taxonomy.
   d. speciation.

   ANS: C   DIF: I   OBJ: 18-1.1

2. Taxonomy is defined as the science of
   a. classifying plants according to their uses in agricultural experiments.
   b. studying ribosomal RNA sequencing techniques.
   c. grouping organisms according to their charateristics and evoluntionary history.
   d. studying reproductive mechanisms and gene flow.

   ANS: C   DIF: I   OBJ: 18-1.1

3. As we move through the biological hierarchy from the kingdom to species level, organisms
   a. vary more and more.
   b. are less and less related to each other.
   c. become more similar in appearance.
   d. always are members of the same order.

   ANS: C   DIF: I   OBJ: 18-1.2

4. A mushroom is difficult to classify in Linnaeus's two-kingdom classification system because
   a. it has another common name, the toadstool.
   b. it doesn't seem to fit into either category.
   c. mushrooms had not yet evolved in Linnaeus's time.
   d. All of the above

   ANS: B   DIF: I   OBJ: 18-1.2

5. Which of the following was *not* a consideration for Carolus Linnaeus when he developed his system of nomenclature of organisms?
   a. It should include detailed descriptions of an organism in its name.
   b. It should assign each organism a unique name.
   c. It should assign names using a language that can be recognized worldwide.
   d. It should enable scientists to classify organisms according to their presumed evolutionary relationships to other organisms.

   ANS: D   DIF: I   OBJ: 18-1.2

6. Which of the following scientists developed the system of classifying organisms by assigning them a genus and species name?
   a. Leakey
   b. Aristotle
   c. Darwin
   d. Linnaeus

   ANS: D   DIF: I   OBJ: 18-1.3

A Comparison of Dolphins and Sharks

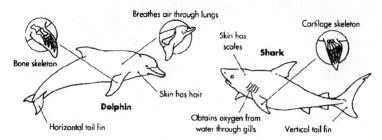

7. Refer to the illustration above. A shark's skeleton is made of cartilage while a dolphin's skeleton is made of bone. This is one reason the two organisms are placed in different
   a. kingdoms.
   b. phyla.
   c. subphyla.
   d. classes.

   ANS: D   DIF: II   OBJ: 18-1.2

8. Refer to the illustration above. Because both organisms in the diagram are vertebrates, they are classified in the same
   a. phylum.
   b. genus.
   c. order.
   d. class.

   ANS: A   DIF: II   OBJ: 18-1.3

9. The organism *Quercus phellos* is a member of the genus
   a. Plantae.
   b. *phellos.*
   c. *Quercus.*
   d. Protista.

   ANS: C   DIF: I   OBJ: 18-1.3

10. Poison ivy is also known as *Rhus toxicodendron.* Its species identifier is
    a. poison.
    b. *Rhus.*
    c. ivy.
    d. *toxicodendron.*

    ANS: D   DIF: I   OBJ: 18-1.3

11. The red maple is also known as *Acer rubrum.* Its scientific name is
    a. red maple.
    b. *Acer.*
    c. *rubrum.*
    d. *Acer rubrum.*

    ANS: D   DIF: I   OBJ: 18-1.3

12. The scientific name of an organism
    a. varies according to the native language of scientists.
    b. is the same for scientists all over the world.
    c. may refer to more than one species.
    d. may have more than one genus name.

    ANS: B   DIF: I   OBJ: 18-1.3

13. Scientists don't use the common names of organisms because
    a. an organism may have more than one common name.
    b. common names are too ambiguous.
    c. an organism rarely has the same name in different languages.
    d. All of the above

    ANS: D   DIF: I   OBJ: 18-1.3

14. An organism can have
    a. one genus name and one species identifier.
    b. one genus name and two species identifiers.
    c. two scientific names if it is found on different continents.
    d. two genus names but only one species identifier.

    ANS: A   DIF: I   OBJ: 18-1.3

15. Scientific names are written in what language?
    a. English   c. Arabic
    b. Greek   d. Latin

    ANS: D   DIF: I   OBJ: 18-1.3

16. Two organisms in the same class but different orders will
    a. be in different kingdoms.   c. be in the same phylum.
    b. have the same genus name.   d. be members of the same species.

    ANS: C   DIF: I   OBJ: 18-1.3

17. Organisms in different genera
    a. may share the second word of their scientific names.
    b. may be in the same family.
    c. may be in different orders.
    d. All of the above

    ANS: D   DIF: I   OBJ: 18-1.3

18. Two organisms in the same order but different families may
    a. be more similar than two organisms in different classes.
    b. be in the same class.
    c. have the same species identifier.
    d. All of the above

    ANS: D   DIF: I   OBJ: 18-1.3

19. Kingdoms are divided into phyla, and a phylum is divided into
    a. families.   c. orders.
    b. classes.   d. genera.

    ANS: B   DIF: I   OBJ: 18-1.3

20. The correct order of the biological hierarchy from kingdom to species is
    a. kingdom, class, family, order, phylum, genus, species.
    b. kingdom, phylum, order, family, class, genus, species.
    c. kingdom, phylum, class, order, family, genus, species.
    d. kingdom, class, order, phylum, family, genus, species.

    ANS: C   DIF: I   OBJ: 18-1.3

21. The lowest hierarchy level in biological classification is the
    a. genus.   c. family.
    b. species.   d. order.

    ANS: B   DIF: I   OBJ: 18-1.3

22. Which of the following is the *least* inclusive classification group?
    a. class   c. phylum
    b. genus   d. species

    ANS: D   DIF: I   OBJ: 18-1.3

23. *Quercus rubra* : *Quercus phellos* ::
    a. *Anolis carolinensis* : *Parus carolinensis*
    b. *Erithacus rubicula* : *Turdus migratoria*
    c. *Aphis pomi* : *Aphis gossypii*
    d. carp : goldfish

    ANS: C   DIF: II   OBJ: 18-1.3

24. class : family ::
    a. order : phylum   c. species : genus
    b. genus : class   d. phylum : order

    ANS: D   DIF: II   OBJ: 18-1.3

25. Today, biologists classify organisms by their
    a. physical similarities.   c. behavioral similarities.
    b. chemical similarities.   d. All of the above

    ANS: D   DIF: I   OBJ: 18-1.4

26. Phylogenetic trees depict
    a. known evolutionary relationships between organisms.
    b. presumed evolutionary relationships based on morphological evidence.
    c. only living organisms.
    d. presumed evolutionary relationships based on a variety of types of evidence.

    ANS: D   DIF: I   OBJ: 18-2.1

27. The organism at the base of a phylogenetic tree is
    a. the oldest living organism among those depicted in the tree.
    b. the common ancestor of all the organisms depicted in the tree.
    c. the modern form of the common ancestor of all the organisms depicted in the tree.
    d. the simplest organisms among those depicted in the tree.

    ANS: B   DIF: III   OBJ: 18-2.1

28. The DNA sequences of two species of sharks would
    a. be more similar than the DNA sequences of a shark and a dolphin.
    b. show no discernible differences.
    c. be very close to the DNA sequences of a dolphin.
    d. indicate how the sharks evolved.

    ANS: A   DIF: I   OBJ: 18-2.2

29. Which of the following types of characteristics is used in systematic taxonomy to organize organisms?
    a. patterns of embryological development
    b. morphology
    c. amino acid sequences of proteins
    d. All of the above

    ANS: D   DIF: I   OBJ: 18-2.2

30. If an early arthropod and early vertebrate embryo are split,
    a. both halves of both organisms will become whole, twin organisms.
    b. both halves of both organisms will die.
    c. both halves of the arthropod embryo will become whole, twin organisms, while both halves of the vertebrate embryo will die.
    d. both halves of the arthropod embryo will die, while both halves of the vertebrate embryo will become whole, twin organisms.

    ANS: D   DIF: I   OBJ: 18-2.3

31. analogous characters : convergent evolution ::
    a. two members of the same genus : same species
    b. cladogram : evolutionary relationships
    c. common names : universal identification
    d. cladograms : exact, direct information

    ANS: B   DIF: II   OBJ: 18-2.4

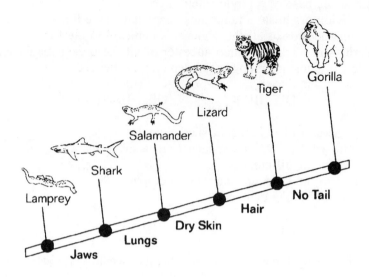

32. Refer to the illustration above. A branching diagram like the one shown is called a
    a. phenetic tree.
    b. cladogram.
    c. family tree.
    d. homology.

    ANS: B   DIF: II   OBJ: 18-2.4

33. Refer to the illustration above. Each unique character, such as dry skin, that is used to assign an organism to a group is known as a(n)
    a. special character.
    b. analogous character.
    c. derived character.
    d. homologous character.

    ANS: C   DIF: I   OBJ: 18-2.4

34. Nearly all single-celled eukaryotes that are either heterotrophic or photosynthetic belong to the kingdom
    a. Animalia.
    b. Fungi.
    c. Plantae.
    d. Protista.

    ANS: D   DIF: I   OBJ: 18-3.1

35. Most multicellular, nucleated autotrophs that carry on photosynthesis belong to the kingdom
    a. Animalia.
    b. Eubacteria.
    c. Fungi.
    d. Plantae.

    ANS: D   DIF: I   OBJ: 18-3.1

36. Multicellular, nucleated heterotrophs that always obtain food by absorbing nutrients from the environment belong to the kingdom
    a. Animalia.
    b. Eubacteria.
    c. Fungi.
    d. Plantae.

    ANS: C   DIF: I   OBJ: 18-3.1

Phylogenetic Tree of the Six Kingdoms

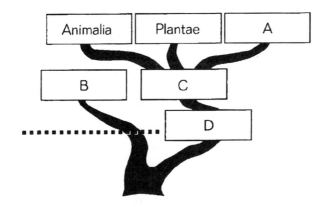

37. Refer to the illustration above. The kingdom represented in box "C" is
    a. Archaebacteria.
    b. Protista.
    c. Eubacteria.
    d. Fungi.

    ANS: B   DIF: II   OBJ: 18-3.1

38. Refer to the illustration above. The kingdom represented in box "B" is
    a. Archaebacteria.
    b. Protista.
    c. Eubacteria.
    d. Fungi.

    ANS: C   DIF: II   OBJ: 18-3.1

39. Refer to the illustration above. The kingdom represented in box "A" is
    a. Archaebacteria.
    b. Protista.
    c. Eubacteria.
    d. Fungi.

    ANS: D   DIF: II   OBJ: 18-3.1

40. An organism that breaks down organic matter, which it then absorbs, is in the kingdom
    a. Fungi.
    b. Plantae.
    c. Animalia.
    d. Protista.

    ANS: A   DIF: I   OBJ: 18-3.1

41. Archaebacteria can be distinguished from eubacteria because of differences in their
    a. cell walls.
    b. cell membranes.
    c. gene architecture.
    d. All of the above

    ANS: D   DIF: I   OBJ: 18-3.2

42. Simple, non-nucleated organisms that use hydrogen to produce methane are in the kingdom
    a. Archaebacteria.
    b. Eubacteria.
    c. Protista.
    d. Fungi.

    ANS: A   DIF: I   OBJ: 18-3.2

43. The catchall kingdom is kingdom
   a. Protista.
   b. Plantae.
   c. Animalia.
   d. Fungi.

   ANS: A   DIF: I   OBJ: 18-3.3

44. The three-domain system of classification is based on ____ evidence.
   a. embryological
   b. fossil
   c. molecular
   d. morphological

   ANS: C   DIF: I   OBJ: 18-3.4

45. The three domain system of classification is based on similarities and differences in ____
   evidence. The six-kingdom system is based on similarities and differences in ____ evidence.
   a. DNA; DNA, fossil, embryological, and morphological
   b. molecular structure; embryological, fossil, morphological, and molecular structure
   c. ribosomal RNA; embryological, fossil, morphological, and a variety of molecular
   d. morphological; embryological, fossil, morphological, and a variety of molecular

   ANS: C   DIF: II   OBJ: 18-3.5

COMPLETION

1. Aristotle classified plants into three categories on the basis of differences in their
   _____.

   ANS: stems   DIF: I   OBJ: 18-1.1

2. The science of naming and classifying organisms is called _____.

   ANS: taxonomy   DIF: I   OBJ: 18-1.1

3. _____ devised the two-name system of naming organisms.

   ANS: Linnaeus   DIF: I   OBJ: 18-1.2

4. The more classification categories two species share, the more _____
   they have in common.

   ANS: traits, characteristics DIF: I   OBJ: 18-1.2

5. Biologists of Linnaeus's time classified every living thing as either plant or
   _____.

   ANS: animal   DIF: I   OBJ: 18-1.2

6. A genus is subdivided into smaller groups called _____.

   ANS: species   DIF: I   OBJ: 18-1.3

7. Each kind of organism on Earth is assigned a unique two-word _____.

   ANS: scientific name   DIF: I   OBJ: 18-1.3

8. All scientific names are made up of two words that are often derived from the _____ language.

    ANS: Latin   DIF: I   OBJ: 18-1.3

9. The first word of a scientific name is the _____ to which the organism belongs.

    ANS: genus   DIF: I   OBJ: 18-1.3

10. The term _____ is used in place of phylum when plants are classified.

    ANS: division   DIF: I   OBJ: 18-1.3

11. The evolutionary history of a species is called its _____.

    ANS: phylogeny   DIF: I   OBJ: 18-1.4

12. Most invertebrates, such as the arthropods, follow a pattern of development in which the blastopore becomes the _____.

    ANS: anterior end of the digestive system (the mouth)

    DIF: I   OBJ: 18-2.3

A   B   C   D

13. Refer to the illustration above. Organism "D" is classified in the kingdom _____.

    ANS: Fungi   DIF: II   OBJ: 18-3.1

14. Eukaryotic organisms that lack specialized tissue systems are members of the kingdom _____.

    ANS: Protista   DIF: I   OBJ: 18-3.1

15. Corals, spiders, and rodents all belong to the kingdom _____.

    ANS: Animalia   DIF: I   OBJ: 18-3.1

16. The domains of the three-domain system of classification are _____, _____, and _____.

    ANS: Archaea, Bacteria, Eukarya   DIF: I   OBJ: 18-3.4

PROBLEM

1. You are given three organisms that all have wings. You are asked to determine how closely related these organisms are to each other. Because you have only simple laboratory facilities, you cannot analyze the DNA of these organisms. You also do not have embryos of your organisms to study.

   a. Select from among the following list of characteristics those that you would use in order to determine how closely related your organisms are. Circle your answers, or write them on a separate piece of paper.

      Presence or absence of a backbone
      Presence or absence of the ability to fly
      Presence or absence of feathers
      Presence or absence of limbs or appendages
      Presence or absence of mammary glands
      Presence or absence of scales
      Presence or absence of a tail
      Presence or absence of teeth or a jaw

   Write your answers to the following in the space below or on a separate sheet of paper.

   b. Consider now that you have collected the following data on your organisms: Organism A does not have a backbone, is able to fly, does not have feathers, has limbs or appendages, does not have mammary glands, does not have scales, does not have a tail, and does have a jaw. Organism B has a backbone, is able to fly, does not have feathers, has limbs or appendages, does have mammary glands, does not have scales, does have a tail, and does have teeth and a jaw. Organism C has a backbone, is able to fly, does have feathers, has limbs or appendages, does not have mammary glands, has some scales, has a tail, and has teeth and a jaw. Which two of these three organisms are most closely related to each other?

   c. What types of animals are your organisms? Make your best estimate based on the information you have gathered and what you know about different types of animals.

   d. For each of the three organisms, identify the phylum and class to which they belong.

   e. Is the presence of wings on all three of these animals an example of convergent or divergent evolution?

   ANS:
   a. Presence or absence of a backbone
      Presence or absence of feathers
      Presence or absence of mammary glands
   b. "B" and "C"
   c. "A" is an insect, "B" is a flying mammal such as a bat or a flying squirrel, and "C" is a bird.
   d. Organism "A:" Phylum Arthropoda, Class Insecta
      Organism "B:" Phylum Chordata, Class Mammalia
      Organism "C:" Phylum Chordata, Class Aves
   e. Convergent evolution

   DIF: III   OBJ: 18-2.2

2. The following table presents data on some characteristics found in vertebrates. A "+" indicates that an organism has a particular characteristic and a "–" indicates that an organism does not have a particular characteristic.

Organism	Characteristics				
	Jaws	Limbs	Hair	Lungs	Tail
Lamprey	–	–	–	–	+
Turtle	+	+	–	+	+
Cat	+	+	+	+	+
Gorilla	+	+	+	+	+
Lungfish	+	–	–	+	+
Trout	+	–	–	–	+
Human	+	+	+	+	–

Using these data, construct a cladogram illustrating the evolutionary relationships among these organisms. Each branch point should indicate a common ancestor. Write in the name of the shared derived character that is common to all organisms above each branching point. A shared derived character can be the absence of a structure common to organisms below that point on the tree. Write your answer in the space below.

ANS:
Students' cladograms should look something like the one depicted below. The positions of the gorilla and the human are also correct if they are placed in opposite positions.

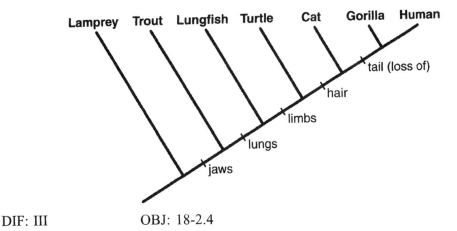

DIF: III   OBJ: 18-2.4

ESSAY

1. Why might the use of common names to describe organisms sometimes cause confusion? Give several examples to support your answer. Write your answer in the space below.

ANS:
The use of common names to describe organisms may sometimes cause confusion because common names may not describe an organism accurately. For example, a jellyfish is not a fish. Sometimes the same common name is used for different species. For instance, a maple tree might be a sugar maple, a silver maple, or a red maple. Also, some organisms have more than one common name, depending on the region in which they are found.

DIF: II   OBJ: 18-1.3

2. While on a biological expedition to a tropical rain forest, you discover a new animal. Explain how you would determine the genus and species name of the animal. Write your answer in the space below.

ANS:
Based on the animal's physical characteristics, you would decide if it belongs in a known genus. If it does, it must be given that generic name. If a new generic name is needed, it should be descriptive. The species identifier may describe the appearance or lifestyle of the organism or may be given in honor of an individual. The given scientific name must be Latin or constructed according to the rules of Latin grammar.

DIF: II   OBJ: 18-1.3

3. The red fox (*Vulpes vulpes*), the coyote (*Canis latrans*), and the dog (*Canis familiaris*) are all members of the Family Canidae. The mountain lion (*Felis concolor*) is a member of the Family Felidae. Describe the relationships among these animals. Write your answer in the space below.

ANS:
Since the coyote and the dog are both members of the same genus, they are the most closely related. The red fox is more closely related to these two animals than to the mountain lion since the mountain lion is in a different family.

DIF: II   OBJ: 18-1.3

4. A species is defined as a group of organisms that are similar and can interbreed and produce fertile offspring in nature. Horses and donkeys can interbreed and produce mules, which cannot produce offspring. Is it possible that horses and donkeys belong to the same species? Explain. Write your answer in the space below.

ANS:
Horses and donkeys cannot belong to the same species because their offspring, mules, are infertile.

DIF: II   OBJ: 18-3.1

CHAPTER 19—INTRODUCTION TO ECOLOGY

TRUE/FALSE

1. While an understanding of the interactions between organisms and their environment was very important to early hunter and gatherer humans, it is even more important today because humans are having significant effects on the environment.

   ANS: T   DIF: I   OBJ: 19-1.1

2. Cutting down trees in a forest alters the habitat of the organisms living in the forest.

   ANS: T   DIF: I   OBJ: 19-1.1

3. If CFCs were to be banned by all countries tomorrow, the destruction of the ozone layer would quickly be stopped.

   ANS: F   DIF: I   OBJ: 19-1.2

4. CFCs are the only chemicals that destroy ozone in the atmosphere.

   ANS: F   DIF: I   OBJ: 19-1.2

5. The world's climate is warming as large amounts of CO_2 are released into the atmosphere.

   ANS: T   DIF: I   OBJ: 19-1.2

6. A community includes all the species within an area.

   ANS: T   DIF: I   OBJ: 19-1.3

7. Ecologists call the physical location of a community its habitat.

   ANS: T   DIF: I   OBJ: 19-2.1

8. Ecosystems include only the biotic factors in an area.

   ANS: F   DIF: I   OBJ: 19-2.1

9. An organism's range can be determined by its tolerance to only one environmental variable.

   ANS: T   DIF: I   OBJ: 19-2.2

10. An organism's niche includes its habitat.

    ANS: T   DIF: I   OBJ: 19-2.4

11. An organism's niche is the sum of all its interactions in its environment, including interactions with other organisms.

    ANS: T   DIF: I   OBJ: 19-2.4

MULTIPLE CHOICE

1. Ecology is the study of the interaction of living organisms
   a. with each other and their habitat.
   b. and their communities.
   c. with each other and their physical environment.
   d. and the food they eat.

   ANS: C   DIF: I   OBJ: 19-1.1

2. The destruction of the ozone layer may be responsible for an increase in
   a. cataracts.
   b. melanoma.
   c. cancer of the retina.
   d. All of the above

   ANS: D   DIF: I   OBJ: 19-1.2

3. CFCs in the atmosphere
   a. stick to frozen water vapor.
   b. change oxygen into ozone.
   c. convert sunlight into ozone.
   d. convert ozone into methane.

   ANS: A   DIF: I   OBJ: 19-1.2

4. Chlorofluorocarbons (CFCs) are a problem because they
   a. corrode aerosol cans and release iron oxide into the atmosphere.
   b. are released by air conditioners into the groundwater.
   c. attack ozone molecules in the upper atmosphere.
   d. were once thought to be a hazard, but this now causes unnecessary expense for industry.

   ANS: C   DIF: I   OBJ: 19-1.2

5. CFCs were once
   a. thought to be chemically inert.
   b. used as refrigerants.
   c. used as aerosol propellants.
   d. All of the above

   ANS: D   DIF: I   OBJ: 19-1.2

6. Ozone in the atmosphere
   a. leads to formation of acid precipitation.
   b. combines readily with water vapor.
   c. absorbs harmful radiation from the sun.
   d. All of the above

   ANS: C   DIF: I   OBJ: 19-1.2

7. As a result of the discovery of the ozone hole,
   a. tall smokestacks were placed on power plants.
   b. the production of most CFCs will end during the 1990s.
   c. methane has been substituted for nitrous oxides in some chemicals.
   d. large greenhouses were built in Europe, the United States, and Canada.

   ANS: B   DIF: I   OBJ: 19-1.2

8. The heat-trapping ability of some gases in the atmosphere can be compared to
   a. the melting of snow.
   b. the way glass traps heat in a greenhouse.
   c. condensation due to heating.
   d. heating water on a stove.

ANS: B   DIF: I   OBJ: 19-1.2

9. Temperatures may increase on Earth because
   a. decomposers essential to recycling matter are being destroyed.
   b. too much oxygen is now given off by plants.
   c. increasing carbon dioxide would trap more heat.
   d. Earth tilts toward the sun in the summer.

ANS: C   DIF: I   OBJ: 19-1.2

10. Rising coastal sea levels are expected to result from
    a. increased ocean floor volcanic activity.
    b. global warming.
    c. ozone layer depletion.
    d. acid rain.

ANS: B   DIF: II   OBJ: 19-1.2

11. sulfur and water : acid rain ::
    a. acid rain and ozone : carbon dioxide   c. oxygen and CFCs : ozone
    b. CFCs and ozone : oxygen   d. ozone and carbon dioxide : acid rain

ANS: B   DIF: II   OBJ: 19-1.2

12. burning fossil fuels : atmospheric carbon dioxide ::
    a. greenhouse effect : CFCs
    b. atmospheric carbon dioxide : global warming
    c. ground level ozone : CO_2
    d. ozone : global warming

ANS: B   DIF: II   OBJ: 19-1.2

13. Which of the following statements provides the best explanation for the disruption of ecosystems by pollutants?
    a. Pollutants differ chemically from naturally-occurring substances.
    b. Only humans have uses for pollutant chemicals.
    c. There are no adaptive mechanisms that can deal with the pollutants.
    d. Pollutants are chemicals that cannot be broken down and so they accumulate in ecosystems.

ANS: C   DIF: III   OBJ: 19-1.2

14. A group of organisms of different species living together in a particular place is called
    a. a community.   c. a biome.
    b. a population.   d. a habitat.

ANS: A   DIF: I   OBJ: 19-1.3

15. An ecosystem consists of
    a. a community of organisms.
    b. energy.
    c. the soil, water, and weather.
    d. All of the above

    ANS: D   DIF: I   OBJ: 19-1.3

16. All organisms in an ecosystem are linked together in a network of interactions. This quality is called
    a. geochemical processes.
    b. isolation.
    c. interconnectedness.
    d. ecology.

    ANS: C   DIF: I   OBJ: 19-1.4

17. Ecological models are useful for
    a. making predictions about future ecological changes.
    b. testing predictions about future ecological changes.
    c. evaluating proposed solutions to environmental problems.
    d. All of the above

    ANS: D   DIF: I   OBJ: 19-1.5

18. In ecology, models are typically expressed as
    a. graphs.
    b. diagrams.
    c. mathematical equations.
    d. All of the above

    ANS: D   DIF: I   OBJ: 19-1.5

19. The physical location of an ecosystem in which a given species lives is called a
    a. habitat.
    b. tropical level.
    c. community.
    d. food zone.

    ANS: A   DIF: I   OBJ: 19-2.1

20. The areas of a tolerance curve that lie at the extreme high or low for the environmental variable represent the
    a. optimal range of an environmental variable for an organism.
    b. zones of physiological stress of an environmental variable for an organism.
    c. zones of physiological intolerance of an environmental variable for an organism.
    d. None of the above

    ANS: C   DIF: I   OBJ: 19-2.2

21. Which of the following is *not* an adaptation for avoiding unfavorable conditions?
    a. acclimation
    b. body temperature regulation
    c. dormancy
    d. migration

    ANS: A   DIF: II   OBJ: 19-2.3

22. An organism's niche includes
    a. what it eats.
    b. where it eats.
    c. when it eats.
    d. All of the above

    ANS: D   DIF: I   OBJ: 19-2.4

23. Which of the following would *not* be included in a description of an organism's niche?
   a. its trophic level
   b. the humidity and temperature it prefers
   c. its number of chromosomes
   d. when it reproduces

   ANS: C   DIF: I   OBJ: 19-2.4

The diagrams below illustrate experiments performed with two species of barnacles that live in the same area.

A. The barnacle *Chthamalus stellatus* can live in both shallow and deep water on a rocky coast.

B. The barnacle *Balanus balanoides* prefers to live in deep water.

C. When the two live together, *Chthamalus* is restricted to shallow water.

24. Refer to the illustration above. Diagram "A" indicates that the barnacle *Chthamalus stellatus* can live in both shallow and deep water on a rocky coast. This is the barnacle's
   a. competitive niche.   c. fundamental niche.
   b. realized niche.   d. exclusive niche.

   ANS: C   DIF: II   OBJ: 19-2.5

25. Refer to the illustration above. Diagram "B" indicates that the barnacle *Balanus balanoides* prefers to live in deep water. Deep water is the barnacle's
   a. competitive niche.   c. fundamental niche.
   b. realized niche.   d. exclusive niche.

   ANS: C   DIF: II   OBJ: 19-2.5

26. Refer to the illustration above. Diagram "C" indicates that when the two barnacles live together, *Chthamalus* is restricted to shallow water. Shallow water is the barnacle's
   a. competitive niche.   c. fundamental niche.
   b. realized niche.   d. exclusive niche.

   ANS: B   DIF: II   OBJ: 19-2.5

27. When two species compete, the niche that each organism ultimately occupies is its
    a. competitive niche.
    b. realized niche.
    c. fundamental niche.
    d. exclusive niche.

    ANS: B   DIF: I   OBJ: 19-2.5

28. If the niches of two organisms overlap,
    a. the organisms may have to compete directly.
    b. the two organisms will always form a symbiotic relationship.
    c. both organisms will disappear from the habitat.
    d. one organism usually migrates to a new habitat.

    ANS: A   DIF: I   OBJ: 19-2.5

29. Most ecosystems tend to be complex because
    a. they are found in all climates.
    b. potential competitors in the ecosystem often occupy slightly different niches.
    c. they all contain a wide variety of producers.
    d. of symbiotic relationships within them.

    ANS: B   DIF: II   OBJ: 19-2.5

COMPLETION

1. _____ is the study of how organisms interact with each other and
   with their environment.

   ANS: Ecology   DIF: I   OBJ: 19-1.1

2. The phenomenon known as the _____ is the mechanism that
   insulates Earth from the deep freeze of space.

   ANS: greenhouse effect   DIF: I   OBJ: 19-1.2

3. CFCs catalyze the conversion of ozone into molecular _____.

   ANS: oxygen   DIF: I   OBJ: 19-1.2

4. Pollutants called _____ can convert ozone in the atmosphere into
   oxygen, thereby diminishing the protective ozone layer.

   ANS: CFCs or chloroflurocarbons   DIF: I   OBJ: 19-1.2

5. The heat-trapping ability of carbon dioxide, methane, and nitrous oxide in the
   atmosphere is known as the _____.

   ANS: greenhouse effect   DIF: I   OBJ: 19-1.2

6. Many scientists think that the increased levels of carbon dioxide in the atmosphere are
   causing global _____.

   ANS: warming   DIF: I   OBJ: 19-1.2

7. An ecosystem consists of the living and _____ environment.

   ANS: nonliving   DIF: I   OBJ: 19-1.3

8. The term _____ is used to describe the physical area in which an organism lives.

   ANS: habitat   DIF: I   OBJ: 19-1.3

9. A model is limited in its application because no model can account for every _____ in an environment.

   ANS: variable   DIF: I   OBJ: 19-1.5

10. Organisms that do not regulate their internal conditions are called _____, while those that do are called _____.

    ANS: conformers; regulators   DIF: I   OBJ: 19-2.3

11. A _____ describes the habitat, feeding habits, other aspects of an organism's biology, and its interactions with other organisms and the environment.

    ANS: niche   DIF: I   OBJ: 19-2.4

ESSAY

1. Describe the greenhouse effect. Write your answer in the space below.

   ANS:
   The greenhouse effect is the natural phenomenon that results in the warming of Earth due to carbon dioxide and water vapor in the atmosphere, which absorb and reflect heat back onto Earth. This effect is intensified by increased levels of carbon dioxide in the atmosphere due to the combustion of fossil fuels. The increase in levels of carbon dioxide causes an increase in the ability of the atmosphere to trap heat, thus causing temperatures to rise gradually.

   DIF: II   OBJ: 19-1.2

2. Explain how a change in the habitat of a species affects the entire ecosystem. Write your answer in the space below.

   ANS:
   A change in habitat may disturb the interactions of plants and animals in the ecosystem. A drastic change in the factors of a habitat that affects one species can have an effect on the whole ecosystem because it affects the natural cycling of nutrients, food chains, and food webs. This disruption could result in endangerment or extinction of species in the ecosystem.

   DIF: II   OBJ: 19-1.4

3. A plant disease infects most of the vegetation in a particular area, destroying it. How might the destruction of this vegetation affect the animal life in the area? Write your answer in the space below.

ANS:
The ecosystem would be seriously disrupted. Herbivores that ate the vegetation would be affected as their major source of food was eliminated. The carnivores in the area would soon die or leave the area because their source of energy—the herbivores—could not remain.

DIF: II   OBJ: 19-1.4

4. What adaptation do many plant species have that enables them to survive through very cold winters? Write your answer in the space below.

ANS:
They produce seeds that can survive very cold winters.

DIF: III   OBJ: 19-2.3

5. Which type of organisms are most likely to survive, those that have a narrow ecological niche or those that have a broad niche? Explain. Write your answer in the space below.

ANS:
Organisms having broad niches are more likely to survive because they are not likely to depend on a single food source or a single habitat. If one food source becomes scarce, they can turn to another; or if one habitat is destroyed, they can move to another. An organism having a narrow niche may depend totally on a single food source or require a specific habitat. If the food source or habitat is disrupted, the organism may not survive.

DIF: II   OBJ: 19-2.5

Modern Biology Assessment Item Listing
190

CHAPTER 20—POPULATIONS

TRUE/FALSE

1. Clumped population distributions result from organisms seeking clumped resources.

   ANS: T   DIF: I   OBJ: 20-1.2

2. The study of demographics helps predict changes in the size of a population.

   ANS: T   DIF: I   OBJ: 20-2.1

3. Very small populations are less likely to become extinct than larger populations.

   ANS: F   DIF: I   OBJ: 20-2.4

4. The human population began to increase dramatically in 500 AD.

   ANS: F   DIF: I   OBJ: 20-3.1

5. The population of Earth has not changed very much over the last 350 years.

   ANS: F   DIF: I   OBJ: 20-3.2

6. The human birth rate has remained about the same for the last 350 years.

   ANS: T   DIF: I   OBJ: 20-3.2

7. The population of every country is steadily increasing.

   ANS: F   DIF: I   OBJ: 20-3.4

MULTIPLE CHOICE

1. Because individuals in a population usually tend to produce more than one offspring,
   a. populations tend to increase in size.
   b. populations remain stable in size.
   c. individuals tend to die quickly.
   d. the number of individuals declines rapidly.

   ANS: A   DIF: I   OBJ: 20-1.1

2. Which of the following does *not* represent a population?
   a. all the robins in Austin, Texas
   b. all the grass frogs in the pond of Central Park, New York City
   c. all the birds in Chicago, Illinois
   d. all the earthworms in Yosemite National Park

   ANS: C   DIF: I   OBJ: 20-1.1

3. Demographic studies of populations must take into consideration
    a. population size.
    b. population density.
    c. population dispersion.
    d. All of the above

    ANS: D   DIF: I   OBJ: 20-1.1

4. Regarding population dispersion patterns, which of the following is an *improper* pairing?
    a. randomly spaced — chance
    b. evenly spaced — regular intervals
    c. clumped — clusters
    d. dispersive — randomly distributed

    ANS: D   DIF: I   OBJ: 20-1.2

5. Trees growing along the banks of a river but not growing in the surrounding area would best be described as a ____ dispersion of the trees.
    a. clumped
    b. even
    c. random
    d. mixture of clumped, even, and random

    ANS: A   DIF: II   OBJ: 20-1.2

6. If a population is composed of a balance of people of pre-reproductive, reproductive, and post-reproductive age, what will most likely happen to the size of the population?
    a. It will grow steadily.
    b. It will experience no growth for a time and then increase rapidly.
    c. It will decrease steadily.
    d. It will experience no growth for a time and then decrease rapidly.

    ANS: A   DIF: II   OBJ: 20-1.3

7. A population of organisms grows
    a. with no natural restrictions except the availability of food.
    b. when the birth rate exceeds the death rate.
    c. only in the absence of predators or natural diseases.
    d. All of the above

    ANS: B   DIF: I   OBJ: 20-1.3

8. Which organism is incorrectly paired with its survivorship curve type.
    a. humans/Type I
    b. some species of birds/Type II
    c. sea turtles/Type II
    d. fish/Type III

    ANS: C   DIF: I   OBJ: 20-1.4

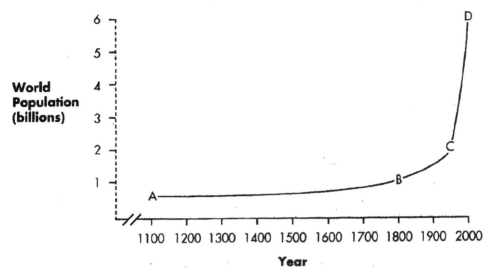

World Population Growth

9. Refer to the illustration above. Which time period shows exponential growth of the population?
   a. period A–B
   b. period B–D
   c. period C–D
   d. period D

   ANS: B   DIF: II   OBJ: 20-2.1

10. Refer to the illustration above. Which of the following contributed to the change in world population during the 1900s shown in the graph?
    a. better sanitation
    b. improved health care
    c. agricultural improvements
    d. All of the above

    ANS: D   DIF: II   OBJ: 20-3.1

11. Refer to the illustration above. Which letter in the graph indicates the approximate world population in the year 1950?
    a. Letter "A"
    b. Letter "B"
    c. Letter "C"
    d. Letter "D"

    ANS: C   DIF: II   OBJ: 20-3.3

12. Refer to the illustration above. The American Revolution began in 1776. According to the graph, what was the approximate world population at that time?
    a. 500 thousand
    b. 1 million
    c. 1 billion
    d. 2 billion

    ANS: C   DIF: II   OBJ: 20-3.2

13. population density : number of individuals in a given area ::
    a. population : an area where organisms live
    b. logistic model : how populations grow in nature
    c. logistic growth curve : rate of growth
    d. population size : population density

    ANS: B (describes)   DIF: II   OBJ: 20-2.2

14. birth and death rates : constant on exponential growth curve ::
    a. birth rates : equal to death rates
    b. *r*-strategists : equal to *K*-strategists
    c. birth and death rates : not constant on logistic growth curve
    d. exponential models : same as logistic models

    ANS: C (are assumed to be)   DIF: II   OBJ: 20-2.2

Population Growth Over Time

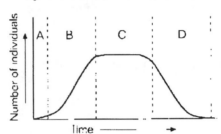

15. Refer to the illustration above. During which time period are the birth rate and death rate equal?
    a. period "A"   c. period "C"
    b. period "B"   d. period "D"

    ANS: C   DIF: II   OBJ: 20-2.2

16. Refer to the illustration above. The rate of growth of a population is represented by *r*. During which time period will *r* = 0?
    a. period "A"   c. period "C"
    b. period "B"   d. period "D"

    ANS: C   DIF: II   OBJ: 20-2.2

17. Refer to the illustration above. The time period during which *r* would have a negative value is
    a. period "A."   c. period "C."
    b. period "B."   d. period "D."

    ANS: D   DIF: II   OBJ: 20-2.2

18. As a population reaches its carrying capacity, there is an increase in competition for
    a. food.
    b. shelter.
    c. mates.
    d. All of the above

    ANS: D   DIF: I   OBJ: 20-2.3

19. Which of the following is a density-independent regulatory factor?
    a. food
    b. water
    c. temperature
    d. number of nesting sites

    ANS: C   DIF: I   OBJ: 20-2.3

20. All of the following are problems arising from inbreeding, *except*
    a. production of a genetically uniform population.
    b. increases in the diversity within a population.
    c. increased chance of homozygous recessive alleles occurring.
    d. reduction of a population's ability to adapt to environmental changes.

    ANS: B   DIF: I   OBJ: 20-2.4

21. Which population might be least likely to be devastated by a disease outbreak?
    a. a small population who are all offspring of healthy, related parents
    b. a large, genetically-diverse population
    c. a small, genetically-uniform population
    d. a few strong, healthy individuals

    ANS: B   DIF: I   OBJ: 20-2.4

22. The agricultural revolution enabled Earth's human population to increase dramatically because it
    a. allowed people to live in one place instead of moving from place to place in search of food.
    b. stabilized and increased available food supplies.
    c. resulted in people being healthier and therefore better able to resist diseases.
    d. provided plenty of work for most of Earth's population.

    ANS: B   DIF: II   OBJ: 20-3.1

Human Population Growth

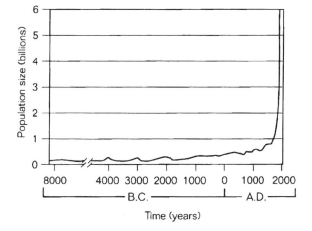

23. Refer to the illustration above. According to the graph, the human population
    a. remained essentially unchanged for thousands of years.
    b. doubled in size from 2000 BC to 1000 BC
    c. reached 1 billion in 1492.
    d. will stop growing in the year 2000.

    ANS: A   DIF: II   OBJ: 20-3.2

24. Refer to the illustration above. According to the graph,
    a. there were no humans on Earth around 6000 BC.
    b. the human population has never decreased in size.
    c. increase in the food supply was responsible for the increase in the population.
    d. the human population is currently rising dramatically.

    ANS: D   DIF: II   OBJ: 20-3.3

25. Human population growth is most rapid in
    a. Europe.   c. Japan.
    b. the United States.   d. developing countries.

    ANS: D   DIF: I   OBJ: 20-3.4

COMPLETION

1. Population density refers to how many _____ are present in a particular location.

    ANS: individual members of a species   DIF: I   OBJ: 20-1.1

2. The way in which members of a population are arranged in a given area is referred to as _____.

    ANS: dispersion   DIF: I   OBJ: 20-1.1

3. A population of organisms will grow when its _____ exceeds its death rate.

    ANS: birth rate   DIF: I   OBJ: 20-1.3

4. A _____ is the mortality rate data of a species modeled as one of three different curves on a graph, Type I, Type II, or Type III.

    ANS: survivorship curve   DIF: I   OBJ: 20-1.4

5. _____ is the measurement of the factors that determine how populations grow.

    ANS: Demography   DIF: I   OBJ: 20-2.1

6. _____ is defined as the amount by which a population's size changes in a given time.

    ANS: Growth rate   DIF: I   OBJ: 20-2.1

7. The _____ is the population size that can be sustained by an environment.

ANS: carrying capacity   DIF: I   OBJ: 20-2.2

8. The main reason Earth's human population has increased over the past 350 years is because of a decrease in the _____ rate.

ANS: death   DIF: I   OBJ: 20-3.3

9. The _____ countries are experiencing the greatest increase in population growth.

ANS: developing   DIF: I   OBJ: 20-3.4

PROBLEM

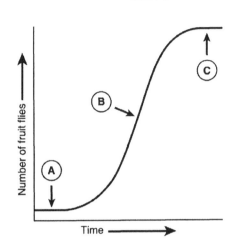

1. Refer to the illustration above. The graph depicts the growth of a population of fruit flies over time. Write your answers to the following in the spaces below.
   a. Why does the population stop increasing after it reaches the point on the curve labeled "C"?
   b. Would a density-dependent limiting factor have a greater impact on the population at point "A," "B," or "C" on the curve? Why?
   c. Name one density-independent limiting factor that could affect this population of fruit flies. Would you expect this limiting factor to have a greater impact on the population at any particular point on the curve, and if so, which one?

ANS:
   a. The population has reached the carrying capacity of the ecosystem in which it lives. The ecosystem cannot support any more flies than this number.
   b. It would have the greatest impact on the population at point "C." This is because it is at point "C" on the curve that there is the greatest population density. Density-dependent limiting factors impact populations more as they increase in size.
   c. A number of abiotic factors would be suitable answers. The most obvious answer and the most commonly important abiotic factor would be a temperature extreme (e.g. freezing). Other abiotic factors could be floods, hurricanes, fires, and volcanic eruptions. Such a limiting factor would not be expected to have a greater impact on the population at any particular point on the curve.

DIF: III   OBJ: 20-2.3

ESSAY

1. Explain the advantage a high reproductive rate might give an organism with a Type III survivorship curve. Write your answer in the space below.

   ANS:
   Organisms with a Type III survivorship curve, such as salmon or frogs, produce many young. A large number of these individuals die while young. Each surviving individual must produce many offspring to offset this enormous early mortality.

   DIF: II   OBJ: 20-1.4

2. Contrast exponential growth with logistical growth by completing the chart below.

Criteria	Exponential Population Growth	Logistic Population Growth
Graph of Growth Rate		
Assumptions		
Birth and death Rates		

   ANS:

Criteria	Exponential Population Growth	Logistic Population Growth
Graph of Growth Rate		
Assumptions	unlimited resources	resources limit population growth; stabilizes at the carrying capacity
Birth and death Rates	constant—rates do not change	vary with population size

   DIF: II   OBJ: 20-2.2

TRUE/FALSE

1. Predation is an example of a symbiotic interaction.

   ANS: T   DIF: I   OBJ: 21-1.1

2. When two dissimilar species live together in a close association, they are part of a symbiotic relationship.

   ANS: T   DIF: I   OBJ: 21-1.1

3. Mimicry results in confusion on the part of a predator, resulting in the predator eating both harmless and poisonous species.

   ANS: F   DIF: I   OBJ: 21-1.2

4. Plants and the herbivores that eat them have evolved independently of one another.

   ANS: F   DIF: I   OBJ: 21-1.3

5. The competitive exclusion principle states that competition usually results in the establishment of cooperation between two species.

   ANS: F   DIF: I   OBJ: 21-1.4

6. When two species compete for limited resources, competitive exclusion is sure to take place.

   ANS: F   DIF: I   OBJ: 21-1.4

7. A long-term relationship in which both participating species benefit is known as parasitism.

   ANS: F   DIF: I   OBJ: 21-1.5

8. Mutualism is a symbiotic relationship in which only one party benefits.

   ANS: F   DIF: I   OBJ: 21-1.5

9. A measure of the number of tree species in a community is a measure of the species diversity of trees in that community.

   ANS: F   DIF: I   OBJ: 21-2.1

10. Climate is not a factor in determining the ecosystem types found in the United States.

    ANS: F   DIF: I   OBJ: 21-2.2

11. Larger land areas usually have more species living in them because they contain a greater variety of habitats than smaller land areas do.

ANS: T   DIF: I   OBJ: 21-2.3

12. The term *species-area effect* is used to describe the lower species richness found in large areas compared with small areas.

ANS: F   DIF: I   OBJ: 21-2.3

13. In a stable community, effects of a disturbance are apparently dispersed because of the large number of links that exist between the large number of species present.

ANS: T   DIF: I   OBJ: 21-2.4

14. The major difference between primary succession and secondary succession is that primary succession occurs only on land and secondary succession occurs in ponds and lakes.

ANS: F   DIF: I   OBJ: 21-3.1

15. When succession takes place where there has been previous growth, it is called secondary succession.

ANS: T   DIF: I   OBJ: 21-3.1

16. Because of their small size, pioneer species have small root systems that can survive where there is not much soil.

ANS: T   DIF: II   OBJ: 21-3.2

17. The critical resource required for plant growth that is usually absent in newly formed habitats is water.

ANS: F   DIF: I   OBJ: 21-3.3

18. Secondary succession typically proceeds from deciduous trees to shrubs and then finally grasses.

ANS: F   DIF: I   OBJ: 21-3.4

MULTIPLE CHOICE

1. A relationship between a producer and consumer is best illustrated by
   a. a snake eating a bird.   c. a lion eating a zebra.
   b. a fox eating a mouse.   d. a zebra eating grass.

ANS: D   DIF: I   OBJ: 21-1.1

2. Parasites
   a. coevolve with their hosts.   c. rarely kill their hosts.
   b. are usually smaller than their hosts.   d. All of the above

ANS: D   DIF: I   OBJ: 21-1.1

3. A tick feeding on a human is an example of
   a. parasitism.
   b. mutualism.
   c. competition.
   d. predation.

   ANS: A   DIF: I   OBJ: 21-1.1

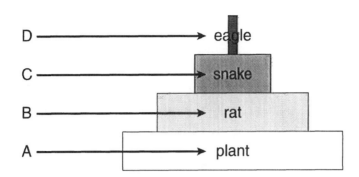

4. Refer to the illustration above. Level "A" is composed of
   a. carnivores.
   b. herbivores.
   c. producers.
   d. omnivores.

   ANS: C   DIF: II   OBJ: 21-1.1

5. Which of the following is an example of mimicry?
   a. a poisonous species that resembles a harmless species
   b. coloration that causes an animal to blend in with its habitat
   c. a harmless species that resembles a poisonous species
   d. similarly colored body parts on two poisonous species

   ANS: C   DIF: I   OBJ: 21-1.2

6. Characteristics that enable plants to protect themselves from herbivores include
   a. thorns and prickles.
   b. sticky hairs and tough leaves.
   c. chemical defenses.
   d. All of the above

   ANS: D   DIF: I   OBJ: 21-1.3

7. Which of the following usually results when members of the same species require the same food and space?
   a. primary succession
   b. competition
   c. secondary succession
   d. interspecific competition

   ANS: B   DIF: I   OBJ: 21-1.4

8. Competitive exclusion occurs when
   a. a species is eliminated from a community because of competition.
   b. new species enter an ecosystem.
   c. species reproduce.
   d. a species occupies a fundamental niche.

   ANS: A   DIF: I   OBJ: 21-1.4

The diagrams below illustrate experiments performed with two species of barnacles that live in the same area.

A. The barnacle *Chthamalus stellatus* can live in both shallow and deep water on a rocky coast.

B. The barnacle *Balanus balanoides* prefers to live in deep water.

C. When the two live together, *Chthamalus* is restricted to shallow water.

9. Refer to the illustration above. Because the two species of barnacles attempt to use the same resources, they are
    a. parasitic.
    b. in competition with one another.
    c. mutualistic.
    d. symbiotic.

    ANS: B   DIF: II   OBJ: 21-1.4

10. An ecologist studying an ocean ecosystem found that the removal of the sea stars (starfish) from the ecosystem drastically affected it. In this ecosystem the sea stars were a(n)
    a. predatory species.
    b. keystone species.
    c. competitive species.
    d. primary species.

    ANS: A   DIF: II   OBJ: 21-1.4

11. Sea stars are fierce predators of marine organisms such as clams and mussels. An ecologist studying an ocean ecosystem performed an experiment in which the sea stars were removed from the ecosystem. After the removal of the sea stars,
    a. the ecosystem became more diverse.
    b. food webs in the ecosystem became more complex.
    c. the size of the ecosystem was reduced.
    d. the number of species in the ecosystem was reduced.

    ANS: D   DIF: I   OBJ: 21-1.4

12. In his experiments with two species of paramecia, G. F. Gause proved that two competitors cannot coexist on the same limited resources. This outcome demonstrated the principle of
    a. competitive exclusion.
    b. secondary succession.
    c. intraspecific competition.
    d. symbiosis.

    ANS: A   DIF: I   OBJ: 21-1.4

13. The relationship between plants and the bees that pollinate them is an example of
    a. commensalism.
    b. competition.
    c. mutualism.
    d. parasitism.

    ANS: C   DIF: I   OBJ: 21-1.5

14. The relationship between a whale and barnacles growing on its skin is an example of
    a. commensalism.
    b. competition.
    c. mutualism.
    d. parasitism.

    ANS: A   DIF: I   OBJ: 21-1.5

The diagrams below show different kinds of interactions between species.

The ant keeps predators away from the acacia tree.

Ant → Acacia

The acacia provides shelter and food for the ant.

1

The cow eats grass.

Cow → Sheep

The sheep eats same grass.

2

Orchid → Tree

The tree provides nutrients and a sun-lit location for the orchid living on it.

3

Tapeworm → Dog

The dog provides nutrients and shelter for the tapeworm living in its intestines.

4

15. Refer to the illustration above. The relationship shown in Diagram "4" above is
    a. commensalism.
    b. competition.
    c. mutualism.
    d. parasitism.

    ANS: D   DIF: II   OBJ: 21-1.1

16. Refer to the illustration above. The relationship shown in Diagram "2" above is
    a. commensalism.
    b. competition.
    c. mutualism.
    d. parasitism.

    ANS: B   DIF: II   OBJ: 21-1.4

17. Refer to the illustration above. The relationship shown in Diagram "1" above is
    a. commensalism.
    b. competition.
    c. mutualism.
    d. parasitism.

    ANS: C   DIF: II   OBJ: 21-1.5

18. Refer to the illustration above. The relationship shown in Diagram "3" above is
   a. commensalism.
   b. competition.
   c. mutualism.
   d. parasitism.

   ANS: A   DIF: II   OBJ: 21-1.5

1	Both organisms benefit from the activity of each other.
2	One organism benefits, and the other organism neither benefits nor suffers harm.
3	One organism obtains its nutrients from another, and the other organism may weaken due to deprivation.

19. Refer to the chart above. The table represents three types of
   a. competition.
   b. rhythmic patterns.
   c. symbiosis.
   d. secondary succession.

   ANS: C   DIF: II   OBJ: 21-1.5

20. Refer to the chart above. Which pair of organisms generally exhibits the type of relationship that corresponds to number "1" in the table?
   a. coyotes and sheep
   b. shrimp and sea cucumbers
   c. parasitic worms and white-tailed deer
   d. clams and algae

   ANS: D   DIF: II   OBJ: 21-1.5

21. Refer to the chart above. The relationship that corresponds to number "2" in the table is known as
   a. parasitism.
   b. commensalism.
   c. mutualism.
   d. predation.

   ANS: B   DIF: II   OBJ: 21-1.5

22. commensalism : one organism ::
   a. parasitism : both organisms
   b. predation : neither organism
   c. mutualism : one organism
   d. mutualism : both organisms

   ANS: D   DIF: II   OBJ: 21-1.5

23. Species diversity is a measure of
   a. the number of species in a community.
   b. the total number of individuals in a community.
   c. the number of plant species relative to the number of animal species in a community.
   d. the number of species and the relative abundance of each in a community.

   ANS: D   DIF: I   OBJ: 21-2.1

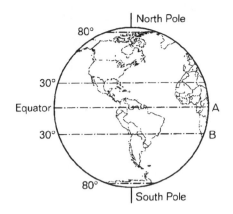

24. Refer to the illustration above. An ecosystem located along latitude "A" would
    a. have a shorter growing season than an ecosystem on latitude "B."
    b. probably contain fewer species than an ecosystem at latitude "B."
    c. probably be more diverse than an ecosystem at latitude "B."
    d. probably have less rainfall than an ecosystem at latitude "B."

    ANS: C   DIF: II   OBJ: 21-2.2

25. The closer an ecosystem is to the equator,
    a. the longer its growing season.   c. the warmer its temperature.
    b. the greater its diversity.   d. All of the above

    ANS: D   DIF: I   OBJ: 21-2.2

26. Generally, the closer an area is to the equator, the greater the diversity in species.
    Following are the latitudes of four cities. Which city would you predict to have the
    greatest diversity of species?
    a. Berlin, Germany (52 degrees 32' North latitude)
    b. Montreal, Canada (45 degrees 0' North latitude)
    c. Denver, Colorado (39 degrees 44' North latitude)
    d. Brisbane, Australia (27 degrees 30' South latitude)

    ANS: D   DIF: I   OBJ: 21-2.2

27. Extinction of many species of organisms is expected to occur in tropical areas because of
    a. global warming.
    b. destruction of habitats.
    c. people hunting many species of animals.
    d. predation by introduced animals.

    ANS: B   DIF: I   OBJ: 21-2.3

28. Which of the following is *not* a characteristic of a stable community?
    a. good resistance to insect pests
    b. the ability to recover rapidly from a drought
    c. a high species richness
    d. a low number of predators

    ANS: D   DIF: II   OBJ: 21-2.4

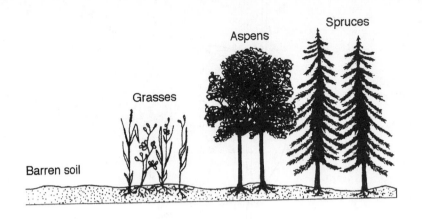

Spruces

Aspens

Grasses

Barren soil

29. Refer to the illustration above. The process shown in the diagram is known as
   a. competitive exclusion.
   b. succession.
   c. symbiosis.
   d. oligotrophy.

   ANS: B   DIF: II   OBJ: 21-3.1

30. Succession is
   a. an organism's ability to survive in its environment.
   b. the number of species living in an ecosystem.
   c. the regular progression of species replacement in an environment.
   d. the transfer of energy through a food chain.

   ANS: C   DIF: I   OBJ: 21-3.1

31. Which of the following types of succession would most likely occur after a forest fire?
   a. primary succession
   b. old field succession
   c. secondary succession
   d. lake succession

   ANS: C   DIF: I   OBJ: 21-3.1

32. Secondary succession occurs
   a. as one generation of organisms replaces the previous one.
   b. as a previously existing community is replaced.
   c. after a new food web is established.
   d. None of the above

   ANS: B   DIF: I   OBJ: 21-3.1

33. When the settlers arrived in New England, many forests were turned into fields.
   Eventually, some fields were abandoned and then grew back into forests. This is best
   described as
   a. primary succession.
   b. coevolution.
   c. secondary succession.
   d. niche realization.

   ANS: C   DIF: I   OBJ: 21-3.1

34. secondary succession : cleared forest ::
    a. pile of rock and gravel : secondary succession
    b. secondary succession : bare soil
    c. primary succession : new volcanic island
    d. succession : the absence of plants

    ANS: C   DIF: II   OBJ: 21-3.1

35. primary succession : areas of no previous plant growth ::
    a. secondary succession : abandoned farm fields
    b. rain forest : a desert
    c. tundra : a desert
    d. secondary succession : bare rock

    ANS: A   DIF: II   OBJ: 21-3.1

36. Which of the following is *not* a characteristic of pioneer species?
    a. They are small.   c. They reproduce slowly.
    b. They grow quickly.   d. They disperse many seeds.

    ANS: C   DIF: I   OBJ: 21-3.2

37. The end stage of primary succession in a northern latitude would be characterized by the predominance of
    a. lichens.   c. small plants and shrubs.
    b. needle-leaved evergreen trees.   d. grasses.

    ANS: B   DIF: I   OBJ: 21-3.3

38. Common types of plants found in areas in the early stages of secondary succession are
    a. shrubs.   c. grasses.
    b. lichens.   d. trees.

    ANS: C   DIF: I   OBJ: 21-3.4

COMPLETION

1. In a parasitic relationship, the organism that provides benefits to another organism at its own expense is called the _____.

    ANS: host   DIF: I   OBJ: 21-1.1

2. The general term for the symbiotic relationship in which one organism feeds upon another is _____.

    ANS: predation   DIF: I   OBJ: 21-1.1

3. A symbiotic relationship in which one organism benefits and another is often harmed but not killed is called _____.

    ANS: parasitism   DIF: I   OBJ: 21-1.1

4. The term _____ is used for a close relationship between two dissimilar organisms in which one organism usually benefits.

   ANS: symbiosis   DIF: I   OBJ: 21-1.1

5. Colored bands on the body of a harmless king snake that resemble the bands on a poisonous coral snake is an example of _____.

   ANS: mimicry   DIF: I   OBJ: 21-1.2

6. The production of secondary compounds by plants protects them from _____.

   ANS: herbivores   DIF: I   OBJ: 21-1.3

7. The struggle among organisms for the same limited natural resources is called _____.

   ANS: competition   DIF: I   OBJ: 21-1.4

8. The symbiotic relationship in which one organism benefits and the other neither benefits nor suffers harm is called _____.

   ANS: commensalism   DIF: I   OBJ: 21-1.5

9. A fish called a cleaner wrasse eats the tiny parasites that cling to and feed upon much larger fish. Therefore, the cleaner wrasse has a _____ relationship to the larger fish.

   ANS: mutualistic   DIF: I   OBJ: 21-1.5

10. The sequential replacement of populations in an area that has not previously supported life is called _____.

    ANS: primary succession   DIF: I   OBJ: 21-3.1

11. Pioneer species are adapted for growing well in _____ habitats.

    ANS: new   DIF: I   OBJ: 21-3.2

12. Secondary succession is typically completed in less time than primary succession because there is _____ present in the habitat to begin with.

    ANS: soil   DIF: I   OBJ: 21-3.4

PROBLEM

1. The data in the table shown below were taken during a study of an abandoned agricultural field. Scientists counted the number of different kinds of herbs, shrubs, and trees present in the field one, 25, and 40 years after it had been abandoned.

	Time after abandonment of agricultural field		
	1 year	25 years	40 years
Number of herb species	31	30	36
Number of shrub species	0	7	19
Number of tree species	0	14	22
Total number of species	31	51	77

  a. In the space below, write three conclusions that you can draw from these data.
  b. Make a prediction of the relative numbers of herbs, shrubs, trees, and of the total number of plant species that you would expect to see 100 years after abandonment of the field.

ANS:
  a. The following are some possible conclusions: (1) The total number of plant species present in the field increased over the 40 year time period. (2) The plants that grew initially in the field were all herbs. (3) Over the 40 year time period, the relative proportions of herbs, shrubs, and trees changed. The relative number of herbs decreased while the relative number of shrubs and trees increased. (4) The total number of herbs present did not change significantly over the 40 year time period.
  b. It is likely that the total number of species present would be even greater 100 years after abandonment. There would probably be relatively fewer herbs, about the same or relatively more shrubs, and relatively more trees.

DIF: I   OBJ: 21-2.4

ESSAY

1. Describe the type of symbiotic interaction called competition. Write your answer in the space below.

ANS:
All organisms compete for food, water, space, and other resources. One type of competition occurs between members of the same species, and another type of competition occurs between different species.

DIF: II   OBJ: 21-1.4

2. Can two species occupy the same realized niche? Explain. Write your answer in the space below.

ANS:
No two species can have the exact same niche. The principle of competitive exclusion states that if two species are competing for the same resource, the species that uses the resource more efficiently will eventually eliminate the other.

DIF: II   OBJ: 21-1.4

3. Some species of orchids grow high in the trees of tropical forests. The trees provide the orchids with the support to grow and allow them to capture more sunlight than they would on the forest floor. What form of symbiosis is illustrated by this occurrence? Explain your answer. Write your answer in the space below.

ANS:
Commensalism is the form of symbiosis illustrated; in commensalism one organism benefits and the other organism neither benefits nor suffers harm. In this example, the orchids benefit from the presence of the trees, but the trees are not harmed since the orchids neither feed on their tissues nor prevent significant amounts of sunlight from reaching their leaves.

DIF: II   OBJ: 21-1.5

4. Why is species diversity a more meaningful measure than species richness? Write your answer in the space below.

ANS:
Species richness takes into consideration only the number of different species in a community. Species diversity, on the other hand, takes into consideration the number of different species as well as the relative abundance of each in a community. Thus, species diversity indicates the relative importance of each species in a community.

DIF: II   OBJ: 21-2.1

5. What is the difference between primary and secondary succession? Write your answer in the space below.

ANS:
Primary succession is the replacement of species in an area that had not previously supported life, such as bare rock or sand dune. Secondary succession involves species replacement habitats that have been disrupted due to natural disaster or human activity but still possess a small amount of soil and vegetation.

DIF: II   OBJ: 21-3.1

6. Describe the reasons why primary succession in Glacier Bay, Alaska, spanned about 200 years. Write your answer in the space below.

ANS:
The process of primary succession in Glacier Bay, Alaska, began when the ground consisted of pulverized bare rocks. The rock was likely first colonized by lichens that secreted acids that slowly broke down some of the rock into smaller pieces. Eventually, a thin layer of soil formed from the accumulation of small fragments of rock and dead lichens. Grasses were then able to colonize the area. As these plants died, their decomposing bodies added organic matter to the soil, and the soil became able to support the growth of larger plants. Shrubs began to grow in the area, and then finally trees were able to grow. After about 200 years, the area became dominated by large, slow-growing trees that are able to grow on thin soil.

DIF: III   OBJ: 21-3.3

TRUE/FALSE

1. Omnivores feed only on primary producers.

    ANS: F   DIF: I   OBJ: 22-1.1

2. When an organism dies, the nitrogen in its body is released by decomposers.

    ANS: T   DIF: I   OBJ: 22-1.2

3. A food chain is made up of interrelated food webs.

    ANS: F   DIF: I   OBJ: 22-1.3

4. All organisms in an ecosystem are part of the food web of that ecosystem.

    ANS: T   DIF: I   OBJ: 22-1.3

5. A change in the number of predators in a food web can affect an entire ecosystem.

    ANS: T   DIF: I   OBJ: 22-1.3

6. Decomposers absorb energy from organisms by breaking down living tissue.

    ANS: F   DIF: I   OBJ: 22-1.4

7. The number of organisms in a trophic level is always directly proportional to the amount of energy at that level.

    ANS: F   DIF: I   OBJ: 22-1.4

8. The source of energy of an organism determines its trophic level.

    ANS: T   DIF: I   OBJ: 22-1.4

9. A trophic level is a group of organisms whose energy sources are the same level away from the sun.

    ANS: T   DIF: I   OBJ: 22-1.4

10. Organisms at higher trophic levels tend to be fewer in number than those at lower trophic levels.

    ANS: T   DIF: I   OBJ: 22-1.4

11. Producers in an ecosystem transfer all of their energy to primary-level consumers.

    ANS: F   DIF: I   OBJ: 22-1.4

12. Organisms are critical for completion of all of the biogeochemical cycles.

    ANS: F   DIF: III   OBJ: 22-2.1

13. Plants release water into the atmosphere through transpiration.

    ANS: T   DIF: I   OBJ: 22-2.2

14. Water and nutrients continue to cycle normally in a forest ecosystem after the trees are cut down.

    ANS: F   DIF: I   OBJ: 22-2.2

15. Nitrogen gas makes up about 79 percent of the Earth's atmosphere.

    ANS: T   DIF: I   OBJ: 22-2.3

16. During nitrification, decomposers break down the roots of plants to produce nitrates.

    ANS: F   DIF: I   OBJ: 22-2.3

17. On land, there are 10 major types of ecosystems, which are called biomes.

    ANS: F   DIF: I   OBJ: 22-3.1

18. Broad, flat leaves are an adaptation of plants found on the tundra.

    ANS: F   DIF: I   OBJ: 22-3.1

19. Permafrost is a characteristic of the taiga.

    ANS: F   DIF: I   OBJ: 22-3.1

20. Tropical rain forests have the most fertile soil on Earth.

    ANS: F   DIF: I   OBJ: 22-3.1

21. Deserts are most extensive in the interiors of continents.

    ANS: T   DIF: I   OBJ: 22-3.3

22. Some animals of the deciduous forest hibernate during the winter.

    ANS: T   DIF: I   OBJ: 22-3.4

23. There are three major types of ecosystems found in the ocean.

    ANS: T   DIF: I   OBJ: 22-4.1

24. All planktonic organisms are photosynthetic.

ANS: F   DIF: I   OBJ: 22-4.2

25. Some clams living near deep-sea vents lack a digestive system and instead harbor chemosynthetic bacteria in their bodies.

ANS: T   DIF: I   OBJ: 22-4.3

26. Oligotrophic lakes fill in and disappear more quickly than eutrophic ones.

ANS: F   DIF: I   OBJ: 22-4.4

MULTIPLE CHOICE

1. Organisms that manufacture organic nutrients for an ecosystem are called
   a. primary consumers.
   b. predators.
   c. primary producers.
   d. scavengers.

   ANS: C   DIF: I   OBJ: 22-1.1

2. The primary producers in a grassland ecosystem would most likely be
   a. insects.
   b. bacteria.
   c. grasses.
   d. algae.

   ANS: C   DIF: I   OBJ: 22-1.1

3. The organic material in an ecosystem is called
   a. trophic level.
   b. biomass.
   c. energy level.
   d. ecomass.

   ANS: B   DIF: I   OBJ: 22-1.1

4. cows : herbivores ::
   a. horses : carnivores
   b. plants : producers
   c. algae : consumers
   d. caterpillars : producers

   ANS: B   DIF: II   OBJ: 22-1.1

5. When an organism dies, the nitrogen in its body
   a. can never be reused by other living things.
   b. is immediately released into the atmosphere.
   c. is released by the action of decomposers.
   d. None of the above

   ANS: C   DIF: I   OBJ: 22-1.2

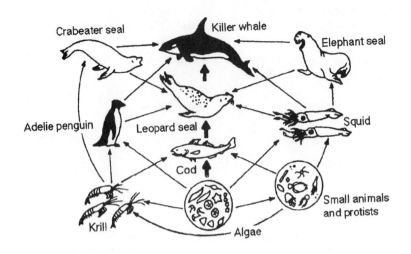

6. Refer to the illustration above. The photosynthetic algae are
   a. producers.
   b. consumers.
   c. parasites.
   d. decomposers.

   ANS: A   DIF: II   OBJ: 22-1.1

7. Refer to the illustration above. The diagram, which shows how energy moves through an ecosystem, is known as a
   a. habitat.
   b. food chain.
   c. food net.
   d. food web.

   ANS: D   DIF: II   OBJ: 22-1.3

8. Refer to the illustration above. Leopard seals are
   a. producers.
   b. omnivores.
   c. herbivores.
   d. carnivores.

   ANS: D   DIF: II   OBJ: 22-1.3

9. Refer to the illustration above. Killer whales feed at the
   a. first and second trophic levels.
   b. second trophic level only.
   c. second and third trophic levels.
   d. third and fourth trophic levels.

   ANS: D   DIF: II   OBJ: 22-1.3

10. In a food web, which type of organism receives energy from every other type?
   a. producer
   b. carnivore
   c. decomposer
   d. herbivore

   ANS: C   DIF: I   OBJ: 22-1.3

11. A forest ecosystem is considered self-supporting because
   a. the sun directly provides its needed chemical energy.
   b. the ecosystem energy is transferred only among its animals.
   c. no additional energy sources or materials need to be added to the system from the outside.
   d. it consists only of organic matter.

ANS: C   DIF: I   OBJ: 22-1.4

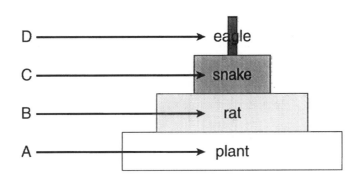

12. Refer to the illustration above. On the pyramid, animals that feed on plant eaters are no lower than
   a. level "A."   c. level "C."
   b. level "B."   d. level "D."

ANS: C   DIF: II   OBJ: 22-1.4

13. Refer to the illustration above. How much energy is available to the organisms in level "C"?
   a. all of the energy in level "A" plus the energy in level "B"
   b. all of the energy in level "A" minus the energy in level "B"
   c. 10 percent of the energy in level "B"
   d. 90 percent of the energy in level "B"

ANS: C   DIF: II   OBJ: 22-1.4

14. Animals that feed on plants are at least in the
   a. first trophic level.   c. third trophic level.
   b. second trophic level.   d. fourth trophic level.

ANS: B   DIF: I   OBJ: 22-1.4

15. The number of trophic levels in an ecological pyramid
   a. is limitless.
   b. is limited by the amount of energy that is lost at each trophic level.
   c. never exceeds four.
   d. never exceeds three.

ANS: B   DIF: I   OBJ: 22-1.4

Modern Biology Assessment Item Listing
215

16. In going from one trophic level to the next higher level,
    a. the number of organisms increases.
    b. the amount of usable energy increases.
    c. the amount of usable energy decreases.
    d. diversity of organisms increases.

    ANS: C   DIF: I   OBJ: 22-1.4

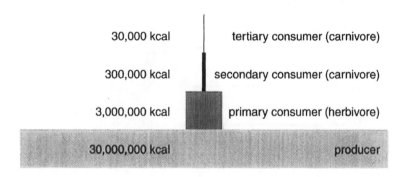

17. Refer to the illustration above. The diagram represents the decrease in
    a. the number of organisms between lower and higher trophic levels.
    b. available energy between lower and higher trophic levels.
    c. diversity of organisms between lower and higher trophic levels.
    d. All of the above

    ANS: D   DIF: II   OBJ: 22-1.4

18. Refer to the illustration above. At each trophic level, the energy stored in the organisms
    in that level is
    a. about one-tenth of the energy in the level below it.
    b. about one-tenth of the energy in the level above it.
    c. 50 percent of the energy in the level below it.
    d. 100 percent of the energy in the level below it.

    ANS: A   DIF: II   OBJ: 22-1.4

19. Because energy diminishes at each successive trophic level, few ecosystems can contain
    more than
    a. two trophic levels.   c. five trophic levels.
    b. four trophic levels.   d. eight trophic levels.

    ANS: C   DIF: II   OBJ: 22-1.4

20. Water and minerals needed by all organisms on Earth pass back and forth between the
    biotic and abiotic portions of the environment in a process known as
    a. recycling.   c. a biogeochemical cycle.
    b. a pathway.   d. transpiration.

    ANS: C   DIF: I   OBJ: 22-2.1

21. Precipitation and evaporation are important components of the
    a. nitrogen cycle.
    b. water cycle.
    c. carbon cycle.
    d. All of the above

    ANS: B   DIF: I   OBJ: 22-2.2

22. Which of the following is part of the nitrogen cycle?
    a. conversion of atmospheric nitrogen into usable organic compounds by bacteria
    b. conversion of nitrogen from decaying organisms into ammonia
    c. nitrogen fixation
    d. All of the above

    ANS: D   DIF: I   OBJ: 22-2.3

23. Nitrogen is a component of
    a. proteins.
    b. fats.
    c. carbohydrates.
    d. water.

    ANS: A   DIF: I   OBJ: 22-2.3

24. In the nitrogen cycle, plants use nitrates and nitrites to form
    a. ammonia.
    b. nitrogen gas.
    c. nutrients.
    d. amino acids.

    ANS: D   DIF: I   OBJ: 22-2.3

25. Which of the following is common to the carbon cycle, the nitrogen cycle, *and* the water cycle?
    a. The substance is rearranged into different types of molecules as it moves through its cycle.
    b. The substance must pass through organisms in order to complete its cycle.
    c. The largest reserves of the substance are always in organisms.
    d. The substance is required by all living things and is involved in many processes that occur in all living things.

    ANS: D   DIF: III   OBJ: 22-2.3

26. Coal, oil, and natural gas
    a. are formed from decayed plants.
    b. are fossil fuels.
    c. release carbon dioxide when they are burned.
    d. All of the above

    ANS: D   DIF: I   OBJ: 22-2.4

27. Humans are affecting the carbon cycle by
    a. burning fossil fuels.
    b. destroying vegetation that absorbs carbon dioxide.
    c. using electrical labor-saving devices.
    d. All of the above

    ANS: D   DIF: I   OBJ: 22-2.4

28. air pump : tire pressure ::
    a. more rain : transformation of rain forests
    b. more transpiration : arid weather
    c. burning fossil fuels : carbon in the atmosphere
    d. slowing of evaporation : transpiration

    ANS: C   DIF: II   OBJ: 22-2.4

29. Major ecosystems that occur over wide areas of land are called
    a. communities.   c. biomes.
    b. habitats.   d. food chains.

    ANS: C   DIF: I   OBJ: 22-3.1

Biome	Average yearly temperature range	Vegetation
1	–10°C–14°C	Needle-leafed evergreen trees
2	0°C–25°C	Tall grasses in moist areas; short grasses in drier areas
3	24°C–34°C	Succulent plants and scattered grasses
4	25°C–27°C	Broad-leafed evergreen trees and shrubs
5	10°C–20°C	Giant needle-leafed evergreen trees

30. Refer to the table above. Which biome generally has the lowest average yearly precipitation?
    a. "2"   c. "4"
    b. "3"   d. "5"

    ANS: B   DIF: II   OBJ: 22-3.1

31. Refer to the table above. Biome "1" is called the
    a. deciduous forest.   c. coniferous forest.
    b. tropical rain forest.   d. temperate rain forest.

    ANS: C   DIF: II   OBJ: 22-3.1

32. Which of the following biomes is characterized by evergreen trees and mammals such as moose, bears, and lynx?
    a. taiga   c. temperate rain forest
    b. polar   d. tundra

    ANS: A   DIF: I   OBJ: 22-3.1

33. Herds of grazing animals are most likely to be found in a
    a. savanna.   c. deciduous forest.
    b. tropical rain forest.   d. taiga

    ANS: A   DIF: I   OBJ: 22-3.2

34. The biome that makes up most of the central part of the United States is
    a. rain forest.
    c. tundra.
    b. temperate grassland.
    d. deciduous forest.

    ANS: B   DIF: I   OBJ: 22-3.2

35. Which of the following is *not* an adaptation for water conservation found in desert organisms?
    a. nocturnal lifestyle
    c. waxy leaf coatings
    b. deep root system
    d. burrowing in the ground

    ANS: B   DIF: II   OBJ: 22-3.3

36. Which of the following animals would most likely be found in a temperate rain forest?
    a. monkeys
    c. deer
    b. caribou
    d. leopards

    ANS: C   DIF: I   OBJ: 22-3.4

37. Tropical ecosystems are more diverse than temperate zone ecosystems because
    a. the growing season in tropical ecosystems never stops.
    b. the climate in tropical ecosystems does not vary much from year to year.
    c. a greater amount of food is produced in tropical ecosystems.
    d. All of the above

    ANS: D   DIF: II   OBJ: 22-3.4

38. Almost all of Earth's surface water is contained in
    a. ocean ecosystems.
    c. tropical rain forests.
    b. freshwater biomes.
    d. ponds and lakes.

    ANS: A   DIF: I   OBJ: 22-4.1

39. Which of the following is characteristic of the photic zone of the ocean but not the aphotic zone?
    a. fish
    c. bacteria
    b. tides
    d. photosynthesis

    ANS: D   DIF: I   OBJ: 22-4.1

40. Plankton are
    a. a major formation ingredient of most fossil fuels.
    b. found in the deep-water zone of most lakes and oceans.
    c. the base of most aquatic food webs.
    d. usually in the third and fourth trophic levels of ocean ecosystems.

    ANS: C   DIF: I   OBJ: 22-4.2

41. Organisms with light-producing body parts would most likely be found in
    a. the deep-water zone of lakes.
    c. open ocean surfaces.
    b. shallow ocean waters.
    d. deep ocean waters.

    ANS: D   DIF: II   OBJ: 22-4.2

42. The greatest diversity of life in the ocean is found in
    a. shallow ocean waters.
    b. the ocean surface.
    c. deep ocean waters.
    d. tidal areas.

    ANS: A   DIF: I   OBJ: 22-4.2

43. many fish : shallow ocean water habitat ::
    a. nutrients : deep-sea waters
    b. plankton : deep-sea-water habitat
    c. plankton : open-sea surface habitat
    d. animals producing own light : shallow-ocean-water habitat

    ANS: C   DIF: II   OBJ: 22-4.2

44. Which of the following processes harnesses energy for organisms living near deep-sea vents?
    a. photosynthesis
    b. heterotrophy
    c. chemosynthesis
    d. respiration

    ANS: C   DIF: I   OBJ: 22-4.3

45. Eutrophic and oligotrophic lakes differ primarily in the amount of ____ they contain.
    a. animal life
    b. algae
    c. salt
    d. organic matter

    ANS: D   DIF: I   OBJ: 22-4.4

COMPLETION

1. The biological structures of many of the Earth's ecosystems have been determined largely by the ways plants avoid being eaten and the ways by which _____ succeed in eating them.

   ANS: herbivores   DIF: I   OBJ: 22-1.1

2. The niche of a deer in a forest is that of a herbivore. The niche of a cougar that eats the deer is that of a _____.

   ANS: carnivore   DIF: I   OBJ: 22-1.1

3. Animals known as _____ eat only primary producers.

   ANS: herbivores   DIF: I   OBJ: 22-1.1

4. An organism that eats a primary consumer is called a _____ consumer.

   ANS: secondary   DIF: I   OBJ: 22-1.1

5. The term _____ is given to the bacteria that break down dead tissue.

   ANS: decomposers   DIF: I   OBJ: 22-1.2

6. The interrelated food chains in an ecosystem are called a _____.

ANS: food web   DIF: I   OBJ: 22-1.3

7. The primary productivity of an ecosystem is a measure of the amount of organic material that the _____ organisms in the ecosystem produce.

ANS: photosynthetic   DIF: I   OBJ: 22-1.3

8. A path of energy through the energy levels of an ecosystem is called a _____.

ANS: food chain   DIF: I   OBJ: 22-1.3

9. In an ecosystem, _____ diminishes at each successive trophic level.

ANS: energy   DIF: I   OBJ: 22-1.4

10. An energy pyramid shows the amount of energy contained in the bodies of organisms at each _____ level.

ANS: trophic   DIF: I   OBJ: 22-1.4

11. Every time energy is transferred in an ecosystem, potential energy is lost as _____.

ANS: heat   DIF: I   OBJ: 22-1.4

12. Cellular respiration and photosynthesis are the two processes that form the biogeochemical cycle known as the _____ cycle.

ANS: carbon   DIF: I   OBJ: 22-2.1

13. When forests are cut down, both water and nutrient _____ are broken.

ANS: cycles   DIF: I   OBJ: 22-2.2

14. Water that seeps into the soil is called _____ water.

ANS: ground   DIF: I   OBJ: 22-2.2

15. The conversion of nitrogen gas to ammonia by the action of bacteria is called _____.

ANS: nitrogen fixation.   DIF: I   OBJ: 22-2.3

16. The process of _____ occurs when anaerobic bacteria break down nitrates and release nitrogen gas back into the atmosphere.

ANS: denitrification   DIF: I   OBJ: 22-2.3

17. Coniferous trees are predominantly found in the _____ biome.

ANS: taiga   DIF: I   OBJ: 22-3.1

18. The thick, continually frozen layer of ground found in the northern tundra is called
_____.

ANS: permafrost   DIF: I   OBJ: 22-3.1

19. Elk and moose may live in _____, areas that are also the primary
source of the world's lumber.

ANS: coniferous forests   DIF: I   OBJ: 22-3.1

20. A _____ is open, windswept ground that is always frozen.

ANS: tundra   DIF: I   OBJ: 22-3.1

21. Bison, elephants, and kangaroos are most likely found in the biome known as the
_____.

ANS: temperate grassland   DIF: I   OBJ: 22-3.2

22. The biome that makes up most of the central part of the continental United States is the
_____.

ANS: temperate grassland   DIF: I   OBJ: 22-3.2

23. A dry grassland, known as a _____, has open, widely spaced trees and
seasonal rainfall and is the home of elephants, giraffes, and lions.

ANS: savanna   DIF: I   OBJ: 22-3.2

24. Some plants are adapted for living in the desert because they open their
_____ only at night.

ANS: stomata   DIF: I   OBJ: 22-3.3

25. Trees that lose their leaves every year are known as _____.

ANS: deciduous   DIF: I   OBJ: 22-3.4

26. _____ are characterized by lush vegetation, abundant rain, and year-
round warm temperatures.

ANS: Tropical rain forests   DIF: I   OBJ: 22-3.4

27. _____ ocean waters are small in area but contain most of the ocean's
diversity.

ANS: Shallow   DIF: I   OBJ: 22-4.2

28. The raw material that is the ultimate source of energy for deep-sea vent organisms is

_____.

ANS: hydrogen sulfide DIF: I OBJ: 22-4.3

PROBLEM

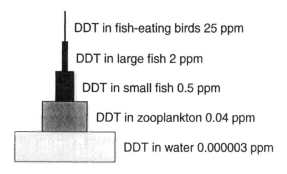

30,000 kcal	tertiary consumer (carnivore)
300,000 kcal	secondary consumer (carnivore)
3,000,000 kcal	primary consumer (herbivore)
30,000,000 kcal	producer

The diagram above is a typical energy pyramid, which shows how energy is lost as it is transferred from one level to another in a food chain. The diagram below shows the concentration of DDT, a pesticide, in water and in a number of organisms that make up a food chain.

DDT in fish-eating birds 25 ppm

DDT in large fish 2 ppm

DDT in small fish 0.5 ppm

DDT in zooplankton 0.04 ppm

DDT in water 0.000003 ppm

1. Refer to the illustrations above. Explain how DDT and other toxic substances can become concentrated in organisms as it is transferred up through a food chain. Write your answer in the space below.

ANS:
As energy is passed from one level of a food chain to another, only a small amount of it is retained by the next organism up in the food chain. This occurs in part because all energy conversions involve a loss of energy in the form of heat. It is also partly due to the fact that each successive organism in a food chain requires more energy to maintain its body's activities. If there are toxic substances, such as DDT, in an organism's food, it will pass through the organism's body. These substances can be taken up and stored in body tissues. When another organism ingests food containing stored toxins, it can also take up and store the toxins. The toxic substances become increasingly concentrated as they move up through the food chain because each successive organism requires more food energy than the one below it in order to survive.

DIF: III OBJ: 22-1.3

Modern Biology Assessment Item Listing
223

2. Nitrogen fertilizer is added to soils in virtually all agricultural areas of the world. The use of nitrogen fertilizer greatly increases the amount of food produced. However, it can also affect the ecology of areas near agricultural areas. The data presented in the table below were obtained in an experiment conducted to evaluate the effects of nitrogen fertilizer on grass species diversity. Nitrogen fertilizer was applied yearly to an experimental plot, beginning in 1856.

Year	1856	1872	1949
Total number of grass species	49	15	3
Number of species producing more than 10% of the total dry weight of all species combined	2	3	1
Number of species producing more than 50% of the total dry weight of all species combined	0	1	1
Number of species producing more than 99% of the total dry weight of all species combined	0	0	1

Write your answers to the following in the space below.
a. Write three conclusions that you can draw from these data.
b. How could this experiment have been designed differently to make it a better experiment?

ANS:
a. The following are some possible conclusions:
  1. The total number of grass species decreased over time and with exposure to nitrogen fertilizer.
  2. At the beginning of the experiment, there was no one dominant species of grass. Over time and with exposure to nitrogen fertilizer, a few species became dominant.
  3. Prolonged use of nitrogen fertilizer encourages the growth of one or at least only a few dominant species.
b. It should have been designed to have a control plot that did not receive nitrogen fertilizer. As the experiment was designed, the effects of nitrogen fertilizer cannot be distinguished from the effects of time.

DIF: III   OBJ: 22-1.3

ESSAY

1. Clover plants, rabbits, and coyotes are some of the organisms that occupy a particular ecosystem. Assign the roles of primary producers, primary consumers, and secondary consumers to these three groups of organisms and explain your answer. Write your answer in the space below.

ANS:
In this ecosystem, the clover plants are the primary producers. These autotrophs help manufacture the organic nutrients necessary to sustain the ecosystem. Rabbits are herbivores that consume the primary producers (the clover plants), so they are classified as primary consumers. Coyotes eat the primary consumers (the rabbits), so they are classified as secondary consumers.

DIF: II   OBJ: 22-1.1

2. Why are decomposers necessary for the continuation of life on Earth? Write your answer in the space below.

ANS:
Matter for life cycles through ecosystems. Decomposers release matter from waste materials and dead organisms. Were it not for the action of decomposers, the Earth would eventually be depleted of usable essential matter such as carbon and nitrogen that organisms need. Decomposers are essential to the recycling of matter. Without decomposers we would not be able to recycle essential materials such as nitrogen and carbon.

DIF: II   OBJ: 22-1.2

3. Describe how energy is transferred from one trophic level to another. Write your answer in the space below.

ANS:
A portion of the energy available to the organisms at each level of the food chain is stored in the chemical bonds of nutrients that are not used by an organism in order to sustain life. When that organism is eaten by another, the stored chemical energy is transferred to the new organism and used to sustain its life.

DIF: II   OBJ: 22-1.4

4. Why is it cheaper for a farmer to produce a pound of grain than a pound of meat? Write your answer in the space below.

ANS:
Animals are on higher trophic levels than plants. Consequently, it takes several pounds of grain to produce one pound of meat.

DIF: II   OBJ: 22-1.4

5. Explain and give an example of what is meant by the statement "Climate has an important influence on the type of ecosystem found in an area." Write your answer in the space below.

ANS:
The climate of an area refers to the daily atmospheric conditions—the temperature, amount of rainfall, and amount of sunlight in a given area. The physical features of the Earth and amount of solar energy reaching an area influence the climate. Ecosystems vary based on the types of living organisms—plants and animals—that can survive in an area.

Areas receiving large amounts of sunlight and precipitation tend to be warm and moist and support different types of organisms than colder, dry areas. Areas that are warm and dry, such as parts of southern Arizona, promote the growth of fewer plants than areas with heavy rainfall. The plants that survive, such as cacti, have developed structures that promote water conservation. Areas with mild temperatures and heavier rainfall, such as Virginia and North Carolina, promote the growth of dense forests with tall trees that shed their leaves and consume large amounts of water on a daily basis. (Other examples also are acceptable that establish a link between the type of organisms that can survive and the climate.)

DIF: II   OBJ: 22-3.4

6. Why are plankton important in freshwater ecosystems? Are plankton important in land ecosystems as well? Explain. Write your answer in the space below.

ANS:
Plankton, a diverse biological community of microscopic organisms, live near the surface of lakes and ponds. Plankton contain photosynthetic organisms that are the base of aquatic food webs. Plankton are important in land ecosystems because these ecosystems are closely connected to freshwater habitats. Many land animals come to water to feed on aquatic animals that rely on plankton or plankton-eating organisms for food.

DIF: II   OBJ: 22-4.4

CHAPTER 23—ENVIRONMENTAL SCIENCE

TRUE/FALSE

1. Some of the effects of El Niño are beneficial to humans.

   ANS: T   DIF: I   OBJ: 23-1.2

2. Because of human efforts in the past decade, the preservation of nonrenewable resources such as topsoil, ground water, and our diverse species are no longer concerns for environmentalists.

   ANS: F   DIF: I   OBJ: 23-1.4

3. The exploding human population is the single greatest threat to the world's future.

   ANS: T   DIF: I   OBJ: 23-1.4

4. About one-half of Earth's tropical rain forests have been destroyed.

   ANS: T   DIF: I   OBJ: 23-2.2

5. The primary reason for loss of biodiversity is habitat destruction.

   ANS: T   DIF: I   OBJ: 23-2.3

6. In a debt-for-nature swap, richer countries pay off the debt of developing countries. In exchange, the developing countries agree to protect their biodiversity.

   ANS: T   DIF: I   OBJ: 23-2.3

7. The belief that organisms have value simply because they exist is a utilitarian view of biodiversity.

   ANS: F   DIF: I   OBJ: 23-2.4

8. Current efforts in the United States to conserve migratory birds focus on the development of wildlife refuges along the birds' flyways.

   ANS: T   DIF: I   OBJ: 23-3.2

9. Damage to the Florida Everglades ecosystem occurred primarily because of the removal of trees and grasses from the area.

   ANS: F   DIF: I   OBJ: 23-3.4

MULTIPLE CHOICE

1. atmospheric air circulation : ocean circulation patterns ::
   a. leeward mountainside : windward weather
   b. desert : mountain weather
   c. landmass : ocean circulation patterns
   d. landmass : latitude

   ANS: C   DIF: II   OBJ: 23-1.1

2. El Niño results in a cutoff in the upwelling of _____ in the ocean.
   a. oxygen-rich water   c. anchovies
   b. nutrients   d. warm water

   ANS: B   DIF: I   OBJ: 23-1.2

3. Which of the following is *not* a result of El Niño?
   a. reduced catches of anchovies   c. reduced grain production
   b. reduced guano production   d. reduced summer air temperatures

   ANS: D   DIF: I   OBJ: 23-1.2

4. Which of the following is *not* a human-induced alteration in Earth's environment?
   a. global warming   c. reduction of the ozone layer
   b. El Niño   d. increased carbon dioxide levels

   ANS: B   DIF: II   OBJ: 23-1.3

5. The extinction of species
   a. is a problem limited to the tropics.
   b. has been speeded up by the activities of people.
   c. is a problem only where topsoil and ground water are limited.
   d. is not a problem in the twentieth century.

   ANS: B   DIF: I   OBJ: 23-1.4

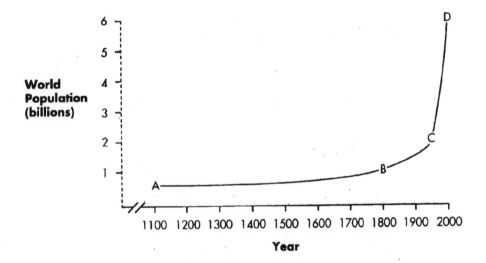

6. Refer to the illustration above. The current rate of population growth will result in a doubling of the world population every 39 years. Based on information in the graph, what will be the approximate world population in the year 2039 if nothing is done to change this rate?
   a. 6 billion
   b. 10 billion
   c. 12 billion
   d. 24 billion

   ANS: C   DIF: II   OBJ: 23-1.4

7. Which of the following groups of organisms has the greatest species richness?
   a. mammals
   b. insects
   c. plants
   d. vertebrates

   ANS: B   DIF: I   OBJ: 23-2.1

8. Destruction of the tropical rain forests
   a. threatens the existence of thousands of species.
   b. provides for more pasture and farmlands.
   c. is done partly because of the need for lumber.
   d. All of the above

   ANS: D   DIF: I   OBJ: 23-2.2

9. During which of the following periods in the history of life on Earth is/was there the greatest biodiversity?
   a. Cretaceous
   b. Jurassic
   c. Cambrian
   d. present

   ANS: D   DIF: I   OBJ: 23-2.2

10. Which of the following is a utilitarian use of biodiversity?
    a. food
    b. timber
    c. recreation
    d. All of the above

    ANS: D   DIF: I   OBJ: 23-2.4

11. Which of the following is *not* a utilitarian value of biodiversity?
    a. development of medicinal drugs from wild plant species
    b. harvesting and sale of ornamental plant species present in the wild
    c. preservation of organisms because they are alive
    d. use of wild plants and animals for food

    ANS: C   DIF: II   OBJ: 23-2.4

12. The steps needed to solve environmental problems include
    a. waiting for the affected species to leave an ecosystem that is in trouble.
    b. leaving them to United Nations committees to address.
    c. educating the public about them and the costs of their solution.
    d. taking any necessary action, regardless of the consequences or adverse effects.

    ANS: C   DIF: I   OBJ: 23-3.1

13. The biggest threat to the survival of migratory birds is
    a. insufficient numbers of nesting sites in their summer habitats.
    b. habitat destruction along their flyways and in their winter habitats.
    c. hunting during migration.
    d. increasingly cooler winter habitats.

    ANS: B   DIF: II   OBJ: 23-3.2

14. Gray-wolf populations in the United States became endangered because of
    a. the killing of wolves by people.
    b. declines in populations of the prey these carnivores eat.
    c. loss of habitat as ranches increased in size.
    d. unusually severe winters for a number of years.

    ANS: A   DIF: I   OBJ: 23-3.3

15. The primary justification for the wolf reintroduction plan was
    a. to help control elk populations.
    b. to return a well-known species to a national park.
    c. to increase enjoyment of a national park for visitors.
    d. All of the above

    ANS: D   DIF: I   OBJ: 23-3.3

16. Which of the following is *not* a component of the wolf reintroduction plan?
    a. provisions for compensation to ranchers who lose livestock to the wolves
    b. financial incentives offered for landowners who let wolves breed on their property
    c. laws preventing anyone from killing a wolf
    d. monitoring of reintroduced wolf populations

    ANS: C   DIF: II   OBJ: 23-3.3

17. The efforts to restore Everglades National Park focus on
    a. planting native trees and grasses that had previously been removed.
    b. building a dam to prevent further water loss from the area.
    c. restoring water pathways to their previous, natural courses.
    d. purchasing the rest of the Everglades ecosystem not already in the Everglades National Park.

    ANS: C   DIF: I   OBJ: 23-3.4

COMPLETION

1. The circulation of the Earth's atmosphere is caused by _____ heating.

    ANS: solar   DIF: I   OBJ: 23-1.1

2. The field of study called _____ uses biological principles to look at the relationships between humans and Earth.

    ANS: environmental science   DIF: I   OBJ: 23-1.1

3. Warming and cooling air form loops called _____ in Earth's atmosphere.

ANS: convection cells   DIF: I   OBJ: 23-1.1

4. The first step in addressing an environmental problem is _____.

ANS: assessment   DIF: I   OBJ: 23-1.1

5. Many scientists believe that the release of large quantities of chlorofluorocarbons has resulted in a diminishing of the _____ in the upper atmosphere.

ANS: ozone layer   DIF: I   OBJ: 23-1.3

6. Evidence has been collected suggesting that the atmospheric levels of _____ have increased significantly in the last 200 years and will result in a significant warming of Earth's atmosphere.

ANS: carbon dioxide   DIF: I   OBJ: 23-1.3

7. The population of the Earth is expected to exceed _____ billion people by the year 2000.

ANS: 6   DIF: I   OBJ: 23-1.4

8. A location that has 17 species of birds has greater _____ than a location that has 10 species.

ANS: biodiversity   DIF: I   OBJ: 23-2.1

9. If the rate of destruction of the biome known as the _____ remains at its current rate, it is likely that one-fifth of the world's species of plants and animals will become extinct.

ANS: tropical rain forest   DIF: I   OBJ: 23-2.2

10. Ecotourism is a method that has been developed to promote the conservation of _____ in developing countries.

ANS: biodiversity   DIF: I   OBJ: 23-2.3

11. A strategy for conserving biodiversity in developing countries is _____ in which people who want to see the ecosystem pay money for guides, food, and lodging.

ANS: ecotourism   DIF: I   OBJ: 23-2.3

12. A crucial argument that promoters of biodiversity conservation make is that there are many _____ in the wild that have potential value to humans and are primarily located in areas being subjected to habitat destruction.

ANS: undiscovered species   DIF: I   OBJ: 23-2.4

13. The field of study called _____ seeks to identify and maintain natural areas.

ANS: conservation biology   DIF: I   OBJ: 23-3.1

14. Many migratory birds have winter _____ outside the United States and so conservation efforts must be international.

ANS: habitats   DIF: I   OBJ: 23-3.2

15. The amount of wetland habitat present in the Florida Everglades declined by _____ percent in only 50 years.

ANS: 50   DIF: I   OBJ: 23-3.4

ESSAY

1. Explain how species richness and species evenness differ. Write your answer in the space below.

ANS:
Species richness is the number of species in an area. Species Evenness takes into account the number of individuals of each species there are in an area.

DIF: I   OBJ: 23-2.1

2. How many species of organisms are there? Explain your answer. Write your answer in the space below.

ANS:
No one is certain how many species there are. Fewer than 3 million have been named and described, but the total number may be between 10 million and 30 million.

DIF: I   OBJ: 23-2.2

3. Compare and contrast restoration biology and conservation biology. Write your answer in the space below.

ANS:
Restoration biology is concerned with rebuilding badly damaged ecosystems. Conservation biology is concerned with protecting areas that retain most of their biodiversity. Both disciplines use biological knowledge to help conserve biodiversity.

DIF: I   OBJ: 23-3.1

4. Why must efforts to conserve migratory birds be international? Give two examples of such efforts. Write your answer in the space below.

ANS:
Migratory birds fly long distances and live in different countries at different times of the year. Two international partnerships are the Western Hemisphere Shorebird Reserve Network and Partners in Flight—Aves de las Americas.

DIF: I   OBJ: 23-3.2

5. Identify three reasons why wolves are being restored to Yellowstone National Park. Write your answer in the space below.

ANS:
Answers include that wolves are being restored to help control herbivore populations, to provide enjoyment to the park's visitors, and to return part of the park's former biodiversity.

DIF: I   OBJ: 23-3.3

6. How did the diversion of water from the Everglades lead to environmental problems? Write your answer in the space below.

ANS:
The diversion of water from the Everglades reduced the recharge of ground water, leading to water shortages in Miami and surrounding areas. Florida Bay, south of the Everglades, became excessively salty because it no longer received the fresh water that had passed through the Everglades.

DIF: I   OBJ: 23-3.4

CHAPTER 24—BACTERIA

TRUE/FALSE

1. Gram-negative bacteria have a thick layer of peptidoglycan that stains purple.

   ANS: F   DIF: I   OBJ: 24-1.4

2. Bacteria lack nuclei and therefore also lack genetic material.

   ANS: F   DIF: I   OBJ: 24-2.1

3. Bacterial cells have membrane-bound organelles and chromosomes.

   ANS: F   DIF: I   OBJ: 24-2.1

4. Bacterial cells are usually much larger than eukaryotic cells.

   ANS: F   DIF: I   OBJ: 24-2.1

5. Bacteria are incapable of movement themselves; they can only get to new locations by growing toward them or by forming endospores and being carried in air or water.

   ANS: F   DIF: I   OBJ: 24-2.2

6. Some bacteria cannot survive in the presence of oxygen.

   ANS: T   DIF: I   OBJ: 24-2.4

7. When bacteria undergo nonreproductive genetic recombination, their bacterial chromosome is altered.

   ANS: F   DIF: III   OBJ: 24-2.5

8. Certain antibiotics have become ineffective against certain strains of bacteria. These bacteria have developed a resistance, which may be passed on from one generation of bacteria to the next.

   ANS: T   DIF: I   OBJ: 24-3.2

9. The photoautotrophic bacteria are the only bacteria that are indirectly beneficial to humans.

   ANS: F   DIF: I   OBJ: 24-3.3

MULTIPLE CHOICE

1. The earliest known group of living organisms on Earth was
   a. viruses.
   b. fungi.
   c. bacteria.
   d. protists.

   ANS: C   DIF: I   OBJ: 24-1.1

2. Bacteria are the only organisms characterized as
   a. unicellular.
   b. prokaryotic.
   c. eukaryotic.
   d. photosynthetic.

   ANS: B   DIF: I   OBJ: 24-1.1

3. Bacteria can be classified according to their
   a. type of cell walls.
   b. methods of obtaining energy.
   c. Gram-staining characteristics.
   d. All of the above

   ANS: D   DIF: I   OBJ: 24-1.2

Organism A   Organism B   Organism C

4. Refer to the illustration above. Which of the diagrams has a shape like the *Bacillus* bacterial genus?
   a. Organism "A"
   b. Organism "B"
   c. Organism "C"
   d. None of the above

   ANS: B   DIF: II   OBJ: 24-1.2

5. Refer to the illustration above. The shape represented by Organism "C" is called
   a. coccus.
   b. spirillum.
   c. bacillus.
   d. filamentous.

   ANS: B   DIF: I   OBJ: 24-1.2

6. When tested with a Gram stain, gram-positive bacteria are stained
   a. green.
   b. yellow.
   c. pink.
   d. purple.

   ANS: D   DIF: I   OBJ: 24-1.4

7. It is important to distinguish between Gram-positive and Gram-negative bacteria in diagnosing a bacterial infection because
   a. Gram-negative bacteria do not respond to many antibiotics.
   b. Gram-positive bacteria never cause fatal diseases.
   c. Gram-positive bacteria destroy antibiotics, preventing them from working.
   d. Gram-positive bacteria respond to many antibiotics.

   ANS: A   DIF: I   OBJ: 24-1.4

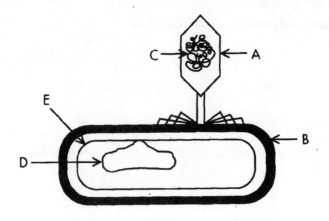

8. Refer to the illustration above. If the bacterium in the diagram is Gram-negative, what two types of molecules would be found in the structure labeled "B"?
   a. protein and lipids
   b. protein and polysaccharides
   c. polysaccharides and lipids
   d. nucleic acid and lipids

ANS: C   DIF: I   OBJ: 24-1.4

9. Bacteria lack a true nucleus and membrane-bound organelles; therefore, they are classified as
   a. prokaryotes.
   b. aerobes.
   c. anaerobes.
   d. eukaryotes.

ANS: A   DIF: I   OBJ: 24-2.1

10. The cytoplasm of bacteria
    a. contains numerous types of organelles.
    b. is divided into compartments.
    c. has varying numbers of chromosomes, depending on the species of bacteria.
    d. contains a single molecule of DNA.

ANS: D   DIF: I   OBJ: 24-2.1

11. Which of the following comparisons is *incorrect*?

	PROKARYOTES	EUKARYOTES
a.	smaller	larger
b.	circular chromosomes	linear chromosomes
c.	binary fission	mitosis
d.	chloroplasts	mitochondria

ANS: D   DIF: I   OBJ: 24-2.1

12. One difference between human body cells and bacterial cells is that bacterial cells have
    a. an outer cell wall made up of phosphates.
    b. a cell wall made up of peptidoglycan.
    c. no DNA.
    d. no ribosomes.

ANS: B   DIF: I   OBJ: 24-2.1

13. Structures found in a eukaryotic cell but not in a bacterial cell are
    a. cell nuclei.
    b. chromosomes.
    c. membrane-bound organelles.
    d. All of the above

    ANS: D   DIF: I   OBJ: 24-2.1

14. Which of the following might be found in the cytoplasm of a bacterial cell?
    a. chloroplasts
    b. Golgi bodies
    c. mitochondria
    d. None of the above

    ANS: D   DIF: I   OBJ: 24-2.1

15. Bacterial cells
    a. have a cell wall only.
    b. have a cell membrane only.
    c. have both a cell membrane and cell wall.
    d. have a cell wall inside their cell membrane.

    ANS: C   DIF: I   OBJ: 24-2.1

16. Cell organelles that *E. coli* and other bacteria have in common with eukaryotes are
    a. chloroplasts.
    b. mitochondria.
    c. nuclei.
    d. ribosomes.

    ANS: D   DIF: I   OBJ: 24-2.1

17. Bacterial endospores
    a. occur where there is plenty of available food.
    b. allow certain species to survive harsh environmental conditions.
    c. are similar to human tumors.
    d. can cause growth abnormalities in plants.

    ANS: B   DIF: I   OBJ: 24-2.1

18. *E. coli* is an example of a bacterium that has short, thin, hairlike projections called
    a. pili.
    b. cilia.
    c. cocci.
    d. ribosomes.

    ANS: A   DIF: I   OBJ: 24-2.1

19. Which of the following are used by at least some bacteria for movement?
    a. pili
    b. flagella
    c. cytoplasmic projections
    d. All of the above

    ANS: B   DIF: I   OBJ: 24-2.2

20. Autotrophic eukaryotes and autotrophic prokaryotes differ in that autotrophic eukaroytes
    a. are cyanobacteria.
    b. can only use photosynthesis to manufacture their food.
    c. lack membrane-bound organelles.
    d. cannot manufacture their own food.

    ANS: B   DIF: I   OBJ: 24-2.3

21. photosynthetic bacteria : sunlight::
    a. chemotrophic bacteria : dead organisms
    b. chemoautotrophic bacteria : inorganic molecules
    c. photosynthesis : nitrification
    d. heterotrophic bacteria : inorganic molecules

    ANS: B   DIF: II   OBJ: 24-2.3

22. Which of the following conditions would be unsuitable for any kind of bacteria to grow?
    a. temperature of 110°C (230°F)   c. pH of 5
    b. absence of water   d. absence of oxygen

    ANS: B   DIF: III   OBJ: 24-2.4

23. Bacterial cells such as *E. coli* transfer pieces of genetic material in a process called
    a. binary fission.   c. conjugation.
    b. mitosis.   d. sexual reproduction.

    ANS: C   DIF: I   OBJ: 24-2.5

24. During the process of conjugation
    a. a virus obtains DNA from a host bacterium.
    b. a bacterial cell takes in DNA from the external environment.
    c. one bacterium transfers DNA to another.
    d. two bacteria exchange DNA.

    ANS: C   DIF: II   OBJ: 24-2.5

25. A pathogen is an agent that is
    a. beneficial to humans.   c. harmful to living organisms.
    b. harmful only to plants.   d. nearly extinct.

    ANS: C   DIF: I   OBJ: 24-3.1

26. Which of the following is a fermentation product of bacteria?
    a. ricotta cheese   c. yogurt
    b. ice cream   d. cottage cheese

    ANS: C   DIF: I   OBJ: 24-3.3

27. Antibiotics
    a. include penicillin, tetracycline, and streptomycin.
    b. may prevent bacteria from making new cell walls.
    c. are very effective treatments for bacterial diseases.
    d. All of the above

    ANS: D   DIF: I   OBJ: 24-3.3

COMPLETION

1. Spiral bacteria are called _____.

    ANS: spirilli   DIF: I   OBJ: 24-1.2

2. Spherical bacteria are called _____.

    ANS: cocci   DIF: I   OBJ: 24-1.2

3. Rod-shaped bacteria are called _____.

    ANS: bacilli   DIF: I   OBJ: 24-1.2

4. The procedure used to distinguish between two types of bacterial cell wall structures is called _____.

    ANS: Gram staining   DIF: I   OBJ: 24-1.4

5. Protective structures that some bacteria may form under harsh conditions are

    _____.

    ANS: endospores   DIF: I   OBJ: 24-2.1

6. The cell walls of Gram-negative eubacteria are composed of a combination of polysaccharide and polypeptide called _____.

    ANS: peptidoglycan   DIF: I   OBJ: 24-2.1

7. Bacteria that obtain their energy by removing electrons from inorganic molecules, rather than obtaining energy from the sun, are called _____ bacteria.

    ANS: chemoautotrophic   DIF: I   OBJ: 24-2.3

8. In general, organisms that obtain their energy from sunlight are called

    _____.

    ANS: photoautotrophs   DIF: I   OBJ: 24-2.3

9. Bacteria that are heterotrophic and feed on dead organic matter are called

    _____.

    ANS: saprophytes   DIF: I   OBJ: 24-2.4

10. A(n) _____ is a substance that can be obtained from bacteria or fungi and can be used as a drug to fight pathogenic bacteria.

    ANS: antibiotic   DIF: I   OBJ: 24-3.3

11. Many bacteria are _____ and play an important role in recycling carbon, nitrogen, and other elements, while other bacteria are _____ and assemble organic compounds from carbon dioxide, nitrogen, and other elements.

    ANS: decomposers; photosynthetic   DIF: I   OBJ: 24-3.3

PROBLEM

1. Write your answers to the following in the space below or on a separate sheet of paper.
   a. Design an experiment to test the hypothesis that bacteria are not necessary for the survival of other organisms on earth. You should use some kind of closed containers for your experiments. You should include a variety of eukaryotic organisms in your experiment. Your experiment must be a controlled experiment. Be sure to indicate what chemicals you would need to include in your containers and which you would exclude.
   b. What results do you expect to see from this experiment? Provide explanations for your expected results.

ANS:
a. A good experiment would have at least two containers. Half of the containers would be the experimental containers and half would be the control containers. Both containers should be partly filled with soil. This soil must be sterilized soil, so that it would not contain any bacteria. The activity of bacteria that students will choose to test in their experiment is nitrogen fixation (decomposition would not be a good activity to test because some fungi are also capable of decomposition). Their control container should have soil inoculated with nitrogen-fixing bacteria. For an ideal controlled experiment, the experimental container would receive an inoculation of the same type of bacteria that has been killed by sterilization. Both containers should have some kind of decomposing bacterium added to the soil. There must be a source of air for the containers. Ordinary room air that is passed through filters small enough to trap bacteria would be satisfactory. Some possible eukaryotic organisms to include would be at least several kinds of plants, an insect, a worm, a reptile or an amphibian, a bird, and a mammal (most of the heterotrophs should be herbivores). The plants should be started from seed to avoid possible bacterial contamination. The animals should be treated with antibiotics effective against both gram-positive bacteria and gram-negative bacteria. Once all of the organisms are in place in the containers, they must also be provided with a source of sterilized water and sunlight. The experiment should be conducted for a relatively long period of time, at least several months.

b. The students should expect to first see a big difference in the growth rate of the plants in the control containers and those in the experimental chambers. Those in the control containers should be growing much more rapidly than those in the experimental containers. Later, the students should see plant-eating animals dying off because of a lack of sufficient plant material to eat. Finally, the students should see carnivorous animals dying off because their prey have died. The ultimate cause of the death of organisms in the experimental container is the fact that it does not contain any nitrogen-fixing bacteria. These bacteria provide a means for all eukaryotic organisms to obtain nitrogen. They convert atmospheric (gaseous) nitrogen into forms that can be taken up by plants. Animals then obtain nitrogen by eating either plants or animals that have eaten plants. Fungi obtain nitrogen from decomposition or parasitism of plants or animals.

DIF: III   OBJ: 24-3.3

ESSAY

1. Explain the difference between Gram-positive bacteria and Gram-negative bacteria. Write your answer in the space below.

ANS:
Gram-positive bacteria have a thick peptidoglycan layer that holds a stain. Gram-negative bacteria have a thin peptidoglycan layer and a thick outer membrane that does not retain a stain.

DIF: I   OBJ: 24-1.4

CHAPTER 25—VIRUSES

TRUE/FALSE

1. Although viruses do not consist of cells, biologists consider them to be living because they are capable of reproduction.

   ANS: F   DIF: I   OBJ: 25-1.1

2. Some viruses have a membranous envelope surrounding the protein coat that helps them gain entry into host cells.

   ANS: T   DIF: I   OBJ: 25-1.1

3. Wendell Stanley made the important discovery that viruses are not cellular.

   ANS: T   DIF: I   OBJ: 25-1.2

4. The largest virus is smaller than the smallest bacterium.

   ANS: F   DIF: I   OBJ: 25-1.3

5. Viruses consist of RNA or DNA surrounded by a coat of protein.

   ANS: T   DIF: I   OBJ: 25-1.4

6. Prions are the smallest known particles that are able to replicate.

   ANS: F   DIF: I   OBJ: 25-1.5

7. A virus can only reproduce by controlling a cell.

   ANS: T   DIF: I   OBJ: 25-2.2

8. Once a virus enters either a lytic or a lysogenic cycle, it cannot change to the opposite type of cycle.

   ANS: F   DIF: I   OBJ: 25-2.3

9. Prophages and proviruses can both enter lytic cycles and destroy host cells.

   ANS: T   DIF: I   OBJ: 25-2.4

10. People can contract the influenza virus more than once because the virus tends to mutate rapidly, avoiding the actions of the immune system.

    ANS: T   DIF: I   OBJ: 25-2.5

11. Most scientists believe that viruses appeared on Earth before living cells and that living cells evolved from a virus-like entity.

    ANS: F   DIF: I   OBJ: 25-2.5

12. Smallpox is caused by bacteria.

ANS: F   DIF: I   OBJ: 25-3.1

13. Chickenpox and shingles are caused by the same virus.

ANS: T   DIF: I   OBJ: 25-3.1

14. The viruses that have been linked to human cancers are usually transmitted through the air.

ANS: F   DIF: II   OBJ: 25-3.3

15. Emerging viruses normally do not infect humans, but they can when humans disturb their habitat.

ANS: T   DIF: II   OBJ: 25-3.4

MULTIPLE CHOICE

1. We know viruses are not alive because
   a. they are not cellular.
   b. they cannot make proteins.
   c. they cannot use energy.
   d. All of the above

ANS: D   DIF: I   OBJ: 25-1.1

2. The study of viruses is a part of biology because
   a. they belong to the kingdom Eubacteria.
   b. they are about to become extinct.
   c. they are living organisms.
   d. they are active inside living cells.

ANS: D   DIF: I   OBJ: 25-1.1

3. Biologists now know that viruses
   a. are the smallest organisms.
   b. consist of a protein surrounded by a nucleic acid coat.
   c. contain RNA or DNA in a protein coat.
   d. all form the same crystalline shape.

ANS: C   DIF: I   OBJ: 25-1.1

4. The capsid of a virus is the
   a. protective outer coat.
   b. cell membrane.
   c. nucleus.
   d. cell wall and membrane complex.

ANS: A   DIF: I   OBJ: 25-1.1

5. A membranous envelope surrounding some viruses may be composed of
   a. lipids.
   b. proteins.
   c. glycoproteins.
   d. All of the above

ANS: D   DIF: I   OBJ: 25-1.1

6. All viruses have
   a. cytoplasm.
   b. ribosomes.

   c. mitochondria.
   d. None of the above

   ANS: D   DIF: I   OBJ: 25-1.1

7. viruses : nucleic acids::
   a. water : ice
   b. brick : wood

   c. simplicity : complexity
   d. a jigsaw puzzle : individual pieces

   ANS: D   DIF: II   OBJ: 25-1.1

8. Tobacco mosaic virus
   a. is able to be crystallized.
   b. causes disease in tobacco plants.

   c. is smaller than a bacterium.
   d. All of the above

   ANS: D   DIF: I   OBJ: 25-1.2

9. The largest known virus is about
   a. 20 nm in diameter.
   b. 250 nm in diameter.

   c. 20 µm in diameter.
   d. 250 µm in diameter.

   ANS: B   DIF: I   OBJ: 25-1.3

10. Viruses that use reverse transcriptase to cause their host cells to transcribe DNA from an RNA template are called
    a. bacteriophages.
    b. antibodies.

    c. retroviruses.
    d. capsoviruses.

    ANS: C   DIF: I   OBJ: 25-1.4

11. Which of the following contains only a nucleic acid?
    a. prion
    b. virus

    c. viroid
    d. All of the above

    ANS: C   DIF: II   OBJ: 25-1.5

12. Unlike viruses, prions
    a. are capable of reproducing outside of a host cell.
    b. are composed only of protein.
    c. can infect brain cells of mammals.
    d. can be treated with antibiotics.

    ANS: B   DIF: I   OBJ: 25-1.5

13. A typical virus consists of
    a. a protein coat and a cytoplasm core.
    b. a carbohydrate coat and a nucleic acid core.
    c. a protein coat and a nucleic acid core.
    d. a polysaccharide coat and a nucleic acid core.

    ANS: C   DIF: I   OBJ: 25-2.1

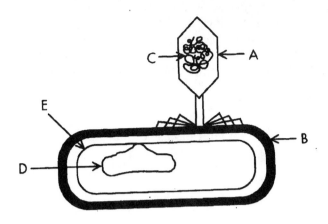

14. Refer to the illustration above. Which labeled structure could possibly be made of RNA?
   a. Structure "B"
   b. Structure "C"
   c. Structure "D"
   d. Structure "E"

ANS: B   DIF: II   OBJ: 25-2.1

15. Viruses
   a. are cellular organisms.
   b. reproduce only in living cells.
   c. have nuclei and organelles.
   d. are surrounded by a polysaccharide coat.

ANS: B   DIF: I   OBJ: 25-2.2

16. Animal viruses often infect only specific host cells because
   a. they must have the same DNA as their host cell.
   b. the host cell has specific receptors for the glycoprotein on the virus.
   c. viruses have receptors for host cell glycoproteins.
   d. the enzymes of the virus can attach only to specific host cells.

ANS: B   DIF: I   OBJ: 25-2.2

17. In which type of cell cycle(s) does viral DNA become integrated into the host cell's DNA?
   a. lytic
   b. lysogenic
   c. neither lytic nor lysogenic
   d. lytic and lysogenic

ANS: B   DIF: I   OBJ: 25-2.3

18. A prophage differs from a provirus in that
   a. a prophage contains DNA, while a provirus contains RNA.
   b. a prophage is formed during a lysogenic cycle, while a provirus is formed during a lytic cycle.
   c. a prophage contains DNA found in the infecting virus particle, while a provirus contains DNA produced from viral RNA.
   d. a prophage becomes integrated into a host cell's DNA, while a provirus cannot become integrated into a host cell's DNA.

ANS: C   DIF: II   OBJ: 25-2.4

19. Antibiotics are ineffective against viral infections because
    a. viruses are protected inside their host cells.
    b. viruses have enzymes that inactivate the antibiotics.
    c. antibiotics interfere with metabolic processes that viruses do not perform.
    d. viral protein coats block the antibiotics from entering the virus.

    ANS: C   DIF: I   OBJ: 25-3.1

20. Which of the following is *not* a viral disease of humans?
    a. hepatitis
    b. rabies
    c. shingles
    d. All of the above are viral diseases of humans.

    ANS: D   DIF: I   OBJ: 25-3.1

21. Which of the following is *not* a virus linked to cancer?
    a. Ebola   c. hepatitis B
    b. human papillomavirus   d. Epstein-Barr

    ANS: A   DIF: I   OBJ: 25-3.3

22. Which of the following human activities is most closely associated with emerging viruses?
    a. absence of a vaccination program   c. clearcutting of forests
    b. crowded living conditions   d. eating uncooked meat

    ANS: C   DIF: I   OBJ: 25-3.4

COMPLETION

1. The protein coat of a virus is called a(n) _____.

    ANS: capsid   DIF: I   OBJ: 25-1.1

2. Most viruses occur in the shape of a(n) _____ or a(n)
    _____.

    ANS: icosahedron; helix   DIF: I   OBJ: 25-1.3

3. A virus that transcribes DNA from an RNA template is called a(n)
    _____.

    ANS: retrovirus   DIF: I   OBJ: 25-1.4

4. An enzyme called _____ manufactures DNA that is complementary
    to a virus's RNA.

    ANS: reverse transcriptase   DIF: I   OBJ: 25-1.4

5. _____ are bacterial viruses with a polyhedral head and a helical tail.

    ANS: Bacteriophages   DIF: I   OBJ: 25-2.1

6. All viruses reproduce by taking over the reproductive machinery of a

   _____.

   ANS: cell   DIF: I   OBJ: 25-2.2

7. Viruses that infect a host cell and have their nucleic acid replicated but do not harm the host cell are in a _____ cycle.

   ANS: lysogenic   DIF: I   OBJ: 25-2.3

8. A viral DNA molecule formed from an RNA virus is called a(n)

   _____.

   ANS: provirus   DIF: I   OBJ: 25-2.4

9. The virus that causes AIDS is called _____.

   ANS: human immunodeficiency virus or HIV DIF: I   OBJ: 25-3.1

10. Some viruses are thought to induce _____, a disease characterized by uncontrolled cell division.

    ANS: cancer   DIF: I   OBJ: 25-3.3

11. An example of an emerging virus is the _____ virus.

    ANS: Ebola   DIF: I   OBJ: 25-3.4

PROBLEM

1. A new disease has suddenly appeared and scientists are trying to determine whether the disease agent is a virus or a bacterium. They collect the following information:

   1. The disease can be transmitted through the air.
   2. The disease agent is too small to be seen under a light microscope.
   3. There are no known antibiotics that are effective against the disease.
   4. The genetic material of the disease agent is DNA.
   5. The disease agent cannot be cultured using any known culture medium.

   Is the disease agent most likely a bacterium or a virus? Explain your answer. Write your answer in the space below.

   ANS: The disease agent is most likely a virus. Many viruses can be transmitted through the air, though so can many bacteria. Almost all viruses are too small to be seen under a light microscope, though many bacteria are also too small to be seen under a light microscope. Antibiotics are ineffective against viruses, while there are antibiotics that are effective against most bacteria. The genetic material of viruses may be DNA or RNA and the genetic material of bacteria is always DNA. Viruses cannot be cultured on artificial media, while most bacteria can. Facts #2, 3, and 5 provide the most significant information indicating that the disease agent is a virus.

   DIF: III   OBJ: 25-1.1

ESSAY

1. Viurses are not considered to be living organisms, but they are still studied as part of biology. Explain. Write your answer in the space below.

   ANS: Viruses are active inside living cells, making them an important part of the study of biology. Although viruses contain genetic material and can evolve as this material changes over time, they are not considered living because they are not cellular, cannot make their own protein, and cannot use energy in metabolic processes.

   DIF: II   OBJ: 25-1.1

CHAPTER 26—PROTOZOA

TRUE/FALSE

1. The kingdom Protista contains the eukaryotes that are not plants, animals, or fungi.

   ANS: T   DIF: I   OBJ: 26-1.1

2. Zooplankton protozoan species are unique among protozoa in that they are autotrophic.

   ANS: F   DIF: I   OBJ: 26-1.2

3. Amoebas move by means of pseudopodia.

   ANS: T   DIF: I   OBJ: 26-1.3

4. The first protists were prokaryotes.

   ANS: F   DIF: I   OBJ: 26-1.5

5. Amoebic dysentery is usually passed from person to person by coughing and sneezing.

   ANS: F   DIF: I   OBJ: 26-2.3

6. Protists cause amoebic dysentery, giardiasis, and sleeping sickness.

   ANS: T   DIF: I   OBJ: 26-2.3

MULTIPLE CHOICE

1. All protozoa
   a. are parasites.
   b. have a true nucleus.
   c. move toward light.
   d. use flagella to move.

   ANS: B   DIF: I   OBJ: 26-1.1

2. pseudopodia and cilia : locomotion structures ::
   a. nucleus and gullet : eyespots in euglenoids
   b. food and contractile : vacuoles in *Paramecia*
   c. cilia and pellicle : nuclei in amoebas
   d. "dino" and "zoo" : ciliates

   ANS: B   DIF: II   OBJ: 26-1.1

3. You have been given an unknown organism to identify. You find that it is unicellular and has a cell wall. Which of the following *must* it also have?
   a. chloroplasts
   b. asexual reproduction
   c. pseudopodia
   d. one or more flagella

   ANS: B   DIF: III   OBJ: 26-1.1

4. Which of the following types of protozoa is a primary source of energy for other organisms living in the same ecosystem?
   a. parasitic protozoa
   b. zooplankton
   c. cyst-forming protozoa
   d. soil-inhabiting protozoa

   ANS: B   DIF: I   OBJ: 26-1.2

5. Pseudopodia are used for
   a. *Paramecium* conjugation.
   b. movement by amoebas.
   c. *Euglena* reproduction.
   d. *Paramecium* mitosis.

   ANS: B   DIF: I   OBJ: 26-1.3

6. A resistant structure formed by some protozoa that enables them to survive harsh environmental conditions is a(n)
   a. eyespot.
   b. cyst.
   c. food vacuole.
   d. pseudopod.

   ANS: B   DIF: II   OBJ: 26-1.4

7. The process in which two *Paramecia* come together after meiosis to exchange parts of their genetic material is called
   a. mitosis.
   b. replication.
   c. pollination.
   d. conjugation.

   ANS: D   DIF: I   OBJ: 26-2.2

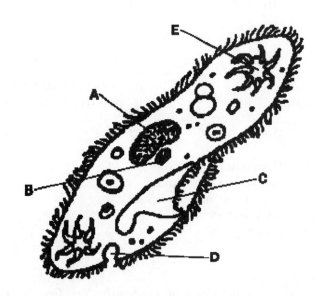

8. Refer to the illustration above. The structure that contains small pieces of DNA is labeled
   a. "A."
   b. "B."
   c. "C."
   d. "E."

   ANS: B   DIF: I   OBJ: 26-2.2

9. A current problem in the treatment of malaria is that *Plasmodium* parasites
   a. have evolved resistance to quinine and its derivatives.
   b. can now be transmitted through sexual contact.
   c. have developed a resistance to the malaria vaccine.
   d. All of the above

   ANS: A   DIF: I   OBJ: 26-2.3

10. Giardiasis is a disease that is spread
    a. by direct person-to-person contact.   c. through water.
    b. through the air.   d. by the *Anopheles* mosquito.

    ANS: C   DIF: I   OBJ: 26-2.3

11. Sleeping sickness is spread by
    a. tsetse flies.   c. contaminated food.
    b. mosquitoes.   d. All of the above

    ANS: A   DIF: I   OBJ: 26-2.3

12. Which of the following are human diseases caused by protists?
    a. amoebic dysentery   c. leishmaniasis
    b. toxoplasmosis   d. All of the above

    ANS: D   DIF: I   OBJ: 26-2.3

13. protists : damp soil or sand ::
    a. cells : cilia
    b. parasitic protists : human tissues or blood
    c. green algae : dry ground
    d. forams : fresh water

    ANS: B   DIF: II   OBJ: 26-2.3

14. giardiasis : contaminated water ::
    a. amoebic dysentery : mosquito   c. malaria : mosquito
    b. amoebic dysentery : giardiasis d. malaria : food contamination

    ANS: C   DIF: II   OBJ: 26-2.3

15. The symptoms of malaria
    a. include anemia and sweating.   c. include severe chills and fever.
    b. follow a cycle.   d. All of the above

    ANS: D   DIF: I   OBJ: 26-2.4

16. The protozoan that causes malaria reproduces in the
    a. intestine of a human.   c. red blood cells of a human.
    b. red blood cells of a mosquito. d. stinger of a mosquito.

    ANS: C   DIF: I   OBJ: 26-2.4

17. Malaria is caused by
    a. *Toxoplasma.*
    b. *Phytophthora.*
    c. *Giardia.*
    d. *Plasmodium.*

    ANS: D   DIF: I   OBJ: 26-2.4

18. The stage in the life cycle of *Plasmodium* that develops in mosquitoes and is injected into humans is called the
    a. gametophyte.
    b. sporozoite.
    c. sporophyte.
    d. zoospore.

    ANS: B   DIF: I   OBJ: 26-2.4

19. Quinine
    a. can be used to relieve the symptoms of malaria.
    b. cures drug-resistant malaria.
    c. was produced in the 1980s using genetic engineering techniques.
    d. is derived from fungi.

    ANS: A   DIF: I   OBJ: 26-2.4

COMPLETION

1. Free-living protozoa live in a _____ environment.

    ANS: water   DIF: I   OBJ: 26-1.2

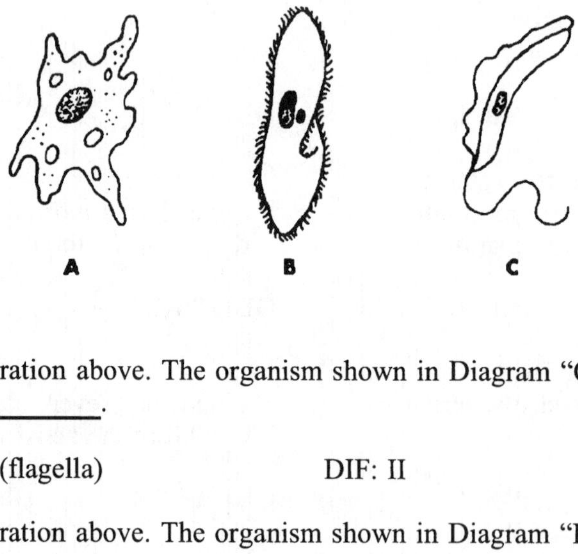

A   B   C

2. Refer to the illustration above. The organism shown in Diagram "C" moves by means of
   _____.

    ANS: a flagellum (flagella)   DIF: II   OBJ: 26-1.3

3. Refer to the illustration above. The organism shown in Diagram "B" moves by means of
   _____.

    ANS: cilia   DIF: II   OBJ: 26-1.3

4. Refer to the illustration above. The organism shown in Diagram "A" moves by means of _____.

   ANS: pseudopodia   DIF: II   OBJ: 26-1.3

5. The formation of _____ helps certain protozoa to survive harsh environmental conditions when they are not infecting either of their two hosts.

   ANS: cysts   DIF: I   OBJ: 26-1.4

6. Forams have porous shells called _____.

   ANS: tests   DIF: I   OBJ: 26-2.1

7. Sleeping sickness is caused by a group of _____ called trypanosomes.

   ANS: zoomastigotes or protozoans   DIF: I   OBJ: 26-2.3

8. Disease-causing protists are transmitted mainly by insects and contaminated _____.

   ANS: water   DIF: I   OBJ: 26-2.3

PROBLEM

1. The diagram below is a generalized sexual life cycle of a protist.

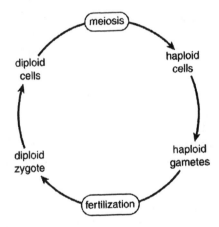

In the space below, redraw this life cycle so that it illustrates the life cycle of the malaria parasite, *Plasmodium*. Indicate which cell types and processes occur in the human host and which occur in the mosquito host. Also indicate where asexual reproduction occurs in this life cycle.

ANS:
The students' diagrams should look something like the following:

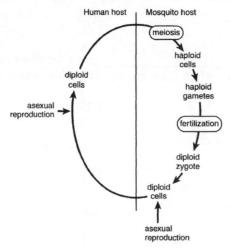

DIF: III   OBJ: 26-2.4

ESSAY

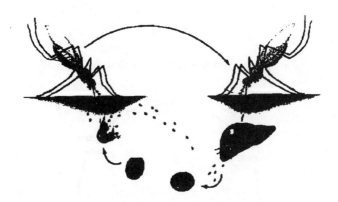

1. Refer to the illustration above. Based on the diagram, describe how the malaria parasite reproduces and spreads from person to person. Write your answer in the space below.

ANS:
Female mosquitoes acquire the malaria parasite *Plasmodium* when they bite infected humans. The mosquito then bites another victim, injecting the parasites into the victim's bloodstream. Once in the blood, the parasites travel to the liver, where they reproduce. Then they reenter the bloodstream, penetrate red blood cells, and reproduce again. Every 48 to 72 hours, a new generation of parasites bursts out of infected red blood cells. This new generation then invades other red blood cells. Some red-blood-cell parasites develop into gametocytes. When gametocytes are taken up by another feeding mosquito, the gametocytes reproduce sexually within the mosquito and produce sporozoites, which enable the mosquito to transmit malaria when it next consumes blood.

DIF: II   OBJ: 26-2.4

CHAPTER 27—ALGAE AND FUNGUSLIKE PROTISTS

TRUE/FALSE

1. Algae and plants both form gametes in single-celled gametangia.

   ANS: F   DIF: I   OBJ: 27-1.2

2. Members of the phyla Phaeophyta and Rhodophyta are commonly referred to as seaweeds.

   ANS: T   DIF: I   OBJ: 27-2.2

3. Diatoms are the only type of protists with shells.

   ANS: F   DIF: I   OBJ: 27-2.4

4. Adverse environmental conditions induce individual cellular slime molds to aggregate, forming a colonial organism.

   ANS: T   DIF: I   OBJ: 27-3.2

5. Water molds release sperm cells from reproductive structures and the sperm cells swim through water to reproductive structures containing egg cells.

   ANS: F   DIF: II   OBJ: 27-3.4

MULTIPLE CHOICE

1. Autotrophic protists are
   a. usually found deep in the oceans.
   b. always unicellular.
   c. often called algae.
   d. All of the above

   ANS: C   DIF: I   OBJ: 27-1.1

2. Algae are
   a. sometimes heterotrophic.
   b. always microscopic in size.
   c. found in both fresh water and salt water.
   d. found only in fresh water.

   ANS: C   DIF: I   OBJ: 27-1.1

3. In which of the following ways do algae differ from most other protists?
   a. All algae are unicellular and photosynthetic.
   b. Algae are photosynthetic and either unicellular or multicellular.
   c. All algae are unicellular and heterotrophic.
   d. All algae are multicellular and heterotrophic.

   ANS: B   DIF: I   OBJ: 27-1.1

4. Green algae and plants
   a. both have photosynthetic pigments.
   b. both use starch to store food.
   c. share a unique form of cell division.
   d. All of the above

   ANS: D   DIF: I   OBJ: 27-1.2

5. Which of the following types of algae are most like plants?
   a. colonial algae
   b. filamentous algae
   c. multicellular algae
   d. unicellular algae

   ANS: C   DIF: II   OBJ: 27-1.3

6. Although algae are relatively unspecialized, they may have structures specialized for
   a. anchoring the thallus to the ocean bottom.
   b. reproduction.
   c. movement.
   d. All of the above

   ANS: D   DIF: I   OBJ: 27-1.3

7. Which of the following is *not* a characteristic used to classify algae?
   a. food storage form
   b. type of chlorophyll
   c. cell wall composition
   d. whether unicellular or multicellular

   ANS: D   DIF: I   OBJ: 27-1.4

8. chloroplasts of green algae : chlorophyll a and b ::
   a. brown algae : phycobilins
   b. red algae : pigments similar to those in diatoms
   c. brown algae : symbionts
   d. red algae : phycobilins

   ANS: D   DIF: II   OBJ: 27-1.4

9. Zoospores are
   a. produced as a result of meiosis.
   b. all parasitic.
   c. produced as a result of mitosis.
   d. All of the above

   ANS: C   DIF: I   OBJ: 27-1.5

10. The haploid, gamete-producing phase in the life cycle of some protists is known as the
    a. zygospore generation.
    b. gametophyte.
    c. conjugation generation.
    d. sporophyte generation.

    ANS: B   DIF: I   OBJ: 27-1.5

11. Which of the following is not characteristic of the phylum Chlorophyta?
    a. presence of chlorophylls a and b
    b. food stored as starch
    c. cell walls made of cellulose
    d. all are unicellular

    ANS: D   DIF: I   OBJ: 27-2.1

12. Which of the following algal phyla has the most characteristics in common with plants?
   a. Rhodophyta
   b. Bacillariophyta
   c. Euglenophyta
   d. Chrysophyta

   ANS: A   DIF: II   OBJ: 27-2.2

13. The algal phylum most essential to the production of photosynthetic products and oxygen for the Earth's heterotrophs is the phylum
   a. Chlorophyta.
   b. Bacillariophyta.
   c. Dinoflagellata.
   d. Phaeophyta.

   ANS: B   DIF: I   OBJ: 27-2.3

14. dinoflagellates : flagella ::
   a. amoebas : pseudopodia
   b. forams : flagella
   c. ciliates : pseudopodia
   d. amoebas : flagella

   ANS: A   DIF: II   OBJ: 27-2.4

15. *Euglena* is an example of a protist that
   a. is both autotrophic and heterotrophic.
   b. is only a parasitic heterotroph.
   c. is always autotrophic.
   d. swims away from light.

   ANS: A   DIF: I   OBJ: 27-2.5

16. A "mass of cytoplasm that can ooze around obstacles" is most likely a(n)
   a. fruiting body.
   b. water mold.
   c. slime mold.
   d. All of the above

   ANS: C   DIF: I   OBJ: 27-3.1

17. Which of the following is *not* characteristic of the slime mold feeding stage?
   a. It is motile.
   b. It produces a fruiting body.
   c. It feeds on decomposing plant matter.
   d. It can change its shape.

   ANS: B   DIF: II   OBJ: 27-3.1

18. Slime molds would most likely be found in which of the following environments?
   a. the surface of a pond
   b. the leaves of a plant
   c. on the floor of a forest
   d. in the soil

   ANS: C   DIF: I   OBJ: 27-3.2

19. The feeding stage of a plasmodial slime mold is best described as
   a. unicellular.
   b. haploid.
   c. multicellular.
   d. multinucleate.

   ANS: D   DIF: II   OBJ: 27-3.3

20. A pseudoplasmodium is a _____ of a _____ slime mold.
    a. feeding-stage structure; plasmodial
    b. feeding-stage structure; cellular
    c. reproductive-stage structure; plasmodial
    d. reproductive-stage structure; cellular

    ANS: B   DIF: I   OBJ: 27-3.3

21. The body of a water mold in the phylum Oomycota is
    a. composed of a colony of individual cells.
    b. multinucleate.
    c. filamentous.
    d. unicellular.

    ANS: C   DIF: I   OBJ: 27-3.4

COMPLETION

1. Unlike _____, multicellular algae lack specialized tissues.

   ANS: plants   DIF: I   OBJ: 27-1.2

2. Some algae have thin, flattened structures that resemble _____ of
   plants; some have long, filamentous structures that resemble _____ of
   plants; and some have anchoring structures that resemble _____ of
   plants.

   ANS: leaves; stems; roots   DIF: I   OBJ: 27-1.3

3. In addition to chlorophyll, algae contain _____, such as carotenoids,
   xanthophyll, and fucoxanthin, that give each type of alga its characteristic color.

   ANS: accessory pigments   DIF: I   OBJ: 27-1.4

Life Cycle of *Chlamydomonas*

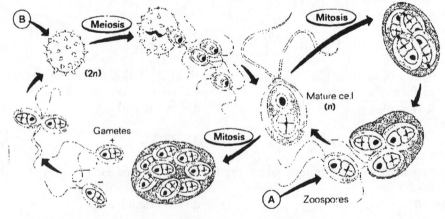

4. Refer to the illustration above. Arrow "B" is pointing to the _____ stage in the life cycle.

   ANS: zygospore   DIF: I   OBJ: 27-1.5

5. Refer to the illustration above. Arrow "A" is pointing to the _____ stage in the life cycle.

   ANS: zoospore   DIF: I   OBJ: 27-1.5

6. Refer to the illustration above. According to the diagram, Chlamydomonas reproduces both sexually and _____.

   ANS: asexually   DIF: I   OBJ: 27-1.5

7. Some protists undergo sexual reproduction only at times of environmental

   _____.

   ANS: stress   DIF: I   OBJ: 27-1.5

8. The greatest diversity of algal form, size, number of body cells, reproductive methods, and habitat is found in the phylum _____.

   ANS: Chlorophyta   DIF: I   OBJ: 27-2.1

9. Brown algae get their name from the pigment _____.

   ANS: fucoxanthin   DIF: I   OBJ: 27-2.2

10. Diatoms form shells containing _____ that are collected and used commercially in the production of substances such as _____.

    ANS: silicon dioxide; detergents/toothpaste/paint removers/fertilizers/insulators (any one of these is acceptable)

    DIF: I   OBJ: 27-2.3

11. The fruiting bodies of slime molds resemble the reproductive structures of _____, with which they were formerly classified.

    ANS: fungi   DIF: I   OBJ: 27-3.1

12. Slime molds take up food from their environment by the process of

    _____.

    ANS: phagocytosis   DIF: I   OBJ: 27-3.2

13. Both types of slime molds produce _____ in a fruiting body when they reproduce.

    ANS: spores   DIF: I   OBJ: 27-3.3

14. Most water molds are free-living and aquatic, but some are parasites of _____.

ANS: plants   DIF: I   OBJ: 27-3.4

ESSAY

1. How do euglenoids illustrate the problems of classifying protists as plants or animals?

ANS:
Some euglenoids are photosynthetic; others lack chloroplasts and are heterotrophic. Some photosynthetic euglenoids may reduce the size of their chloroplasts and become heterotrophic if kept in a dark environment.

DIF: II   OBJ: 27-2.5

CHAPTER 28—FUNGI

TRUE/FALSE

1. All fungi except yeasts have bodies composed of filaments.

   ANS: T   DIF: I   OBJ: 28-1.2

2. The cell walls of fungi are made up of cellulose.

   ANS: F   DIF: I   OBJ: 28-1.2

3. All fungi are heterotrophic.

   ANS: T   DIF: I   OBJ: 28-1.3

4. Fungi obtain nutrients through photosynthesis.

   ANS: F   DIF: I   OBJ: 28-1.3

5. Sporangia are reproductive structures in which spores form asexually.

   ANS: T   DIF: I   OBJ: 28-2.1

6. The Fungi Imperfecti reproduce sexually and asexually.

   ANS: F   DIF: I   OBJ: 28-2.2

7. Some fungi aid in the transfer of minerals from the soil to the roots of plants.

   ANS: T   DIF: I   OBJ: 28-2.4

8. Ringworm is caused by a small wormlike animal.

   ANS: F   DIF: I   OBJ: 28-3.1

MULTIPLE CHOICE

1. Biologists think fungi evolved from
   a. algae.
   b. plants.
   c. protists.
   d. prokaryotes.

   ANS: D   DIF: I   OBJ: 28-1.1

2. Chitin is found in fungi and in
   a. clam shells.
   b. the outer shells of insects.
   c. some plant cell walls.
   d. snail shells.

   ANS: B   DIF: I   OBJ: 28-1.2

3. Fungi
   a. do not contain chloroplasts.
   b. have cell walls that contain chitin.
   c. do not produce their own food.
   d. All of the above

ANS: D   DIF: I   OBJ: 28-1.2

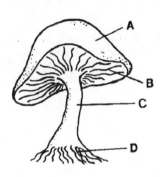

4. Refer to the illustration above. Which features characterize the kingdom of which this organism is a member?
   a. eukaryotic, absorbs nutrients
   b. aquatic, multicellular
   c. autotrophic, ingests nutrients
   d. prokaryotic, photosynthetic

ANS: A   DIF: II   OBJ: 28-1.2

5. Refer to the illustration above. Which structure is responsible for meeting the food requirements of the organism shown?
   a. "A"
   b. "B"
   c. "C"
   d. "D"

ANS: D   DIF: II   OBJ: 28-1.3

6. Fungi obtain energy
   a. directly from the sun.
   b. from inorganic material in their environment.
   c. by absorbing digested nutrients.
   d. from nuclear fusion.

ANS: C   DIF: I   OBJ: 28-1.3

7. Fungi obtain nutrients by
   a. photosynthesis.
   b. the nitrogen fixation process in their hyphae.
   c. digesting organic matter externally before absorbing it.
   d. None of the above

ANS: C   DIF: I   OBJ: 28-1.3

8. Fungi digest organic matter
   a. through photosynthesis.
   b. outside their cell walls.
   c. inside their cell walls.
   d. All of the above

   ANS: B   DIF: I   OBJ: 28-1.3

9. A hypha is a long string of cells divided by
   a. spindle fibers.
   b. an ascus.
   c. mycorrhizae.
   d. septa.

   ANS: D   DIF: I   OBJ: 28-1.4

10. The individual filaments that make up a mycelium are called
    a. vascular tissue.
    b. hyphae.
    c. rhizoids.
    d. stem cells.

    ANS: B   DIF: I   OBJ: 28-1.4

11. fungal food : organic molecules ::
    a. pea plant cell wall : chitin
    b. insect exoskeleton : cellulose
    c. fungus cell wall : cellulose
    d. mycelium : hyphae

    ANS: D   DIF: II   OBJ: 28-1.4

Life Cycle of a Mold

12. Refer to the illustration above. Structure "A" is
    a. a rhizoid.
    b. vascular tissue.
    c. a hypha.
    d. a stem.

    ANS: C   DIF: II   OBJ: 28-1.4

13. Refer to the illustration above. Structure "B" is
    a. commensal.
    b. haploid.
    c. embryonic.
    d. diploid.

ANS: B   DIF: II   OBJ: 28-2.2

14. Refer to the illustration above. The process that takes place at structure "C" is known as
    a. meiosis.
    b. conjugation.
    c. mitosis.
    d. fusion.

ANS: D   DIF: II   OBJ: 28-2.2

15. Mushrooms are examples of
    a. club fungi.
    b. sac fungi.
    c. molds.
    d. yeasts.

ANS: A   DIF: I   OBJ: 28-2.1

16. Mushrooms are members of the phylum
    a. Ascomycota.
    b. Basidiomycota.
    c. Zygomycota.
    d. None of the above

ANS: B   DIF: I   OBJ: 28-2.1

17. All of the following are true of ascomycetes *except*
    a. they have saclike reproductive cells in which spores grow.
    b. some are truffles.
    c. they are often used in the baking of bread.
    d. they form ascocarps during asexual reproduction.

ANS: D   DIF: I   OBJ: 28-2.1

18. Zygospores allow molds to
    a. remain dormant until conditions are favorable for their spores.
    b. digest bread.
    c. grow unusually large.
    d. produce antibiotics.

ANS: A   DIF: I   OBJ: 28-2.1

19. The group of fungi that includes the molds that often grow on bread is the
    a. ascomycetes.
    b. basidiomycetes.
    c. zygomycetes.
    d. deuteromycetes.

ANS: C   DIF: I   OBJ: 28-2.1

20. Reproductive structures in which spores form are known as
    a. septa.
    b. stolons.
    c. mycorrhizae.
    d. sporangia.

ANS: D   DIF: I   OBJ: 28-2.1

21. Refer to the illustration above. The organism shown is a(n)
    a. mycorrhizae.
    b. Zygomycota.
    c. Fungi Imperfecti.
    d. unicellular fungus.

    ANS: D   DIF: II   OBJ: 28-2.1

22. Refer to the illustration above. This organism can reproduce
    a. by fission.
    b. by forming buds.
    c. only sexually.
    d. All of the above

    ANS: B   DIF: II   OBJ: 28-2.2

23. Fungi Imperfecti
    a. cause skin diseases in humans.
    b. do not reproduce sexually.
    c. are used to ferment soy sauce.
    d. All of the above

    ANS: D   DIF: I   OBJ: 28-2.2

24. A lichen
    a. consists of a fungus and a photosynthetic partner in a symbiotic relationship.
    b. is a sac fungus clump.
    c. is found only in temperate climates.
    d. is a mold found on the shady side of trees.

    ANS: A   DIF: I   OBJ: 28-2.3

25. fungus : lichen ::
    a. plant : mycorrhiza
    b. mycelium : hypha
    c. septa : hypha
    d. fungus : alga

    ANS: A   DIF: II   OBJ: 28-2.3

26. Fungi are important to an ecosystem as
    a. producers.
    b. regulators.
    c. decomposers.
    d. controllers.

    ANS: C   DIF: I   OBJ: 28-2.4

27. Which of the following is *not* a means by which fungi cause harm to humans?
    a. inducing allergic reactions
    b. producing toxins
    c. transmitting viral diseases
    d. infecting internal organs

    ANS: C   DIF: II   OBJ: 28-3.1

28. Which of the following is *not* a food product of fungi?
    a. soy sauce
    b. cortisone
    c. bread
    d. truffles

    ANS: B   DIF: I   OBJ: 28-3.2

29. An example of a fungus is
    a. a mushroom.
    b. a bread mold.
    c. *Penicillium.*
    d. All of the above

    ANS: D   DIF: I   OBJ: 28-3.3

30. An economically important use of fungi is
    a. bread making.
    b. the production of antibiotics.
    c. the manufacture of gasohol.
    d. All of the above

    ANS: D   DIF: I   OBJ: 28-3.3

31. yeasts : baking ::
    a. hyphae : wine-making
    b. sporangia : brewing
    c. molds : drug manufacturing
    d. basidiospores : making cheeses

    ANS: C   DIF: II   OBJ: 28-3.3

COMPLETION

1. Unlike plants, fungi lack _____ and cannot carry out photosynthesis.

    ANS: chloroplasts   DIF: I   OBJ: 28-1.2

2. Fungi obtain food by _____ organic matter.

    ANS: decomposing   DIF: I   OBJ: 28-1.3

3. The typical fungus is a eukaryotic heterotroph that has a body consisting of many slender filaments called _____.

    ANS: hyphae   DIF: I   OBJ: 28-1.4

4. When hyphae grow, they form a mass called a(n) _____.

    ANS: mycelium   DIF: I   OBJ: 28-1.4

5. The common name of unicellular fungi is _____.

    ANS: yeast   DIF: I   OBJ: 28-2.1

6. The familiar mushroom belongs to the phylum _____.

    ANS: Basidiomycota   DIF: I   OBJ: 28-2.1

7. Yeasts are examples of phylum _____.

    ANS: Ascomycota   DIF: I   OBJ: 28-2.1

8. Fungi reproduce sexually and _____.

    ANS: asexually   DIF: I   OBJ: 28-2.2

9. A(n) _____ is a saclike structure in which haploid spores are formed.

    ANS: ascus   DIF: I   OBJ: 28-2.2

10. A fungal _____ is a haploid reproductive cell that is capable of developing into a new organism.

    ANS: spore   DIF: I   OBJ: 28-2.2

11. A lichen consists of a fungus and a(n) _____ living together in a symbiotic relationship.

    ANS: photosynthetic partner   DIF: I   OBJ: 28.2.3

12. Fungi in the genus *Penicillium* are important to humans because they produce the antibiotic penicillin but also because they are used to produce food such as _____.

    ANS: cheese   DIF: I   OBJ: 28-3.2

PROBLEM

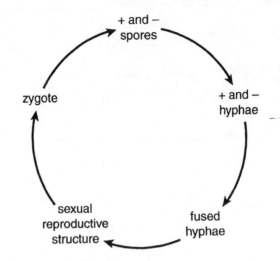

1. Refer to the illustration above. The diagram is a generalized life cycle of sexually reproducing fungi. Write your answers to the following in the space below or on a separate sheet of paper.
   a. Complete the diagram by indicating the ploidy level of each structure shown (i.e., haploid, diploid, or dikaryotic) and the location where meiosis and fertilization occur.
   b. How do the sexual reproductive structures differ in the three groups of fungi that produce them? Name and briefly describe each.

   ANS:
   a. The students' diagrams should look something like the following:

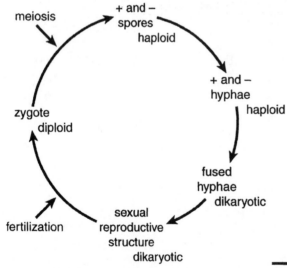

   b. Members of the phylum Zygomycota form zygosporangia. These are small, thick-walled, rounded structures. Members of the phylum Ascomycota form ascocarps. These are often large structures containing many small sac-shaped asci. Members of the phylum Basidiomycota form basidiocarps. These are often large structures, sometimes mushrooms, containing many small club-shaped basidia.

   DIF: III   OBJ: 28-2.2

ESSAY

1. Describe the symbiotic relationship that enables a lichen to exist. Write your answer in the space below.

   ANS:
   A lichen is an organism that consists of a fungus and a photosynthetic partner living in a symbiotic relationship. The fungus absorbs minerals and other nutrients from rocks or logs and retains water the alga needs for photosynthesis. Through photosynthesis, the alga produces carbohydrates that the fungus uses for food.

   DIF: II   OBJ: 28-2.3

CHAPTER 29—THE IMPORTANCE OF PLANTS

TRUE/FALSE

1. Virtually all our food is derived, directly or indirectly, from flowering plants.

   ANS: T   DIF: I   OBJ: 29-1.1

2. Cassava is a starchy root that is the staple food of more than 500 million people around the world.

   ANS: T   DIF: I   OBJ: 29-1.1

3. Wood is used for construction and for the manufacture of paper and rayon.

   ANS: T   DIF: I   OBJ: 29-1.1

4. Cotton cloth is made from thread prepared by spinning strong, fine fibers obtained from cotton seeds.

   ANS: T   DIF: I   OBJ: 29-1.1

5. Most of the rubber being made today is manufactured from naturally obtained latex.

   ANS: F   DIF: I   OBJ: 29-1.1

6. The vegetables that we eat come from the stems, roots, and leaves of plants.

   ANS: T   DIF: I   OBJ: 29-1.2

7. Grains are dry, edible fruits produced by cereal grasses.

   ANS: T   DIF: I   OBJ: 29-1.2

8. Massive food shortages have occurred worldwide because food production has not been able to keep up with the growing world population.

   ANS: F   DIF: I   OBJ: 29-1.3

9. Digitalis, a drug used to treat heart problems, is produced from the plant called foxglove.

   ANS: T   DIF: I   OBJ: 29-1.4

10. Cortisone, a drug used to treat inflammation and allergies, is derived from yew trees.

    ANS: F   DIF: I   OBJ: 29-1.4

11. All terrestrial consumers are ultimately dependent on plants because plants can produce organic compounds from inorganic compounds and sunlight.

    ANS: T   DIF: I   OBJ: 29-2.1

12. Most insect pollinators of plants help the plants reproduce by transferring pollen from one plant to another, but they do not get anything in return for their efforts.

ANS: F   DIF: I   OBJ: 29-2.3

13. Mycorrhizal associations are most commonly found in plants of the legume family.

ANS: F   DIF: I   OBJ: 29-2.4

14. Introduced water hyacinth plants have damaged natural aquatic habitats by shading native, underwater plant species.

ANS: T   DIF: I   OBJ: 29-2.5

MULTIPLE CHOICE

1. Plants used to make fibers for clothing include
   a. nylon.
   b. cotton.
   c. flax.
   d. Both b and c

ANS: D   DIF: I   OBJ: 29-1.1

2. cotton : fibers ::
   a. cotton : rubber
   b. latex : cotton
   c. fiber : sap
   d. rubber : sap

ANS: D   DIF: II   OBJ: 29-1.1

3. All of the following foods come from fruits *except*
   a. rice.
   b. wheat.
   c. spinach.
   d. applesauce.

ANS: C   DIF: I   OBJ: 29-1.2

4. Vegetables that we eat come from various plant parts including
   a. stems.
   b. roots.
   c. leaves.
   d. All of the above

ANS: D   DIF: I   OBJ: 29-1.2

5. Fruits of cereal plants are called
   a. grains.
   b. tubers.
   c. legumes.
   d. vegetables.

ANS: A   DIF: I   OBJ: 29-1.2

6. rice and corn : cereal grains ::
   a. beets and wheat : leaves
   b. sweet potatoes and cassava : roots
   c. turnips and radishes : stems
   d. wheat and corn : roots

ANS: B   DIF: II   OBJ: 29-1.2

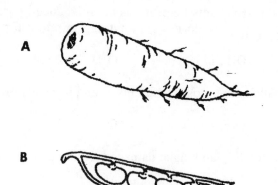

7. Refer to the illustration above. The plant represented in the diagrams that is the highest in protein content is
   a. plant "A."
   b. plant "B."
   c. plant "C."
   d. None of them; all plants are high in carbohydrates, but very low in protein.

   ANS: B   DIF: II   OBJ: 29-1.2

8. Refer to the illustration above. Which plant represented in the diagram would contain nitrogen-fixing bacteria?
   a. plant "A"
   b. plant "B"
   c. plant "C"
   d. None of them would contain nitrogen-fixing bacteria.

   ANS: B   DIF: II   OBJ: 29-2.2

9. Which of the following associations between an agricultural practice and its description is incorrect?
   a. Use of pesticides—control of insects and microorganisms
   b. Use of fertilizers—supplementation with mineral nutrients
   c. Use of irrigation—supplementation with water
   d. Artificial selection of plants—harvesting the highest yielding or highest quality plants

   ANS: D   DIF: II   OBJ: 29-1.3

10. vincristine : rosy periwinkle ::
    a. cortisone : foxglove
    b. digitalis : willow trees
    c. reserpine : sweet potatoes
    d. taxol : yew trees

ANS: D   DIF: II   OBJ: 29-1.4

11. Plant ecology is the study of the interaction between plants and
    a. animals.
    b. microorganisms and animals.
    c. bacteria, fungi, and animals.
    d. the environment.

ANS: D   DIF: II   OBJ: 29-2.1

12. A good reason that a farmer might alternately grow corn and a legume crop in a single field is to
    a. create a varied and more attractive landscape.
    b. allow the legumes to restore nitrogen to the soil that is depleted by the corn.
    c. satisfy the changing needs of the consuming public.
    d. get twice as much productivity out of a single piece of land.

ANS: B   DIF: I   OBJ: 29-2.2

13. An example of a plant and an animal that have evolved together is
    a. a plant flower that resembles the female of an insect species.
    b. an insect obtaining nectar from a flower.
    c. an insect consuming leaves of a flowering plant.
    d. an insect carrying pollen from one plant to another.

ANS: A   DIF: I   OBJ: 29-2.3

14. Mycorrhizae are
    a. symbiotic associations between the roots of a plant and a bacterium.
    b. symbiotic associations between the roots of a plant and a fungus.
    c. symbiotic associations between the stems and leaves of a plant and a bacterium.
    d. associations between the roots of a plant and a fungus in which the fungus benefits but the plant is neither harmed nor benefited.

ANS: B   DIF: I   OBJ: 29-2.4

15. A beneficial relationship between a plant and a bacterium occurs when certain bacteria inhabit the roots of a plant and _____ that the plant can use.
    a. absorb water
    b. absorb minerals
    c. fix nitrogen
    d. fix carbon

ANS: C   DIF: I   OBJ: 29-2.4

16. People have damaged natural plant populations by introducing
    a. foreign plant species that become noxious weeds.
    b. diseases that kill native plants.
    c. animals that consume native plants.
    d. All of the above

ANS: D   DIF: I   OBJ: 29-2.5

COMPLETION

1. _____ is the world's most important plant fiber.

   ANS: Cotton   DIF: I   OBJ: 29-1.1

2. Botanically speaking, a(n) _____ is the ripened ovary of a flower.

   ANS: fruit   DIF: I   OBJ: 29-1.2

3. The fruits of cereal plants such as rice, corn, and oats are called
   _____.

   ANS: grains   DIF: I   OBJ: 29-1.2

4. _____ is stored in root crops, making them an important source of
   calories for human populations.

   ANS: Starch   DIF: I   OBJ: 29-1.2

5. Plants, such as peas, that produce protein-rich seeds in long pods are called
   _____.

   ANS: legumes   DIF: I   OBJ: 29-1.2

6. Water pollution is caused by the use of _____ and
   _____ in agriculture because these chemicals get washed off farmland
   during rains and end up in drinking-water reserves.

   ANS: pesticides; fertilizers   DIF: I   OBJ: 29-1.3

7. Salicin is an extract of willow bark and is used in the production of
   _____.

   ANS: aspirin   DIF: I   OBJ: 29-1.4

8. The substances plants produce that consumers rely on for survival are
   _____ and _____.

   ANS: oxygen; organic compounds DIF: I   OBJ: 29-2.1

9. Legumes may thrive in nitrogen-poor soil because they have root nodules in which there
   are _____.

   ANS: nitrogen-fixing bacteria DIF: I   OBJ: 29-2.1

10. The planting of legumes is useful in crop rotation because they supply
    _____ to the soil.

    ANS: nitrogen   DIF: I   OBJ: 29-2.2

11. Flowers that are large and colorful are most often pollinated by
_____.

    ANS: insects   DIF: I   OBJ: 29-2.3

12. Chestnut blight, which has wiped out American chestnut trees in many parts of the eastern United States, is caused by a _____ that was introduced into the country.

    ANS: fungus   DIF: I   OBJ: 29-2.5

ESSAY

1. Fruits and vegetables are important parts of the human diet. Using examples, distinguish between these two types of foods. Write your answer in the space below.

    ANS:
Fruits are the parts of plants that contain seeds (such as apples, wheat grains, and rice grains), and vegetative parts are nonreproductive plant structures (such as leaves, stems, and roots). When they pertain to foods, the terms fruits and vegetables define agricultural commodities. Fruits, which are also fruits in the botanical sense, are plant parts that are sweet and usually eaten as a dessert. Examples include apples, bananas, oranges, pumpkins, grapes, and strawberries. Vegetables, which may be leaves, stems, roots, flowers, or fruits, are plant parts that are not sweet and are usually eaten with the main part of a meal. Examples include lettuce, cabbage, potatoes, onions, carrots, broccoli, cauliflower, green beans, squash, and tomatoes.

    DIF: II   OBJ: 29-1.2

2. Explain the reason that crop rotation is used as a method to increase crop yields. Write your answer in the space below.

    ANS:
Alternating grain and legume crops in a single field is known as crop rotation. The principle behind this farming method is that legumes, which contain nitrogen-fixing bacteria, convert atmospheric nitrogen into nutrient molecules that plants can use. These nitrogen compounds are used by the legume crop and also remain in the soil as nutrients that can be used by the successive grain crop.

    DIF: I   OBJ: 29-2.2

CHAPTER 30—PLANT EVOLUTION AND CLASSIFICATION

TRUE/FALSE

1. Algae are seedless plantlike organisms, and all true plants produce seeds.

   ANS: F DIF: I OBJ: 30-1.1

2. The surface of a vascular plant is covered by a cuticle in order to reduce water loss.

   ANS: T DIF: I OBJ: 30-1.2

3. Many gymnosperms, such as pine, spruce, and fir trees, produce their seeds in cones.

   ANS: T DIF: I OBJ: 30-1.3

4. Land plants have a complex life cycle that involves an alternation of generations between a haploid gametophyte and a diploid sporophyte.

   ANS: T DIF: I OBJ: 30-1.4

5. The sporophyte of a nonvascular plant is larger and lives longer than the gametophyte.

   ANS: F DIF: I OBJ: 30-1.4

6. The life cycle of nonvascular plants involves alternation of generations.

   ANS: T DIF: I OBJ: 30-1.4

7. Land plants have a complex life cycle that involves an alternation of generations between a haploid gametophyte and a diploid sporophyte.

   ANS: T DIF: I OBJ: 30-2.1

8. Mosses, liverworts, and hornworts all are generally found in moist habitats.

   ANS: T DIF: I OBJ: 30-2.1

9. Nonvascular plants have true leaves but lack true stems and roots.

   ANS: F DIF: I OBJ: 30-2.2

10. Mosses and ferns no longer require the presence of a film of water for reproduction.

    ANS: F DIF: I OBJ: 30-2.3

11. Ferns need water to reproduce because their sperm must swim to eggs.

    ANS: T DIF: I OBJ: 30-2.3

12. Mosses are called pioneer plants because they can promote the development of new communities in barren areas that have been burned or destroyed by humans.

ANS: T   DIF: I   OBJ: 30-2.4

13. Sphagnum moss is used in potting and gardening soils because of its ability to encourage water drainage.

ANS: F   DIF: I   OBJ: 30-2.5

14. The vascular plants are so named because they have conducting tissues that transport water, minerals, and sugars within the plants.

ANS: T   DIF: I   OBJ: 30-3.1

15. The only major difference between seedless vascular plants and seed plants is the production of seeds by the latter.

ANS: F   DIF: II   OBJ: 30-3.2

16. Pines and all other conifers have needle-like leaves.

ANS: F   DIF: I   OBJ: 30-3.3

17. Evidence suggests that monocots may have evolved from primitive dicots.

ANS: T   DIF: I   OBJ: 30-3.5

MULTIPLE CHOICE

1. The ancestors of today's land plants were probably
   a. brown algae.
   b. red algae.
   c. green algae.
   d. lichens.

ANS: C   DIF: I   OBJ: 30-1.1

2. All of the following are derived from angiosperms and used by humans in their daily lives *except*
   a. timber.
   b. textiles.
   c. baker's yeast.
   d. food.

ANS: C   DIF: I   OBJ: 30-1.1

3. Which of the following is *not* characteristic of both green algae and plants?
   a. chlorophylls a and b
   b. motile sperm and nonmotile eggs
   c. energy stored as starch
   d. cellulose cell walls

ANS: B   DIF: II   OBJ: 30-1.1

4. The challenges faced by early land plants included
   a. conserving water.
   b. reproducing on land.
   c. absorbing minerals from the rocky surface.
   d. All of the above

   ANS: D   DIF: I   OBJ: 30-1.2

5. The waxy protective covering of a land plant is called a
   a. cuticle.   c. rhizome.
   b. capsule.   d. stoma.

   ANS: A   DIF: I   OBJ: 30-1.2

6. The cuticle
   a. helps reduce the evaporation of fluids from a plant.
   b. is a plant adaptation to an aquatic environment.
   c. is a reproductive structure in some plants.
   d. is crucial to plant cell nourishment.

   ANS: A   DIF: I   OBJ: 30-1.2

7. Some land plants developed an internal system of interconnected tubes and vessels called
   a. cuticles.   c. the circulatory system.
   b. nonvascular canals.   d. vascular tissues.

   ANS: D   DIF: I   OBJ: 30-1.3

8. The xylem in a plant
   a. transports food from the leaves.
   b. transports water and minerals.
   c. exchanges carbon dioxide with the atmosphere.
   d. All of the above

   ANS: B   DIF: I   OBJ: 30-1.3

9. liverworts, hornworts, mosses : nonvascular plants ::
   a. gymnosperms, angiosperms : bryophytes
   b. ferns : mosses
   c. gymnosperms and angiosperms : vascular plants
   d. bryophytes, liverworts : vascular plants

   ANS: C   DIF: II   OBJ: 30-1.3

10. gymnosperms : naked seeds ::
    a. pollen : mosses   c. liverwort : vascular tissue
    b. liverwort : pollen   d. angiosperms : enclosed seeds

    ANS: D   DIF: II   OBJ: 30-1.3

11. The diploid form in a plant's life cycle is called the
    a. sporophyte.
    b. gametophyte.
    c. parental generation.
    d. alternate generation.

    ANS: A   DIF: I   OBJ: 30-1.4

12. The haploid form in a plant's life cycle is called the
    a. sporophyte.
    b. gametophyte.
    c. parental generation.
    d. alternate generation.

    ANS: B   DIF: I   OBJ: 30-1.4

13. A haploid stage following a diploid stage in a plant's life cycle is called
    a. generational recycling.
    b. periodic gametogenesis.
    c. alternating forms.
    d. alternation of generations.

    ANS: D   DIF: I   OBJ: 30-1.4

14. In plants, haploid gametes are produced as a result of
    a. fertilization.
    b. meiosis.
    c. encapsulation.
    d. mitosis.

    ANS: D   DIF: I   OBJ: 30-1.4

15. The dominant generation in vascular plants is the
    a. gametophyte.
    b. gymnosperm.
    c. angiosperm.
    d. sporophyte.

    ANS: D   DIF: I   OBJ: 30-1.4

16. vascular plants : sporophytes ::
    a. sporophytic plants : gametophytes
    b. nonvascular plants : gametophytes
    c. spores : gametes
    d. plants with seeds : seedless plants

    ANS: B   DIF: II   OBJ: 30-1.4

17. sporophytes : spores ::
    a. sporophytes : gametophytes
    b. gametophytes : gametes
    c. gametophytes : spores
    d. sporophytes : gametes

    ANS: B   DIF: II   OBJ: 30-1.4

18. Which of the following is *not* a bryophyte?
    a. moss
    b. liverwort
    c. hornwort
    d. fern

    ANS: D   DIF: I   OBJ: 30-2.1

19. Which of the following is *not* characteristic of all nonvascular plants?
    a. They produce seeds.
    b. They have an alternation of generations lifestyle.
    c. They produce spores.
    d. They require water for sexual reproduction.

    ANS: A   DIF: I   OBJ: 30-2.2

20. Which of the following is a reason why mosses are good pioneer plants?
    a. They can survive in very wet areas.
    b. They can survive in areas that receive only low levels of sunlight.
    c. They can create a layer of soil on bare rock.
    d. They are very slow growing plants.

    ANS: C   DIF: I   OBJ: 30-2.4

21. The water-retaining ability of sphagnum moss makes it ideal for
    a. using in garden-soil mixes.
    b. use in packing bulbs and flowers for shipping.
    c. use in houseplant soils.
    d. All of the above

    ANS: D   DIF: II   OBJ: 30-2.5

22. All of the following developed in vascular plants and are not present in nonvascular plants *except*
    a. pollen.
    b. deep roots.
    c. chlorophyll.
    d. seeds.

    ANS: C   DIF: I   OBJ: 30-3.1

23. The primary distinguishing characteristics of all vascular plants are
    a. xylem and phloem; true roots, stems, and leaves; pollen; and seeds.
    b. xylem and phloem; true roots, stems, and leaves; and spores.
    c. true roots, stems, and leaves; spores.
    d. xylem and phloem; spores or seeds.

    ANS: D   DIF: I   OBJ: 30-3.1

24. Which of the following is *not* a seed plant?
    a. a flowering plant
    b. a pine tree
    c. a fern
    d. a ginkgo

    ANS: C   DIF: I   OBJ: 30-3.2

25. Which of the following is characteristic of all seed plants?
    a. a seed containing an embryo, a nutrient supply, and a protective coat
    b. enclosure and protection of seeds within a fruit
    c. production of flowers
    d. All of the above

    ANS: A   DIF: II   OBJ: 30-3.2

26. Pines, spruces, and firs are
    a. angiosperms.
    b. gymnosperms.
    c. flowering plants.
    d. sometimes nonvascular.

    ANS: B   DIF: I   OBJ: 30-3.3

27. The tallest trees in the world are species of
    a. conifers.
    b. dicots.
    c. liverworts.
    d. angiosperms.

    ANS: A   DIF: I   OBJ: 30-3.3

28. Which of the following were the first land plants to evolve seeds?
    a. angiosperms
    b. gymnosperms
    c. mosses
    d. ferns

    ANS: B   DIF: I   OBJ: 30-3.3

29. Seed plants are the dominant land plants because
    a. they include the largest plants on Earth.
    b. the seeds they produce enable the plant to survive in a dormant state when conditions
    are not suitable for growth.
    c. they are vascular plants with large root systems, so they can obtain water from any
    kind of environment.
    d. they produce flowers that are pollinated by insects, enabling them to produce many
    offspring.

    ANS: B   DIF: I   OBJ: 30-3.4

30. Similarities shared by monocots and primitive dicots suggest that
    a. monocots and dicots evolved independently.
    b. monocots were on Earth long before dicots.
    c. monocots evolved from dicots.
    d. dicots evolved from monocots.

    ANS: C   DIF: I   OBJ: 30-3.5

31. Monocots have
    a. leaves with branching veins.
    b. flower parts in multiples of four or five.
    c. leaves with parallel veins.
    d. two cotyledons.

    ANS: C   DIF: I   OBJ: 30-3.5

32. Flowering plants are classified as monocots or dicots according to the number of their
    a. leaves.
    b. roots.
    c. meristems.
    d. cotyledons.

    ANS: D   DIF: I   OBJ: 30-3.5

COMPLETION

1. Angiosperms are ultimately the source of much of our _____.

   ANS: food   DIF: I   OBJ: 30-1.1

2. In leaves, the expansion and contraction of the guard cells regulate the opening and closing of the _____.

   ANS: stomata   DIF: I   OBJ: 30-1.2

3. The surface of a vascular plant is covered by a waxy, waterproof layer called a _____.

   ANS: cuticle   DIF: I   OBJ: 30-1.2

4. One of the first environmental challenges that early land plants had to overcome was finding a way to conserve _____.

   ANS: water   DIF: I   OBJ: 30-1.2

5. The tissues that transport water and minerals within a plant make up the _____ system.

   ANS: vascular   DIF: I   OBJ: 30-1.3

6. _____ are seed plants with uncovered ovules.

   ANS: Gymnosperms   DIF: I   OBJ: 30-1.3

7. In alternation of generations, the _____ generation alternates with the diploid generation.

   ANS: haploid   DIF: I   OBJ: 30-1.4

Gametophyte

Spores

Gametes
Fertilization

Sporophyte

8. Refer to the illustration above. The cycle shown in the diagram is referred to as _____.

   ANS: alternation of generations   DIF: I   OBJ: 30-1.4

9. The fusion of two gametes results in the production of a _____ sporophyte.

ANS: diploid   DIF: II   OBJ: 30-1.4

10. The haploid form of plant is known as the _____ generation.

ANS: gametophyte   DIF: II   OBJ: 30-1.4

11. In most vascular plants, the _____ grows within the sporophyte.

ANS: gametophyte   DIF: I   OBJ: 30-1.4

12. The life cycle of a conifer is characterized by a large _____.

ANS: sporophyte   DIF: I   OBJ: 30-1.4

13. The sporophyte generation produces spores by the process of _____.

ANS: meiosis   DIF: I   OBJ: 30-1.4

14. Peat bogs contain organic matter that decomposes very slowly because of its high _____ content.

ANS: acid   DIF: I   OBJ: 30-2.1

15. Bryophytes are characterized as having a dominant _____ generation.

ANS: gametophyte   DIF: I   OBJ: 30-2.2

16. In mosses and liverworts, the _____ generation is the dominant generation.

ANS: gametophyte   DIF: I   OBJ: 30-2.3

17. A rootlike structure that anchors nonvascular plants is called a _____.

ANS: rhizoid   DIF: I   OBJ: 30-2.3

18. The ability of mosses to absorb and retain _____ contributes to their ability to help prevent soil erosion.

ANS: water   DIF: I   OBJ: 30-2.4

19. Partially decomposed sphagnum moss plants are collected and used as a source of _____ for heating and other activities.

ANS: fuel   DIF: I   OBJ: 30-2.5

20. A plant that has flower parts that occur in fours or fives or multiples of four or five is a _____.

ANS: dicot   DIF: I   OBJ: 30-3.5

PROBLEM

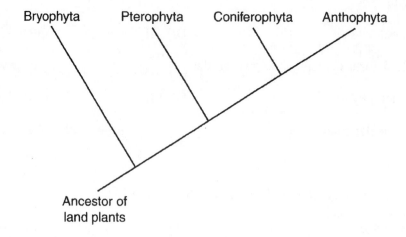

1. Refer to the illustration above. The cladogram depicts the presumed evolutionary relationships between the major phyla of land plants. The list below consists of paired characteristics found in at least some land plants. For each pair of characteristics, choose the one that is the more evolutionarily advanced. Then complete the cladogram by indicating on it where each of the more advanced characteristics first appeared.
   Characteristics:
      cones / flowers
      sporophyte dominant / gametophyte dominant
      waxy cuticle present / waxy cuticle absent
      vascular tissue absent / vascular tissue present
      gametophyte independent of sporophyte / gametophyte dependent on sporophyte
      stomata absent / stomata present
      seeds / spores
      multicellular reproductive structure / unicellular reproductive structure

ANS:
The students' completed cladograms should look like the one shown below. Where two or more evolutionary advancements occur between branch points, their order on the branch is not important.

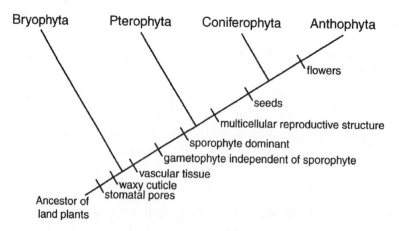

DIF: III   OBJ: 30-3.4

ESSAY

1. Refer to the illustration above. What problems were encountered by the first land plants, such as the one in the diagram? What adaptations evolved to solve these problems? Write your answer in the space below.

ANS:
Before early plants could survive on land, they had to overcome three basic problems: how to avoid drying out, how to reproduce on land, and how to obtain minerals from rocky surfaces. They were able to avoid drying out by developing a waterproof, waxy coating on the stems. Light-weight spores were produced at the tips of the stems, allowing the spores to be distributed by wind to other land areas. Once covered in dew, the spores would germinate, enabling the plants to reproduce with very little water. Mineral absorption was accomplished through the formation of mycorrhizae with fungi.

DIF: II   OBJ: 30-1.2

2. How is a seed an adaptation for life on land? Write your answer in the space below.

ANS:
Seeds enable the dispersal of offspring so that they will not have to compete with their parents for space, light, and nutrients. Additionally, seeds provide an initial food supply (cotyledons) for the embryo. A hard, outer seed coat provides protection from physical injury and drought, allowing the embryo to lie dormant for years and still grow into a healthy plant.

DIF: II   OBJ: 30-3.4

TRUE/FALSE

1. Tracheids and sieve tubes make up a xylem vessel.

    ANS: F   DIF: I   OBJ: 31-1.2

2. The main function of ground tissue is to conduct water and minerals.

    ANS: F   DIF: I   OBJ: 31-1.2

3. Vascular tissue is found within ground tissue, which makes up the outside of the plant.

    ANS: F   DIF: I   OBJ: 31-1.2

4. The outer protective layer of tissue on a vascular plant is known as the meristem.

    ANS: F   DIF: I   OBJ: 31-1.3

5. Secondary tissues result from the extension of apical meristems.

    ANS: F   DIF: I   OBJ: 31-1.3

6. Cell division in meristems decreases the length and girth of a plant.

    ANS: F   DIF: I   OBJ: 31-1.3

7. Monocot stems cannot become large in diameter because they lack lateral meristems.

    ANS: T   DIF: I   OBJ: 31-1.3

8. In plants, xylem tissue is alive at maturity.

    ANS: F   DIF: I   OBJ: 31-1.4

9. Primary plant growth occurs in apical meristems located at the tips of stems and roots.

    ANS: T   DIF: I   OBJ: 31-1.5

10. Sugars are converted to starch in roots.

    ANS: T   DIF: I   OBJ: 31-2.1

11. Primary growth in roots is characterized by an increase in root diameter.

    ANS: F   DIF: III   OBJ: 31-2.3

12. Most of the water absorbed by roots is taken up through cells in the root cap.

    ANS: F   DIF: I   OBJ: 31-2.4

13. Shoots consist of stems and leaves.

    ANS: T   DIF: I   OBJ: 31-3.2

14. The loss of water by transpiration at the leaves helps pull water into the plant at the roots.

    ANS: T   DIF: I   OBJ: 31-3.4

15. The rate of water absorption in roots is influenced by the amount of water lost through transpiration.

    ANS: T   DIF: I   OBJ: 31-3.4

16. The loss of water vapor from a plant can be explained by the pressure-flow model.

    ANS: F   DIF: I   OBJ: 31-3.4

17. The movement of sugar in a plant is called transpiration.

    ANS: F   DIF: I   OBJ: 31-3.5

18. The transport of organic molecules from a leaf to the rest of the plant is called translocation.

    ANS: T   DIF: I   OBJ: 31-3.5

19. The blade of a compound leaf is divided into leaflets.

    ANS: T   DIF: I   OBJ: 31-4.1

MULTIPLE CHOICE

1. Which of the following associations between a plant cell type and its characteristics is *incorrect*?
    a. Collenchyma cell—even, thin cell walls; do not occur in groups
    b. Parenchyma cell—cube-shaped or elongated cells, large vacuole
    c. Sclerenchyma cell—cube-shaped or elongated, thick rigid cell walls
    d. All of the above are correct.

    ANS: A   DIF: I   OBJ: 31-1.1

2. Which of the following types of plant cells provides structural support and is typically dead at functional maturity?
    a. collenchyma   c. sclerenchyma
    b. parenchyma   d. none of the above

    ANS: C   DIF: I   OBJ: 31-1.1

3. The conducting cells of phloem are called
   a. tracheids.
   b. sieve tube members.
   c. sieve plates.
   d. vessel elements.

   ANS: B   DIF: I   OBJ: 31-1.2

4. In xylem tissue, water moves from tracheid to tracheid through
   a. pits.
   b. vessel elements.
   c. sieve tubes.
   d. companion cells.

   ANS: A   DIF: I   OBJ: 31-1.2

5. The outer layers of ground tissue in a stem are known as the
   a. sapwood.
   b. nodes.
   c. pith.
   d. cortex.

   ANS: D   DIF: I   OBJ: 31-1.2

6. vascular tissue: transport of fluids ::
   a. epidermis : support
   b. dermal tissue : storage
   c. dermal tissue : transport of fluids
   d. ground tissue : photosynthesis

   ANS: D   DIF: II   OBJ: 31-1.2

7. Plants grow in regions of active cell division called
   a. meristems.
   b. xylem.
   c. phloem.
   d. dermal tissue.

   ANS: A   DIF: I   OBJ: 31-1.3

8. Meristems are found
   a. only at the tips of roots.
   b. only at the tips of shoots.
   c. at the tips of roots and shoots.
   d. None of the above

   ANS: C   DIF: I   OBJ: 31-1.3

9. Which of the following types of meristems is found in some monocots?
   a. apical meristems
   b. vascular cambium
   c. intercalary meristems
   d. cork cambium

   ANS: C   DIF: I   OBJ: 31-1.3

10. The lengthening of plant roots and shoots is called
    a. secondary growth.
    b. germination.
    c. primary growth.
    d. vascular growth.

    ANS: C   DIF: I   OBJ: 31-1.5

11. During periods of primary growth at apical meristems, stems and roots
    a. become wider.
    b. become longer.
    c. maintain a constant number of cells.
    d. undergo photoperiodism.

    ANS: B   DIF: I   OBJ: 31-1.5

12. secondary growth : width ::
    a. secondary growth : height
    b. lateral meristem : length
    c. apical meristem : width
    d. primary growth : length

    ANS: D   DIF: II   OBJ: 31-1.5

13. The primary function of root hairs is
    a. to strengthen roots as they grow downward.
    b. to transport food up the stem.
    c. the absorption of water and minerals.
    d. water storage.

    ANS: C   DIF: I   OBJ: 31-2.1

14. leaves : carbon dioxide from the air ::
    a. leaves : water from the air
    b. roots : light from the air
    c. roots : carbon dioxide from the air
    d. roots : nutrients from the soil

    ANS: D   DIF: II   OBJ: 31-2.1

15. Which of the following are taproots?
    a. underground roots of grass plants
    b. prop roots of corn plants
    c. roots of radish plants
    d. aerial roots of orchids

    ANS: C   DIF: I   OBJ: 31-2.2

16. Which of the following is *not* characteristic of fibrous roots?
    a. many branch roots
    b. shallow roots
    c. primary root dominant
    d. may develop from the base of the stem

    ANS: C   DIF: I   OBJ: 31-2.2

17. Which of the following is *not* characteristic of secondary growth of roots?
    a. Vascular cambium is formed.
    b. Secondary xylem is produced toward the inside of the root and secondary phloem is produced toward the outside of the root.
    c. Cork cambium is formed.
    d. It occurs in monocot, dicot, and gymnosperm roots.

    ANS: D   DIF: I   OBJ: 31-2.3

18. Which of the following is the function of the endodermis?
    a. water absorption
    b. water storage
    c. regulation of passage of water and minerals into the vascular tissue
    d. production of new cells for secondary growth

    ANS: C   DIF: II   OBJ: 31-2.4

The diagram below shows the stem of a coleus plant.

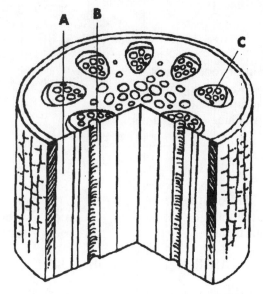

19. Refer to the illustration above. The tissue labeled "A" in the diagram is called
    a. meristem.   c. phloem.
    b. xylem.   d. ground tissue.

    ANS: D   DIF: II   OBJ: 31-3.2

20. Refer to the illustration above. In the diagram, the tissue labeled "B," which conducts
    water and is made of elongated cells that connect end to end, is called
    a. meristem.   c. phloem.
    b. xylem.   d. ground tissue.

    ANS: B   DIF: II   OBJ: 31-3.2

21. Refer to the illustration above. In the diagram, the tissue labeled "C," which transports
    sugars from regions where they are made to regions where they are used, is called
    a. meristem.   c. phloem.
    b. xylem.   d. ground tissue.

    ANS: C   DIF: II   OBJ: 31-3.2

22. The ground tissue in the center of roots and stems
    a. turns into meristem.   c. provides support.
    b. transports food.   d. germinates at least once a year.

    ANS: C   DIF: I   OBJ: 31-3.2

23. Leaves connect to the stems of plants at the
    a. lateral buds.
    b. pith.
    c. nodes.
    d. internodes.

    ANS: C   DIF: I   OBJ: 31-3.2

24. Secondary xylem and phloem form from
    a. cork cambium.
    b. vascular cambium.
    c. apical meristems.
    d. bark.

    ANS: B   DIF: I   OBJ: 31-3.2

25. xylem : inner side of vascular cambium ::
    a. vascular cambium : cork cambium
    b. cork : vascular cambium
    c. phloem : outer side of vascular cambium
    d. phloem : cork cambium

    ANS: C   DIF: II   OBJ: 31-3.2

26. Bark contains
    a. xylem and phloem.
    b. sapwood.
    c. phloem and cork cells.
    d. mesophyll.

    ANS: C   DIF: I   OBJ: 31-3.3

27. In a woody stem, cork cambium
    a. forms phloem.
    b. forms xylem.
    c. produces the cells of the outer bark.
    d. becomes vascular cambium.

    ANS: C   DIF: I   OBJ: 31-3.3

28. The movement of water through a plant is caused by
    a. the attraction of water molecules for each other.
    b. capillary action.
    c. transpiration.
    d. All of the above

    ANS: D   DIF: I   OBJ: 31-3.4

29. The loss of water by the leaves and stem of a plant is called
    a. translocation.
    b. osmosis.
    c. active transport.
    d. transpiration.

    ANS: D   DIF: I   OBJ: 31-3.4

30. The phloem in a plant
    a. transports sugars.
    b. transports water and minerals.
    c. exchanges carbon dioxide and oxygen with the atmosphere.
    d. None of the above

    ANS: A   DIF: I   OBJ: 31-3.4

31. The transport of food from the leaf to the rest of the plant is called
    a. translocation.
    b. osmosis.
    c. active transport.
    d. transpiration.

    ANS: A   DIF: I   OBJ: 31-3.4

32. One model that explains the movement of sugar in a plant is known as the
    a. transpiration model.
    b. translocation model.
    c. pressure-flow model.
    d. source-sink model.

    ANS: C   DIF: I   OBJ: 31-3.4

33. cohesion : adhesion ::
    a. hydrogen : polar
    b. book : pages
    c. hand : people
    d. night : day

    ANS: D   DIF: II   OBJ: 31-3.4

The diagram below shows a portion of a plant's vascular system.

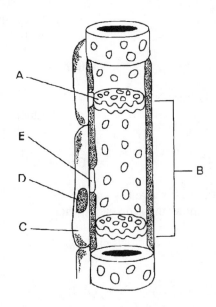

34. Refer to the illustration above. Structure "B" is known as a
    a. tracheid.
    b. companion cell.
    c. vessel element.
    d. sieve tube member.

    ANS: D   DIF: II   OBJ: 31-3.5

35. Refer to the illustration above. Structure "C" is a
    a. tracheid.
    b. companion cell.
    c. vessel element.
    d. sieve tube member.

    ANS: B   DIF: II   OBJ: 31-3.5

36. Refer to the illustration above. Which structure allows the cytoplasm of one cell to connect to the cytoplasm of a neighboring cell?
    a. "A"   c. "D"
    b. "C"   d. "E"

ANS: D   DIF: II   OBJ: 31-3.5

37. The phloem in a plant
    a. transports sugars.
    b. transports water and minerals.
    c. exchanges carbon dioxide and oxygen with the atmosphere.
    d. None of the above

ANS: A   DIF: I   OBJ: 31-3.5

38. Scientists studying the transport of sugars in plants found it difficult to conduct experiments that didn't damage the plants they were studying. Some of them decided to use some insects they knew fed on plants. The insects they chose were aphids, which have mouthparts they insert into plants and use to suck out nutrients. Many of these aphids also release excess sugars from the anal end of their digestive tracts. These substances are called "honeydew," because they are released as sugary droplets. The scientists conducted the following experiments:

    1. They measured the rate at which "honeydew" was released from aphids feeding on cucumber plants. The average rate was two drops per hour.
    2. They froze some aphids and the plant parts they were attached to. They then took cross-sections of the plant parts and examined them using an electron microscope. They found that the tips of the aphids' mouthparts were in individual cells in the phloem tissue.
    3. They anesthetized aphids feeding on plants and then cut away the aphids, leaving the mouthparts in place. They noted that the "honeydew" continued to be released through the mouthparts. The rate at which it was released was measured to be two drops per hour. They also analyzed the "honeydew" and found that it had the same chemical composition as the sugars transported in the plants.

    Which of the following statements is *not* supported by the data obtained in these experiments?
    a. The contents of the phloem are under pressure.
    b. Sugars are transported in the phloem of plants.
    c. Sugars are actively transported into cells of the phloem.
    d. Some aphids take up more sugars from plants than they can use.

ANS: C   DIF: III   OBJ: 31-3.5

39. One model that explains the movement of sugar in a plant is known as the
    a. transpiration model.   c. pressure-flow model.
    b. translocation model.   d. source-sink model.

ANS: C   DIF: I   OBJ: 31-3.4

Four Different Kinds of Leaves

  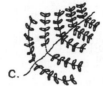 

a. b. c. d.

40. Refer to the illustration above. Which of the leaves is a compound leaf?
    a. Leaf "a"   c. Leaf "c"
    b. Leaf "b"   d. Leaf "d"

    ANS: B   DIF: II   OBJ: 31-4.1

41. The ground tissue in plants that is made up of chloroplast-rich cells is called the
    a. vascular bundle.   c. pith.
    b. petiole.   d. mesophyll.

    ANS: D   DIF: I   OBJ: 31-4.2

42. The tissue of the leaf mesophyll that is located directly below the upper epidermis and
    consists of tightly packed column-shaped cells is the
    a. palisade layer.   c. adventitious layer.
    b. cortex.   d. pith.

    ANS: A   DIF: I   OBJ: 31-4.2

The diagram below shows a leaf cross section.

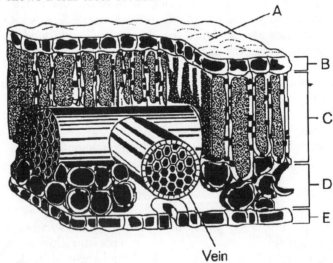

Vein

43. Refer to the illustration above. The spongy layer is indicated at
    a. "B."   c. "D."
    b. "C."   d. "E."

    ANS: C   DIF: II   OBJ: 31-4.2

44. Refer to the illustration above. Structure "A"
    a. is the cuticle.
    b. protects the leaf.
    c. covers the epidermis.
    d. All of the above

    ANS: D   DIF: II   OBJ: 31-4.2

45. Refer to the illustration above. The vein illustrated is made up of
    a. only xylem vessels.
    b. only phloem vessels.
    c. both xylem and phloem vessels.
    d. neither xylem nor phloem vessels.

    ANS: C   DIF: II   OBJ: 31-4.2

46. The tissue of the leaf mesophyll that is located directly below the upper epidermis and consists of tightly packed column-shaped cells is the
    a. palisade layer.
    b. cortex.
    c. adventitious layer.
    d. pith.

    ANS: A   DIF: I   OBJ: 31-4.2

47. Photosynthesis enables plants to produce most of the organic molecules that they need. This process requires the use of all of the following *except*
    a. carbon dioxide.
    b. water.
    c. light.
    d. glucose.

    ANS: D   DIF: I   OBJ: 31-4.3

48. Which of the following is an adaptation found in leaves of shade-grown plants?
    a. high density of chloroplasts
    b. small leaf area
    c. chloroplasts not shading each other
    d. dense hair coatings

    ANS: C   DIF: I   OBJ: 31-4.3

49. The stomata are responsible for
    a. translocation.
    b. leaf growth.
    c. regulating water loss.
    d. the transport of minerals.

    ANS: C   DIF: I   OBJ: 31-4.4

50. The guard cells that surround a stoma
    a. have no walls.
    b. swell with water, causing the stoma to open.
    c. shrivel up when opening the stoma.
    d. are responsible for translocation.

    ANS: B   DIF: I   OBJ: 31-4.4

51. guard cells : stomata ::
    a. can openers : cans
    b. hammers : nails
    c. cushions : rocking chairs
    d. trout : stream

    ANS: A   DIF: II   OBJ: 31-4.4

52. cuticle : above-ground parts ::
    a. ascular system : plant
    b. perm : pollen
    c. guard cell : stoma
    d. wax : root system

ANS: C   DIF: II   OBJ: 31-4.4

COMPLETION

1. Photosynthetic and storage tissues of plants are made up of _____ cells.

ANS: parenchyma   DIF: I   OBJ: 31-1.1

2. _____ are narrow, elongated, thick-walled cells that taper at each end.

ANS: Tracheids   DIF: I   OBJ: 31-1.2

3. A lateral meristem that produces secondary vascular tissue is called the

_____.

ANS: vascular cambium   DIF: I   OBJ: 31-1.3

4. A lateral meristem that produces the cork cells of the outer bark is called the

_____.

ANS: cork cambium   DIF: I   OBJ: 31-1.3

5. Plants grow in regions of active cell division at the tips of roots and shoots called

_____.

ANS: meristems   DIF: I   OBJ: 31-1.3

6. Cell division in the part of the plant called the _____ adds layers of new cells around the outside of a plant's body.

ANS: lateral meristem or cambium   DIF: I   OBJ: 31-1.3

7. Growth that occurs from the formation of new cells at the tip of a plant is called

_____.

ANS: primary growth   DIF: I   OBJ: 31-1.5

8. Growth that causes a plant to increase in width is called _____.

ANS: secondary growth   DIF: I   OBJ: 31-1.5

9. Plant tissues that result from primary growth are called _____.

ANS: primary tissues   DIF: I   OBJ: 31-1.5

10. The thickening of a plant body by the production of new xylem and phloem is called _____ growth.

ANS: secondary   DIF: I   OBJ: 31-1.5

11. The _____ of plants absorb water and minerals necessary for growth.

ANS: roots   DIF: I   OBJ: 31-2.1

12. The two main types of root systems are fibrous root systems and _____ systems.

ANS: taproot   DIF: I   OBJ: 31-2.2

13. Secondary growth in roots occurs as a result of division of cells in the _____ of the primary root.

ANS: pericycle   DIF: I   OBJ: 31-2.3

14. Primary growth in roots occurs in cells of the _____, carbohydrate storage occurs in cells of the _____, water absorption occurs through cells of the _____, and water and carbohydrate transport occur in cells of the _____.

ANS: apical meristem; cortex; epidermis; vascular tissue / xylem and phloem

DIF: II   OBJ: 31-2.4

15. The underground stem of a potato that functions in food storage is called a(n) _____.

ANS: tuber   DIF: I   OBJ: 31-3.1

16. Flexible, soft, and usually green stems are known as _____ stems.

ANS: herbaceous   DIF: I   OBJ: 31-3.1

17. Edible parts of the potato plant are modified stems called _____, which grow underground and store starch.

ANS: tubers   DIF: I   OBJ: 31-3.1

18. The darker wood in the center of a tree trunk is called _____.

ANS: heartwood   DIF: I   OBJ: 31-3.3

19. Wood consists primarily of _____ cells.

ANS: secondary xylem   DIF: I   OBJ: 31-3.3

20. The transport of organic molecules from the leaf to the rest of the plant is called
_____.

ANS: translocation   DIF: I   OBJ: 31-3.5

21. The broad, flat portion of a typical leaf is called the _____.

ANS: blade   DIF: I   OBJ: 31-4.1

22. When the guard cells that surround a stoma fill with water, the stoma
_____.

ANS: opens   DIF: I   OBJ: 31-4.4

23. _____ ions play an important role in opening and closing stomata.

ANS: Potassium   DIF: I   OBJ: 31-4.4

ESSAY

1. Describe the functions of ground tissue in a plant. Write your answer in the space below.

ANS:
Much of the body of a vascular plant is made up of ground tissue. Ground tissue performs photosynthesis, stores water and carbohydrates, assists in transport, and surrounds and supports the conducting tissues.

DIF: II   OBJ: 31-1.2

2. What kinds of plants have lateral meristems, and what kind of growth occurs in these plants that does not occur in plants that lack lateral meristems? Write your answer in the space below.

ANS:
Gymnosperms and most dicots have lateral meristems. One type of lateral meristem is vascular cambium, which is found between xylem and phloem. It produces new vascular tissues, which increase the diameter of the plant. A second type of lateral meristem is cork cambium, which is found outside the phloem. It produces new cork cells.

DIF: III   OBJ: 31-1.3

3. While walking through a forest you notice that someone has carved his or her initials into the bark of a tree. The initials are exactly 1.5 meters from the ground. How far from the ground will the initials be next year and the year after that? Why? Discuss growth tissues in plants in your answer. Write your answer in the space below.

ANS:
The initials will be exactly 1.5 meters from the ground no matter how much the tree grows. Meristems at the tips of roots and shoots enable plants to increase in length. Secondary-growth meristems cause plant bodies to thicken. The initials will get wider but not higher.

DIF: II   OBJ: 31-1.5

4. Secondary growth adds width to a woody stem. Briefly describe the tissues involved and explain how they increase the stem's diameter. Write your answer in the space below.

ANS:
Lateral meristems called cork and vascular cambia produce tissues that contribute to the diameter of a woody stem. Cork cambium produces cells that become part of the outer bark of the plant. Secondary vascular tissues form on opposite sides of the vascular cambium. Secondary xylem forms on the inner side of the vascular cambium, while secondary phloem forms on the outer surface of the vascular cambium, becoming part of the inner bark.

DIF: II   OBJ: 31-3.3

5. Define the terms *source* and *sink* in relation to the transportation of organic molecules in the phloem of plants. Write your answer in the space below.

ANS:
Sugar moves in the phloem of stems. Movement of sugar is from the source, where it is made, to the sink, where it is used or stored.

DIF: II   OBJ: 31-3.5

6. Compare the movement of sugar and water in a plant. Write your answer in the space below.

ANS:
Water only moves upward within the xylem, while sugar moves up and down in the same sieve tube, but at different times. Water can diffuse freely through a plasma membrane, but sugar cannot.

DIF: II   OBJ: 31-3.5

7. Why is it advantageous for mesophyll cells to be more densely packed in the upper part of a plant leaf than in the lower part? Write your answer in the space below.

ANS:
It is advantageous because sunlight hits the upper surface of the leaf directly, so more cells located there would maximize the leaf's photosynthetic rate.

DIF: III   OBJ: 31-4.3

8. Describe how stomata open and close. Write your answer in the space below.

ANS:
Plants control water loss by opening and closing their stomata. Each stoma is formed by two pickle-shaped cells called guard cells. The walls of guard cells are flexible and unevenly thickened. When guard cells are swollen with water, they curve outward and the stoma opens. When the guard cells lose water, they collapse and the stoma closes.

DIF: II   OBJ: 31-4.4

CHAPTER 32—PLANT REPRODUCTION

TRUE/FALSE

1. In ferns, the antheridia and archegonia are produced by different individuals.

   ANS: F   DIF: I   OBJ: 32-1.2

2. Many gymnosperms, such as pine, spruce, and fir trees, produce their seeds in cones.

   ANS: T   DIF: I   OBJ: 32-1.3

3. Seed plants cannot reproduce without a film of water.

   ANS: F   DIF: I   OBJ: 32-1.3

4. In conifers, each pollen grain has a pair of air sacs that help it float on the wind.

   ANS: T   DIF: I   OBJ: 32-1.3

5. Heterosporous plants produce flagellated sperm cells that must swim to nonmotile egg cells.

   ANS: F   DIF: II   OBJ: 32-1.4

6. The flowers of angiosperms are ornamental and have no reproductive function.

   ANS: F   DIF: I   OBJ: 32-2.1

7. Pollen is produced in the tip of the stamen, an area called the sepal.

   ANS: F   DIF: I   OBJ: 32-2.2

8. Brightly colored petals, scents, and nectar are all adaptations of flowers that help ensure pollination.

   ANS: T   DIF: I   OBJ: 32-2.3

9. Plants with colorful flowers are pollinated most commonly by wind.

   ANS: F   DIF: I   OBJ: 32-2.3

10. Pollen tubes grow through the style toward the ovule.

    ANS: T   DIF: I   OBJ: 32-2.4

11. The fusion of a sperm with two nuclei in the ovule produces the endosperm of a seed.

    ANS: T   DIF: I   OBJ: 32-2.4

12. Double fertilization has great survival value because each new generation carries its own initial source of nutrition.

ANS: T   DIF: I   OBJ: 32-2.4

13. In order to avoid extinction, all successful plant species must produce flowers and seeds during each and every growing season.

ANS: F   DIF: I   OBJ: 32-2.5

14. Gymnosperm seeds are enclosed in a fruit.

ANS: F   DIF: I   OBJ: 32-3.3

15. Seeds remain dormant until moisture and temperature conditions favor seedling growth.

ANS: T   DIF: I   OBJ: 32-3.3

16. A plant embryo's shoot develops above the cotyledons, and its roots develop below the cotyledons.

ANS: T   DIF: I   OBJ: 32-3.3

17. Plant clones are individuals genetically identical to one another.

ANS: T   DIF: I   OBJ: 32-3.4

18. Vegetative reproduction in plants does not occur in nature; it occurs only when humans set up conditions conducive to its occurrence.

ANS: F   DIF: I   OBJ: 32-3.5

MULTIPLE CHOICE

1. The structures on a moss gametophyte in which spores are produced are known as
   a. meristems.
   b. pollen grains.
   c. cones.
   d. sporangia.

ANS: D   DIF: I   OBJ: 32-1.1

2. Which of the following statements about moss spores is *not* true?
   a. They are produced by the sporophyte.
   b. They are dispersed and then germinate.
   c. They are produced in a capsule-like top.
   d. They are diploid.

ANS: D   DIF: I   OBJ: 32-1.1

3. The sporophyte generation in mosses produces spores by
   a. meiosis.
   b. mitosis.
   c. sexual reproduction.
   d. None of the above

ANS: A   DIF: I   OBJ: 32-1.1

4. The dominant form of a moss life cycle is the
   a. sporophyte.
   b. gametophyte.
   c. rhizoid.
   d. zygote.

   ANS: B   DIF: I   OBJ: 32-1.1

5. In which of the following structures do liverworts and mosses produce eggs?
   a. antheridia
   b. capsules
   c. archegonia
   d. cones

   ANS: C   DIF: I   OBJ: 32-1.1

6. antheridia : sperm ::
   a. rhizoids : gametes
   b. seeds : gametophytes
   c. archegonia : eggs
   d. megaspores : microspores

   ANS: C   DIF: II   OBJ: 32-1.1

The diagram below shows the plant life cycle.

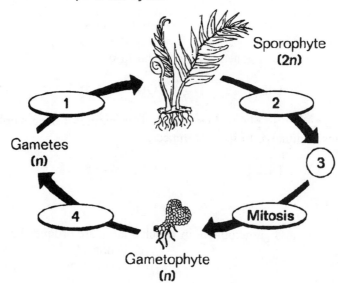

7. Refer to the illustration above. The structures produced at "3" are called
   a. sporangia.
   b. archegonia.
   c. spores.
   d. antheridia.

   ANS: C   DIF: II   OBJ: 32-1.2

8. Refer to the illustration above. At which point in the life cycle does fertilization take place?
   a. "1"
   b. "2"
   c. "3"
   d. "4"

   ANS: A   DIF: II   OBJ: 32-1.2

9. Ferns
   a. are found only in the tropics.
   b. require water for fertilization to occur.
   c. produce diploid spores.
   d. have a dominant gametophyte form.

   ANS: B   DIF: I   OBJ: 32-1.2

10. The fiddlehead of a fern is
    a. a new fern frond.   c. diploid.
    b. part of a fern sporophyte. d. All of the above

    ANS: D   DIF: I   OBJ: 32-1.2

11. Fern sporophytes consist of rhizomes and
    a. flowers.   c. microgametophytes.
    b. stems.   d. fronds.

    ANS: D   DIF: I   OBJ: 32-1.2

12. Which of the following types of plants are homosporous?
    a. mosses
    b. mosses and ferns
    c. mosses, ferns, and gymnosperms
    d. mosses, ferns, gymnosperms, and angiosperms

    ANS: B   DIF: I   OBJ: 32-1.4

13. Pollen is produced in a structure called the
    a. anther.   c. ovary.
    b. stigma.   d. pistil.

    ANS: A   DIF: I   OBJ: 32-2.1

14. The mature microspore of a seed plant is called a
    a. microgametophyte.   c. pollen grain.
    b. sporophyte.   d. sporangium.

    ANS: C   DIF: I   OBJ: 32-2.2

15. Refer to the illustration above. The structure indicated at "f"
    a. supports the anther.
    b. produces pollen.
    c. has tiny structures that look like leaves.
    d. develops into a fruit.

    ANS: B   DIF: II   OBJ: 32-2.2

16. Refer to the illustration above. The structure labeled "c"
    a. produces pollen.   c. is sticky to the touch.
    b. contains sperm cells.   d. contains meristematic tissue.

    ANS: C   DIF: II   OBJ: 32-2.3

17. The process of transferring pollen from a male cone to a female cone in gymnosperms is called
    a. fertilization.   c. pollination.
    b. seed formation.   d. asexual reproduction.

    ANS: C   DIF: I   OBJ: 32-2.3

18. Removing a flower's stigma would initially affect
    a. fertilization.   c. pollination.
    b. seed production.   d. seed dispersal.

    ANS: C   DIF: I   OBJ: 32-2.3

19. If a plant's flowers are very colorful and produce nectar, the plant is probably pollinated by
    a. water.   c. insects.
    b. wind.   d. self-pollination.

    ANS: C   DIF: I   OBJ: 32-2.3

20. Cross-pollination
    a. occurs only in gymnosperms.   c. occurs only in angiosperms.
    b. tends to increase genetic variation.   d. causes the production of sporangia.

    ANS: B   DIF: I   OBJ: 32-2.3

21. Cross-pollination is beneficial because it
    a. produces new genetic variations.
    b. is more efficient.
    c. produces hybrids of two different species of seed-producing plants.
    d. is much quicker than self-pollination.

    ANS: A   DIF: I   OBJ: 32-2.3

Modern Biology Assessment Item Listing
304

22. The flowers produced by angiosperms help ensure the transfer of gametes by
    a. traveling in the air currents.
    b. bursting open and projecting gametes onto the landscape.
    c. attracting a particular bird, insect, or other animal.
    d. All of the above

    ANS: C   DIF: I   OBJ: 32-2.3

23. Immediately following pollination,
    a. the seed develops.   c. fertilization occurs.
    b. an egg cell is formed.   d. the pollen tube begins to form.

    ANS: D   DIF: I   OBJ: 32-2.4

24. Fertilization
    a. involves the union of the egg and sperm.
    b. may not follow pollination at all.
    c. may not occur until weeks or months after pollination has taken place.
    d. All of the above

    ANS: D   DIF: I   OBJ: 32-2.4

25. Double fertilization has great survival value because
    a. two embryos are formed.
    b. if one egg dies, the other can live.
    c. it produces very large plants.
    d. the embryo has its own temporary source of food.

    ANS: D   DIF: I   OBJ: 32-2.4

26. During fertilization in flowering plants, one sperm fuses with an egg to form an embryo, and another fuses with two nuclei to form nutritive tissue. This event is called
    a. self-pollination.   c. maximization.
    b. adaptation.   d. double fertilization.

    ANS: D   DIF: I   OBJ: 32-2.4

27. Which of the following is found in angiosperms but not in gymnosperms?
    a. double fertilization   c. swimming sperm
    b. pollen   d. megaspores and microspores

    ANS: A   DIF: II   OBJ: 32-2.5

28. What function do the fruits produced by angiosperms perform?
    a. provide food for humans and other animals
    b. protect the seeds
    c. disperse the seeds
    d. All of the above

    ANS: D   DIF: I   OBJ: 32-3.1

29. After an egg has been fertilized, a fruit develops from the
    a. style.
    b. ovary.
    c. ovule.
    d. sepal.

    ANS: B   DIF: I   OBJ: 32-3.1

30. The primary purpose of the fruit is
    a. to provide nutrition for the seed.
    b. photosynthesis.
    c. seed dispersal.
    d. to permit cross-fertilization.

    ANS: C   DIF: I   OBJ: 32-3.2

31. The cotyledons in a seed
    a. protect the embryo.
    b. provide a source of food for the embryo.
    c. develop from the seed coat.
    d. are part of the gametophyte.

    ANS: B   DIF: I   OBJ: 32-3.3

32. The partially developed plant found in seeds is known as
    a. a gametophyte.
    b. a spore capsule.
    c. an embryo.
    d. a sporophyte.

    ANS: C   DIF: I   OBJ: 32-3.3

33. A typical seed contains all of the following *except*
    a. a seed coat.
    b. a cotyledon.
    c. an embryo.
    d. a spore case.

    ANS: D   DIF: I   OBJ: 32-3.3

34. A seed or plant may remain inactive for a period of time when it is
    a. dormant.
    b. day-neutral.
    c. photoperiodic.
    d. parthenocarpic.

    ANS: A   DIF: I   OBJ: 32-3.3

35. The development of a seed into a seedling is referred to as
    a. parthenocarpy.
    b. germination.
    c. fertilization.
    d. pollination.

    ANS: B   DIF: I   OBJ: 32-3.3

36. Which of the following enables seeds to germinate?
    a. exposure to temperature changes
    b. seed coat damage
    c. penetration of water and oxygen through the seed coat
    d. All of the above

    ANS: D   DIF: I   OBJ: 32-3.3

37. Once the food stored in a bean's cotyledons is used up,
    a. the cotyledons begin photosynthesizing.
    b. the cotyledons shrivel up and fall off.
    c. the cotyledons become leaves.
    d. new endosperm is produced.

    ANS: B   DIF: I   OBJ: 32-3.3

38. A mature seed forms
    a. when tissues surrounding the zygote and endosperm toughen.
    b. when tissues surrounding the zygote and endosperm become impermeable to water and oxygen.
    c. after the embryo stops growing.
    d. All of the above

    ANS: D   DIF: I   OBJ: 32-3.3

39. fruit : mature ovary ::
    a. gametophyte : sporophyte   c. cotyledon : food reserve
    b. gymnosperm : angiosperm   d. vascular plant : nonvascular plant

    ANS: C   DIF: II   OBJ: 32-3.3

40. Asexual reproduction is advantageous when
    a. the environment is unstable.
    b. plants are well adapted to their environment.
    c. there are a variety of disease agents in the environment.
    d. there is little competition between plants for resources.

    ANS: B   DIF: II   OBJ: 32-3.4

41. Which of the following associations between a vegetative reproductive structure and its characteristics is *incorrect?*
    a. Tuber—fleshy, underground stem specialized for storage
    b. Bulb—thick, underground stem with fleshy leaves
    c. Runner—aboveground root that produces new plants
    d. Rhizome—underground stem that produces new plants

    ANS: C   DIF: I   OBJ: 32-3.5

COMPLETION

1. Plants that produce two different types of spores are known as _____ plants.

    ANS: heterosporous   DIF: I   OBJ: 32-1.4

2. A flower that has all four whorls of appendages is called a(n) _____ flower.

    ANS: complete   DIF: I   OBJ: 32-2.1

3. The transfer of pollen grains from an anther to a stigma is known as

_____.

ANS: pollination   DIF: I   OBJ: 32-2.2

4. Seeds develop from the _____ after an egg has been fertilized.

ANS: ovules   DIF: I   OBJ: 32-2.4

5. The event in which one sperm fertilizes an egg and a second sperm fuses with two nuclei is called _____.

ANS: double fertilization   DIF: I   OBJ: 32-2.4

6. An ovule of an angiosperm contains a structure called a/an _____ while an ovule of a gymnosperm does not.

ANS: embryo sac   DIF: I   OBJ: 32-2.5

7. The seeds of angiosperms are enclosed in _____.

ANS: fruits   DIF: I   OBJ: 32-3.1

8. Because flowering plants are rooted in the ground and cannot move from place to place, they must disperse their _____ so that their offspring can grow in new environments.

ANS: seeds   DIF: I   OBJ: 32-3.2

9. Many fruits are spread by _____ that are attracted to sweet, fleshy fruits, which they use for food.

ANS: animals   DIF: I   OBJ: 32-3.2

10. A _____ is a specialized structure that develops from an ovule and serves to protect a plant embryo from harsh conditions.

ANS: seed   DIF: I   OBJ: 32-3.3

11. Refer to the illustration above. The structure labeled "X" in the diagram is the

_____.

ANS: cotyledon   DIF: II   OBJ: 32-3.3

12. Resumption of growth by a plant embryo in a seed is called _____.

ANS: germination DIF: I OBJ: 32-3.3

13. Seeds typically enter a period of dormancy before they _____.

ANS: germinate DIF: I OBJ: 32-3.3

14. A disadvantage of asexual reproduction is that offspring lack _____, which could enable individuals to survive an attack by a disease agent or a pest.

ANS: genetic variability DIF: I OBJ: 32-3.4

15. Vegetative reproduction usually occurs by growth of new cells, tissues, and organs in _____, _____, or _____ of parent plants.

ANS: roots, stems, leaves DIF: I OBJ: 32-3.5

ESSAY

1. Describe the characteristics of flowers that attract pollinators. Write your answer in the space below.

ANS:
Some flowers have attractive petals or scents. Others secrete a sugary nectar that pollinators use as food. For example, bees locate sources of nectar largely by odor at first, then by homing in on a flower's color and shape; hummingbirds are attracted to red flowers; bats are attracted to heavily scented and pale-colored flowers that open at night.

DIF: II OBJ: 32-2.3

2. Why is insect pollination more efficient than wind pollination? Write your answer in the space below.

ANS:
Insects and plants have coevolved so that certain insects are attracted by particular flowers. A particular insect carries pollen from the flowers of one individual to the flowers of another individual of the same species. Thus, the flowers of insect-pollinated plant species do not need to produce as much pollen as the flowers of wind-pollinated species.

DIF: II OBJ: 32-2.3

TRUE/FALSE

1. Gibberellins are hormones that can stimulate seed germination.

   ANS: T   DIF: I   OBJ: 33-1.1

2. Auxin moves toward the lighted side of a stem, causing the cells on that side to elongate.

   ANS: F   DIF: I   OBJ: 33-1.1

3. Ethylene is the hormone that causes the ripening of bananas.

   ANS: T   DIF: I   OBJ: 33-1.1

4. Seed dormancy is advantageous to plants because it enables them to survive when environmental conditions are not suitable for plant growth.

   ANS: T   DIF: II   OBJ: 33-1.2

5. All parts of a plant exhibit both positive phototropism and positive gravitropism.

   ANS: F   DIF: I   OBJ: 33-2.2

6. Folding of leaves has no particular adaptive advantage; it simply results from the loss of potassium ions and loss of water that occur at night.

   ANS: F   DIF: I   OBJ: 33-2.4

7. A long period of darkness induces flowering in short-day plants.

   ANS: T   DIF: I   OBJ: 33-3.1

8. Biennial plants have a vernalization requirement that must be met before they can flower, so they do not normally flower until their second growing season.

   ANS: T   DIF: I   OBJ: 33-3.2

9. The pigments that produce fall colors are present at all times of the growing season, but their colors are masked by chlorophyll during the spring and summer.

   ANS: T   DIF: I   OBJ: 33-3.3

10. The P_{fr} form of phytochrome is the one that induces phytochrome-mediated responses in plants.

   ANS: T   DIF: III   OBJ: 33-3.4

MULTIPLE CHOICE

The diagrams below illustrate an experiment that was performed to better understand how plants grow toward the light. Diagram "A" illustrates the cut tip of a seedling that was put on a block of agar.

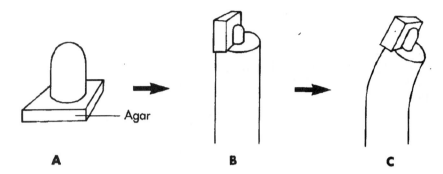

A   B   C

1. Refer to the illustration above. In the diagram, the plant growth hormones that diffused into the agar block from the tip of the seedling are called
   a. meristems.
   b. gibberellins.
   c. auxins.
   d. herbicides.

   ANS: C   DIF: II   OBJ: 33-1.1

2. Refer to the illustration above. These hormones caused the stem in diagram "C" to bend by
   a. exerting a cohesive force on the stem.
   b. causing cells to reproduce at a greater rate.
   c. causing cells to elongate.
   d. translocation.

   ANS: C   DIF: II   OBJ: 33-2.3

3. A plant hormone that is produced primarily in root tips is
   a. auxin.
   b. cytokinin.
   c. ethylene.
   d. gibberellin.

   ANS: B   DIF: I   OBJ: 33-1.1

4. Which of the following hormones normally exists in a gaseous state?
   a. auxin
   b. cytokinin
   c. ethylene
   d. gibberellin

   ANS: C   DIF: I   OBJ: 33-1.1

5. Apical dominance enables plants to
   a. produce large numbers of fruits.
   b. develop an extensive root system.
   c. grow tall and intercept a lot of sunlight.
   d. conserve water during drought conditions.

   ANS: C   DIF: III   OBJ: 33-1.2

6. Apical dominance
   a. is caused by gibberellin in terminal buds.
   b. stimulates terminal buds to elongate.
   c. is the inhibition of lateral bud growth by auxin.
   d. results from gardeners cutting terminal buds in growing plants.

   ANS: C   DIF: I   OBJ: 33-1.3

7. Which of the following is a result of an application of a synthetic auxin to improve crop production?
   a. formation of new roots on stem and leaf cuttings
   b. faster ripening of fruits
   c. larger fruit size
   d. formation of new shoots in tissue culture

   ANS: A   DIF: I   OBJ: 33-1.3

8. Plant movements that occur in response to touch and that are independent of the direction of the stimulus are called
   a. phototropic movements.   c. nyctinastic movements.
   b. thigmonastic movements.   d. chemotropic movements.

   ANS: B   DIF: I   OBJ: 33-2.1

9. shoots : negative gravitropism ::
   a. light stimulations : gravitropism   c. shoots : negative phototropism
   b. gravity movements : phototropism   d. roots : positive gravitropism

   ANS: D   DIF: II   OBJ: 33-2.1

10. All of the following generally cause tropisms in plants *except*
    a. light.   c. touch.
    b. gravity.   d. heat.

    ANS: D   DIF: I   OBJ: 33-2.2

11. When vines grow, they often wrap tendrils around objects for support. The tendrils wrap because of
    a. phototropism.   c. thigmotropism.
    b. gravitropism.   d. chance.

    ANS: C   DIF: I   OBJ: 33-2.2

Newly Germinated Seedling

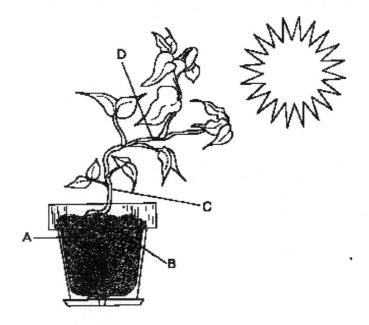

12. Refer to the illustration above. Which part of the plant indicates positive phototropism?
    a. "A"
    b. "B"
    c. "C"
    d. "D"

    ANS: D   DIF: II   OBJ: 33-2.2

13. Refer to the illustration above. Which part of the plant indicates negative gravitropism?
    a. "A"
    b. "B"
    c. "C"
    d. "D"

    ANS: C   DIF: II   OBJ: 33-2.2

14. Which of the following does *not* occur as a result of rapid changes in turgor pressure?
    a. closing of a leaf trap on a Venus' flytrap plant
    b. folding of *Mimosa* leaves
    c. folding of prayer plant leaves
    d. twining of ivy plants around an object

    ANS: D   DIF: I   OBJ: 33-2.4

15. Many plants respond to changes in day length because of
    a. an electronic sensor in their leaves.
    b. a specialized stoma that responds to changes in light and darkness.
    c. a pigment that is sensitive to the amount of darkness.
    d. translocation.

    ANS: C   DIF: I   OBJ: 33-3.1

16. The response of plants to periods of light and dark is called
    a. seasonal.
    b. daily activity.
    c. nocturnal variation.
    d. photoperiodism.

    ANS: D   DIF: I   OBJ: 33-3.1

17. Biennial plants may be kept alive for several years by exposing them to
    a. continuous long nights.
    b. continuous short nights.
    c. continuous cold temperatures.
    d. continuous warm temperatures.

    ANS: D   DIF: I   OBJ: 33-3.2

18. Fall coloration of leaves is caused by
    a. the breakdown of chlorophyll without the production of new chlorophyll.
    b. carotenoids and anthocyanins.
    c. a photoperiodic response.
    d. All of the above

    ANS: D   DIF: I   OBJ: 33-3.2

19. Which of the following is *not* a phytochrome-mediated response, at least in some plants?
    a. flowering
    b. bud dormancy
    c. vernalization
    d. seed germination

    ANS: C   DIF: I   OBJ: 33-3.4

COMPLETION

1. Inhibition of lateral bud growth by auxin is called _____.

   ANS: apical dominance   DIF: I   OBJ: 33-1.1

2. A(n) _____ is a chemical produced in one part of an organism and transported to another part of the organism, where it causes a response.

   ANS: hormone   DIF: I   OBJ: 33-1.1

3. _____ is a hormone that stimulates fruits to ripen.

   ANS: Ethylene   DIF: I   OBJ: 33-1.1

4. A plant hormone that causes elongation of plant cells by enabling them to stretch during cell growth is named _____.

   ANS: auxin   DIF: I   OBJ: 33-1.1

5. Water stress induces the production of _____ in leaves, which causes the closure of _____, which results in the conservation of _____ by the plant.

   ANS: abscisic acid; stomata; water   DIF: II   OBJ: 33-1.2

6. A growth response in plants in which the direction of growth is determined by the direction from which a stimulus comes is called a(n) _____.

    ANS: tropism   DIF: I   OBJ: 33-2.1

7. The accumulation of auxins in _____ promotes cell elongation, while the accumulation of auxins in _____ inhibits cell elongation.

    ANS: stems; roots   DIF: I   OBJ: 33-2.3

8. Plant movements that occur every night as a result of changes in turgor pressure are called _____ movements.

    ANS: nyctinastic   DIF: I   OBJ: 33-2.4

9. In vernalization plants are exposed to _____ in order to induce flowering.

    ANS: cold temperatures   DIF: I   OBJ: 33-2.4

10. Carotenoid pigments produce colors of _____, and anthocyanin pigments produce colors of _____.

    ANS: orange or yellow; red or purplish red   DIF: I   OBJ: 33-3.3

PROBLEM

1. Chrysanthemums are short day plants that normally flower in late fall. Suppose that you are a chrysanthemum grower and would like to produce a chrysanthemum crop for harvesting around Mother's Day (the second Sunday in May). What could you change about the way you grow chrysanthemums in order to postpone flowering from late fall until almost summer? Write your answer in the space below.

    ANS:
Since chrysanthemums are short day plants, they will flower only when nights are of a certain critical length or longer. There are two different ways that a grower could postpone flowering in these plants as the nights lengthen. First, a grower could provide supplemental lighting for the plants, turning on lights in the evenings, for example, and keeping them on for several hours. This would cause the plants to experience shorter nights than their critical period for flowering. An easier and cheaper method would be to expose the plants to a brief flash of bright light in the middle of each night. This would cause the plants to experience essentially two short nights instead of one long one, and they would not flower. Either of these answers should be considered to be correct.

    DIF: III   OBJ: 33-3.1

ESSAY

1. Describe why plants may be more influenced by environmental factors than are animals. Write your answer in the space below.

   ANS:
   Since plants cannot move around the way animals can, plants are likely to be more intimately tied to their immediate surroundings. As the local environment changes in such aspects as light, humidity, temperature, and nutrient availability, plants may respond physiologically by entering or leaving dormancy, dropping or growing leaves, and so forth. Animals, on the other hand, are able to move to new environments when conditions change, thus reducing the influence of the environment.

   DIF: II   OBJ: 33-2.2

2. Describe how auxin causes a plant to bend toward a light source. Write your answer in the space below.

   ANS:
   The plant hormone auxin causes cells to stretch during growth, resulting in elongation of the cells. Under the influence of light, auxin in the plant's terminal bud moves from the lighted side of a shoot to the unlighted side. Cells in the area of the shoot beneath the auxin begin to lengthen. This uneven growth of the cells in the shoot causes bending toward the light; cells on the unlighted side grow slightly longer than those on the lighted side.

   DIF: II   OBJ: 33-2.3

3. Why would it be advantageous for the formation of storage organs in plants to be mediated by phytochrome? Write your answer in the space below.

   ANS:
   Storage organs in plants store carbohydrates to provide energy reserves for plants when environmental conditions are not suitable for photosynthesis, such as in the winter. Phytochrome mediation of storage organ formation would be advantageous because it would result in the formation of these organs during the fall, before the leaves drop from plants and they are no longer able to photosynthesize.

   DIF: III   OBJ: 33-3.4

CHAPTER 34—INTRODUCTION TO ANIMALS

TRUE/FALSE

1. The majority of animal species are classified as invertebrates.

   ANS: T   DIF: I   OBJ: 34-1.1

2. All chordates are classified as vertebrates.

   ANS: F   DIF: I   OBJ: 34-1.1

3. Without exception, all animals are heterotrophs.

   ANS: T   DIF: I   OBJ: 34-1.2

4. All animal cells lack cell walls.

   ANS: T   DIF: I   OBJ: 34-1.2

5. A tissue is a group of dissimilar cells that are organized into a functional unit.

   ANS: F   DIF: I   OBJ: 34-1.3

6. The development of a particular animal's body plan depends on the animal's environment, rather than on the genetic information it carries.

   ANS: F   DIF: I   OBJ: 34-1.4

7. Although animal life is thought to have evolved originally in the sea, the vast majority of animals today are terrestrial.

   ANS: F   DIF: I   OBJ: 34-1.4

8. On an upright, bipedal animal such as a human, the ventral surface is the front side of the body and the dorsal surface is the back side of the body.

   ANS: T   DIF: II   OBJ: 34-2.1

9. Radially symmetric animals have no anterior end and no posterior end, but do have a bottom and a top.

   ANS: T   DIF: II   OBJ: 34-2.2

10. Flatworms are bilaterally symmetrical and cephalized.

    ANS: T   DIF: I   OBJ: 34-2.3

11. An advantage of cephalization is that an animal enters its environment head first, and therefore can immediately sense important stimuli.

    ANS: T   DIF: I   OBJ: 34-2.3

12. The fluid-filled pseudocoelom of roundworms holds the body erect.

    ANS: T   DIF: I   OBJ: 34-2.4

13. The fluid in the body cavity of an animal acts as a medium of transport for nutrients and wastes.

    ANS: T   DIF: I   OBJ: 34-2.4

14. The fluid-filled body cavity found in many invertebrates supports the body, as does the backbone of vertebrates.

    ANS: T   DIF: II   OBJ: 34-2.5

15. All chordates retain their postanal tail in their adult life.

    ANS: F   DIF: I   OBJ: 34-2.6

16. Segmentation occurs in the bodies of annelids and arthropods but is not present in chordates.

    ANS: F   DIF: I   OBJ: 34-3.1

17. Most invertebrates have kidneys that filter waste products from the blood.

    ANS: F   DIF: I   OBJ: 34-3.1

18. Terrestrial animals have a protective outer covering that helps prevent excessive water loss.

    ANS: T   DIF: I   OBJ: 34-3.1

19. Segmentation is evident in vertebrates in the repeating bony units of their backbones and ribs.

    ANS: T   DIF: I   OBJ: 34-3.2

20. Animals with open circulatory systems do not transport respiratory gases in their circulatory fluid, while animals with closed circulatory systems do.

    ANS: F   DIF: I   OBJ: 34-3.3

21. In sponges and cnidarians, nutrients and gases are exchanged directly with the environment by pumps in the animal's body surface.

    ANS: F   DIF: I   OBJ: 34-3.3

22. An advantage of a long digestive tract is that it provides a large surface area over which nutrients can be absorbed.

    ANS: T   DIF: I   OBJ: 34-3.4

23. In cnidarians, nutrients are propelled through a gut that runs the length of the body by the movement of water as the animal swims.

ANS: F   DIF: I   OBJ: 34-3.4

24. During spiral cleavage, each cell of the blastula rests directly above or below an adjacent cell.

ANS: F   DIF: I   OBJ: 34-3.4

25. At the start of gastrulation, the embryo is cup-shaped and has three distinct germ layers.

ANS: F   DIF: I   OBJ: 34-4.1

26. In a cnidarian, endoderm forms the outer tissue and nervous system.

ANS: F   DIF: I   OBJ: 34-4.2

MULTIPLE CHOICE

1. All the members of the kingdom Animalia
   a. are heterotrophs.
   b. are multicellular.
   c. have cells without cell walls.
   d. All of the above

ANS: D   DIF: I   OBJ: 34-1.2

2. Specialized cells
   a. can carry out their tasks more effectively than cells that must do many tasks.
   b. are found only in chordates and echinoderms.
   c. always operate independently of all other cells.
   d. All of the above

ANS: A   DIF: I   OBJ: 34-1.2

3. A group of similar cells organized into a functional unit is called
   a. a nervous system.
   b. specialized cells.
   c. a tissue.
   d. an organ.

ANS: C   DIF: I   OBJ: 34-1.3

4. Which of the following is found only in animals?
   a. the ability to move
   b. sexual reproduction
   c. muscle tissue and nervous tissue
   d. heterotrophy

ANS: B   DIF: II   OBJ: 34-1.3

5. Animals probably evolved from
   a. plants.
   b. photosynthetic protists.
   c. heterotrophic protists.
   d. None of the above

ANS: C   DIF: I   OBJ: 34-1.4

6. Modern organisms that are thought to resemble the earliest animals are
   a. plants.
   b. colonial protists.
   c. unicellular protozoans.
   d. bacteria.

ANS: B   DIF: I   OBJ: 34-1.4

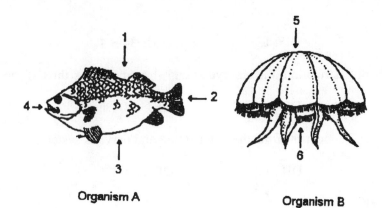

Organism A   Organism B

7. Refer to the illustration above. The position of the arrow labeled ____ can be referred to as anterior.
   a. "1"
   b. "4"
   c. "5"
   d. "6"

ANS: B   DIF: II   OBJ: 34-2.1

8. Most animals have a head that is located at the ____ end of their body and a tail that is located at the ____ end of their body.
   a. ventral; dorsal
   b. dorsal; ventral
   c. anterior; posterior
   d. posterior; anterior

ANS: C   DIF: I   OBJ: 34-2.1

A   B

9. Refer to the illustration above. The organism labeled "B" in the diagram
   a. is asymmetrical.
   b. is bilaterally symmetrical.
   c. exhibits radial symmetry.
   d. has reverse symmetry.

ANS: C   DIF: II   OBJ: 34-2.2

10. Refer to the illustration above. The organism labeled "A" in the diagram
    a. has no symmetry.
    b. is bilaterally symmetrical.
    c. exhibits radial symmetry.
    d. has reverse symmetry.

    ANS: B   DIF: II   OBJ: 34-2.2

11. Radially symmetrical phyla include all of the following *except*
    a. jellyfish.
    b. comb jellies.
    c. hydra.
    d. sponges.

    ANS: D   DIF: I   OBJ: 34-2.2

12. Which of the following has a radial symmetry?
    a. flatworm
    b. annelid
    c. chordate
    d. cnidarian

    ANS: D   DIF: I   OBJ: 34-2.2

13. Cephalization
    a. is a feature of most invertebrates, including the sponges.
    b. is characterized by the concentration of sensory organs in the anterior end.
    c. occurs in marine protozoa.
    d. results when the brain does not develop properly.

    ANS: B   DIF: I   OBJ: 34-2.3

14. Which of the following is found in vertebrates but not in invertebrates?
    a. dorsal nerve cord
    b. coelom
    c. three germ layers
    d. bilateral symmetry

    ANS: A   DIF: II   OBJ: 34-2.5

15. At some stage of their development, all chordates have a supportive rod along their back called the
    a. spinal cord.
    b. pharynx.
    c. notochord.
    d. None of the above

    ANS: C   DIF: I   OBJ: 34-2.6

16. A characteristic shared by all chordates at some stage of their development is
    a. a dorsal hollow nerve cord.
    b. a notochord.
    c. pharyngeal pouches.
    d. All of the above

    ANS: D   DIF: I   OBJ: 34-2.6

17. Which of the following is *not* a vertebrate adaptation to life on land?
    a. lungs
    b. internal fertilization
    c. endoskeleton
    d. brain

    ANS: D   DIF: II   OBJ: 34-3.1

18. Which of the following is *not* a characteristic of the largest phylum of invertebrates, the arthropods?
    a. segmentation
    b. exoskeleton
    c. closed circulatory system
    d. digestive tract

    ANS: C   DIF: I   OBJ: 34-3.2

19. In sponges, digestion occurs in
    a. a gut.
    b. individual cells.
    c. a central cavity with a single opening.
    d. outside of the animal's body.

    ANS: B   DIF: I   OBJ: 34-3.4

20. During which of the following stages of animal development are the germ layers formed?
    a. fertilization
    b. cleavage
    c. gastrulation
    d. organ formation

    ANS: C   DIF: I   OBJ: 34-4.1

21. The acoelomate body type is exemplified by
    a. flatworms.
    b. roundworms.
    c. mollusks.
    d. annelids.

    ANS: D   DIF: I   OBJ: 34-4.2

22. Which of the following is an *incorrect* match?
    a. ectoderm—nervous system
    b. mesoderm—skeletal system
    c. endoderm—muscular system
    d. endoderm—digestive system

    ANS: C   DIF: I   OBJ: 34-4.2

23. As an animal develops, the ectoderm becomes the
    a. heart.
    b. tissue that lines the gut.
    c. skin and nervous system.
    d. muscle tissue.

    ANS: C   DIF: I   OBJ: 34-4.2

24. Which of the following animals is a deuterostome?
    a. annelid
    b. arthropod
    c. mollusk
    d. chordate

    ANS: D   DIF: I   OBJ: 34-4.3

25. Two deuterostome phyla are
    a. annelids and ctenophores.
    b. echinoderms and chordates.
    c. arthropods and chordates.
    d. cnidarians and sponges.

    ANS: C   DIF: I   OBJ: 34-4.3

The diagrams below are cross sections of three types of animal bodies.

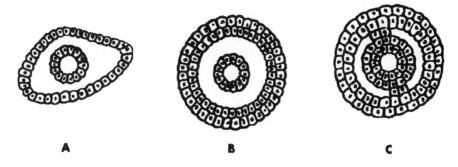

26. Refer to the illustration above. An organism with no body cavity is shown in diagram
    a. "A."
    b. "B."
    c. "C."
    d. None of the above

    ANS: A   DIF: II   OBJ: 34-4.5

27. Refer to the illustration above. The organism shown in diagram "B" is a(n)
    a. acoelomate.
    b. pseudocoelomate.
    c. coelomate.
    d. vertebrate.

    ANS: B   DIF: II   OBJ: 34-4.5

28. Refer to the illustration above. Humans have the type of body cavity shown in diagram
    a. "A."
    b. "B."
    c. "C."
    d. None of the above

    ANS: C   DIF: II   OBJ: 34-4.5

COMPLETION

1. The distinguishing feature of vertebrates is the _____.

   ANS: backbone   DIF: I   OBJ: 34-1.1

2. Because animals cannot make their own food, they are said to be
   _____.

   ANS: heterotrophs   DIF: I   OBJ: 34-1.2

3. Multicellularity allows for the _____ of different cells for different
   tasks.

   ANS: specialization   DIF: I   OBJ: 34-1.2

4. Unlike bacteria and most protists, all animals are _____.

   ANS: multicellular   DIF: I   OBJ: 34-1.2

5. Since sponges do not have body parts that grow around a central point or line as do all other animals, sponges are said to lack _____.

ANS: symmetry   DIF: I   OBJ: 34-2.2

6. An animal whose body parts are arranged around a central point, like spokes around the hub of a wheel, has _____ symmetry.

ANS: radial   DIF: I   OBJ: 34-2.2

7. Organisms that have left and right halves that mirror each other when divided by an imaginary longitudinal plane are said to have _____ symmetry.

ANS: bilateral   DIF: I   OBJ: 34-2.2

8. The concentration of sensory receptors in a head is called _____.

ANS: cephalization   DIF: I   OBJ: 34-2.3

9. The _____ is a fluid-filled cavity that develops within the mesoderm of some animal phyla.

ANS: coelom   DIF: II   OBJ: 34-2.4

10. Embryological evidence suggests that the echinoderms are closely related to the _____.

ANS: chordates   DIF: I   OBJ: 34-2.5

11. An animal without a body cavity is called a(n) _____.

ANS: acoelomate   DIF: I   OBJ: 34-2.5

12. Terrestrial animals have some kind of adaptation for structural support because their bodies are not supported by water. Terrestrial vertebrates have a(n) _____.

ANS: endoskeleton   DIF: I   OBJ: 34-3.1

13. In animals with open circulatory systems, the exchange of gases, nutrients, and wastes occurs between the fluid in the _____ and body cells, while in animals with closed circulatory systems, exchange occurs between circulatory fluid in the _____ and the body cells.

ANS: coelom; vessels   DIF: I   OBJ: 34-3.3

14. The type of coelom formation in which cells at the dorsal part of the archenteron begin dividing rapidly and roll inward is called _____.

ANS: enterocoely   DIF: I   OBJ: 34-3.5

15. During cleavage, the dividing cells become progressively _____.

    ANS: smaller   DIF: I   OBJ: 34-4.1

16. In _____ the blastopore becomes the anus of the adult.

    ANS: deuterostomes   DIF: I   OBJ: 34-4.3

17. During embryonic development, most protostomes undergo _____ cleavage while most deuterostomes undergo _____ cleavage, and the resulting embryos therefore have different arrangements of their cells.

    ANS: spiral; radial   DIF: I   OBJ: 34-4.4

ESSAY

1. Compare the symmetry of body forms observed in the phylum Porifera and the phylum Cnidaria. Write your answer in the space below.

    ANS:
The members of the phylum Porifera, the sponges, are asymmetrical. Their bodies are not arranged in any particular way around a central point or axis. On the other hand, the animals belonging to the phylum Cnidaria, including the jellyfish, hydra, and sea anemones, are radially symmetrical. Their bodies are arranged around a central point.

    DIF: II   OBJ: 34-2.2

2. Distinguish between protostomes and deuterostomes. Write your answer in the space below.

    ANS:
Protostomes are animals in which the blastopore of the embryo becomes the mouth of the organism. In deuterostomes, the anus develops from or near the blastopore.

    DIF: II   OBJ: 34-4.3

3. If cells of an early developing protostome and of an early developing deuterostome are separated from each other, what will be the fate of each type of separated cell? Write your answer in the space below.

    ANS:
The separated cells of the developing protostome will become a portion of a complete embryo and then die. Each of the separated cells of the developing deuterostome will develop into a complete embryo. The embryos will be genetically identical.

    DIF: II   OBJ: 34-4.4

CHAPTER 35—SPONGES, CNIDARIANS, AND CTENOPHORES

TRUE/FALSE

1. Sponges are filter feeders.

    ANS: T   DIF: I   OBJ: 35-1.3

2. Sponges are capable of total regeneration, even from the smallest pieces of their bodies.

    ANS: T   DIF: I   OBJ: 35-1.4

3. Polyps are a body form of cnidarians that are specialized for swimming.

    ANS: F   DIF: I   OBJ: 35-2.1

4. Cnidarians are characterized by stinging nematocysts.

    ANS: T   DIF: I   OBJ: 35-2.2

5. The life cycle of anthozoans includes medusae, planulae, and polyps.

    ANS: F   DIF: I   OBJ: 35-2.3

6. Ctenophores lack a nervous system that coordinates their activities, so their movements are erratic.

    ANS: F   DIF: I   OBJ: 35-2.4

MULTIPLE CHOICE

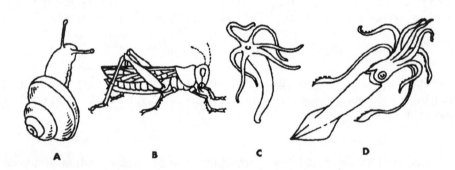

1. Refer to the illustration above. Which organism in the diagrams is most closely related to a jellyfish?
    a. Organism "A"   c. Organism "C"
    b. Organism "B"   d. Organism "D"

    ANS: C   DIF: II   OBJ: 35-1.1

2. Which of the following distinguishes sponges from other invertebrates?
   a. They are not motile in any stage of their life cycle.
   b. They obtain nutrients by diffusion rather than by ingestion.
   c. Their cells are not organized into tissues.
   d. They reproduce only asexually.

   ANS: C   DIF: II   OBJ: 35-1.1

3. Which of the following is characteristic of all invertebrates?
   a. absence of a vertebral column
   b. absence of a vertebral column and radial symmetry
   c. absence of a vertebral column, radial symmetry, and absence of a coelom
   d. absence of a vertebral column, radial symmetry, absence of a coelom, and digestion
      occurring in a gut with only one opening

   ANS: A   DIF: II   OBJ: 35-1.1

4. Sponges
   a. are nonsymmetrical.
   b. lack organization into tissues and organs.
   c. possess cells that are capable of recognizing other sponge cells.
   d. All of the above

   ANS: D   DIF: I   OBJ: 35-1.2

5. Collar cells
   a. are specialized for reproduction.   c. produce cytochrome oxidase.
   b. draw water into the body of a sponge.   d. are parasitic protozoa.

   ANS: B   DIF: I   OBJ: 35-1.2

6. Spicules are
   a. flexible protein fibers.
   b. hard needle-like structures in the wall of a sponge.
   c. similar to seeds; a complete sponge can grow from each spicule.
   d. used for taking in food and water.

   ANS: B   DIF: I   OBJ: 35-1.2

7. Adult sponges
   a. have body walls with many pores.   c. are active swimmers.
   b. possess true tissues.   d. use stinging cells to capture prey.

   ANS: A   DIF: I   OBJ: 35-1.2

8. Skeletal support in sponges may be provided by
   a. spicules of calcium carbonate.   c. spongin fibers.
   b. spicules of silicon dioxide.   d. All of the above

   ANS: D   DIF: I   OBJ: 35-1.2

9. Sponges obtain food
    a. by photosynthesis.
    b. by using their spicules to paralyze protozoa.
    c. by filtering small organisms from the water.
    d. with spongin.

    ANS: C   DIF: I   OBJ: 35-1.3

10. In sponges, currents that draw water through the organism are created by
    a. amoebocytes.   c. gemmules.
    b. collar cells.   d. spicules.

    ANS: B   DIF: I   OBJ: 35-1.3

11. Cells that move throughout the sponge's body wall to deliver food to the organism's cells are
    a. amoebocytes.   c. gemmules.
    b. choanocytes.   d. spicules.

    ANS: A   DIF: I   OBJ: 35-1.3

12. Water leaves the internal cavity of a sponge through the
    a. food vacuoles.   c. body wall.
    b. spicules.   d. osculum.

    ANS: D   DIF: I   OBJ: 35-1.3

13. collar cell : water ::
    a. amoebocyte : nutrients and wastes   c. spicule : water
    b. spongin : food   d. osculum : mesenchyme

    ANS: A   DIF: II   OBJ: 35-1.3

14. The gemmules of sponges
    a. create water currents for feeding.
    b. are equivalent to the sperm cells of higher animals.
    c. are equivalent to the egg cells of higher animals.
    d. are necessary for one form of asexual reproduction.

    ANS: D   DIF: I   OBJ: 35-1.4

15. Hermaphroditic organisms
    a. reproduce only by asexual means.
    b. produce both eggs and sperm.
    c. have gemmules that are fertilized by amoebocytes.
    d. possess only male amoebocytes.

    ANS: B   DIF: I   OBJ: 35-1.4

16. Self-fertilization is avoided in sponges because
    a. there is no way for sperm to enter the sponge.
    b. the sperm do not possess the enzyme needed to penetrate the egg.
    c. sperm and eggs are not produced at the same time.
    d. None of the above is true; self-fertilization is common in sponges.

    ANS: C   DIF: I   OBJ: 35-1.4

17. Sponges can reproduce
    a. by the budding of new sponges from the parent.
    b. by a breakup of the original parent into fragments that each become a new sponge.
    c. sexually, using the production of sperm and eggs.
    d. All of the above

    ANS: D   DIF: I   OBJ: 35-1.4

18. freshwater sponges : gemmules ::
    a. hermaphrodites : eggs and sperm   c. gemmules : sperms
    b. gemmules : eggs   d. amoebocytes : eggs

    ANS: A   DIF: II   OBJ: 35-1.4

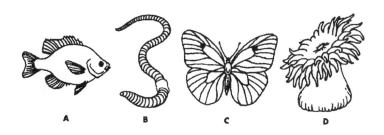

19. Refer to the illustration above. Which organism in the diagrams captures its prey using nematocysts?
    a. Organism "A"   c. Organism "C"
    b. Organism "B"   d. Organism "D"

    ANS: D   DIF: II   OBJ: 35-2.1

20. Many cnidarians have two distinct life stages called
    a. the gametophyte and the sporophyte.
    b. the polyp and the medusa.
    c. egg and adult.
    d. egg and larva.

    ANS: B   DIF: I   OBJ: 35-2.1

21. *Obelia* : polyp ::
    a. *Hydra* : jellyfish   c. Coral : colony
    b. jellyfish : polyp   d. Coral : medusa

    ANS: C   DIF: II   OBJ: 35-2.1

22. Nematocysts
    a. contain harpoonlike structures called cnidocytes.
    b. create water currents in sponges.
    c. can spear a sea anemone's prey.
    d. are found in most predatory eumetazoans.

    ANS: C   DIF: I   OBJ: 35-2.2

23. The cnidarian's inner layer of tissue is specialized for
    a. extracellular digestion.   c. capturing prey.
    b. reproduction.   d. All of the above

    ANS: A   DIF: I   OBJ: 35-2.2

24. The outer cell layer of a cnidarian is the
    a. ectoderm.   c. endoderm.
    b. mesoglea.   d. epidermis.

    ANS: D   DIF: I   OBJ: 35-2.2

25. A characteristic shared between all fungi and cnidarians is
    a. the possession of nematocysts.   c. tentacles for catching food.
    b. extracellular digestion.   d. radial symmetry.

    ANS: B   DIF: I   OBJ: 35-2.2

26. Which of the following is a characteristic associated *only* with cnidarians?
    a. a digestive tract with a single opening
    b. tentacles with stinging cells
    c. choanocytes containing nematocysts
    d. a parasitic life cycle

    ANS: B   DIF: I   OBJ: 35-2.2

27. sponges : fewer than three body layers ::
    a. eumetazoans : no body symmetry   c. cnidarians : extracellular digestion
    b. sponges : bilateral symmetry   d. cnidarians : choanocytes

    ANS: C   DIF: II   OBJ: 35-2.2

28. The phylum Cnidaria includes all of the following *except*
    a. jellyfish.   c. sea anemones.
    b. squids.   d. corals.

    ANS: B   DIF: I   OBJ: 35-2.3

29. Planula larvae of hydrozoans
    a. result from fertilization of eggs by sperm.
    b. swim freely through the water.
    c. settle to the ocean bottom and grow into polyps.
    d. All of the above

    ANS: D   DIF: I   OBJ: 35-2.3

30. The hydra is unique among the hydrozoans because it
    a. is an active swimmer.
    b. feeds without tentacles.
    c. is strictly a marine species.
    d. has no medusa stage.

    ANS: D   DIF: I   OBJ: 35-2.3

31. Which of the following is *not* sessile as an adult?
    a. sponge
    b. hydra
    c. sea anemone
    d. Portuguese man-of-war

    ANS: D   DIF: I   OBJ: 35-2.3

32. Sea anemones are
    a. medusae.
    b. polyps.
    c. larvae.
    d. eggs.

    ANS: B   DIF: I   OBJ: 35-2.3

The diagram below illustrates the life cycle of the jellyfish.

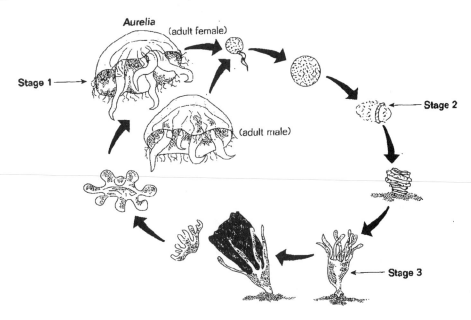

33. Refer to the illustration above. Which stage is called a planula?
    a. Stage "1"
    b. Stage "2"
    c. Stage "3"
    d. None of the above

    ANS: B   DIF: II   OBJ: 35-2.3

34. Refer to the illustration above. Which of the indicated stages reproduces asexually?
    a. Stage "1"
    b. Stage "2"
    c. Stage "3"
    d. None of the above

    ANS: C   DIF: II   OBJ: 35-2.3

35. Anthozoans include organisms known as
  a. jellyfish.
  b. hydras.
  c. Portuguese men-of-war.
  d. sea anemones and corals.

  ANS: D   DIF: I   OBJ: 35-2.3

36. Scyphozoans, such as jellyfish, spend most of their lives as
  a. polyps.
  b. medusae.
  c. corals.
  d. parasites.

  ANS: B   DIF: I   OBJ: 35-2.3

37. The class of cnidarians that typically live only as polyps is the
  a. Anthozoa.
  b. Hydrozoa.
  c. Scyphozoa.
  d. None of the above

  ANS: A   DIF: I   OBJ: 35-2.3

38. Which of the following is *not* a characteristic of ctenophores?
  a. are nonsymmetrical
  b. movement by means of beating cilia
  c. capture of prey by use of cnidocytes
  d. hermaphrodism

  ANS: C   DIF: I   OBJ: 35-2.4

COMPLETION

1. _____ is drawn into a sponge through pores and leaves through the osculum.

  ANS: Water   DIF: I   OBJ: 35-1.2

2. A network of tough protein fibers that provide support in some sponges is called

  _____.

  ANS: spongin   DIF: I   OBJ: 35-1.2

3. Needle-like objects in the middle layers of sponges that make up the skeleton of these organisms are called _____.

  ANS: spicules   DIF: I   OBJ: 35-1.2

4. Spicules may be composed of either _____ or

  _____.

  ANS: calcium carbonate, silicon dioxide   DIF: I   OBJ: 35-1.2

5. Food molecules are carried throughout a sponge's body by _____.

  ANS: amoebocytes   DIF: I   OBJ: 35-1.3

6. Food-filled balls of sponge amoebocytes that are involved in asexual reproduction are called _____.

    ANS: gemmules   DIF: I   OBJ: 35-1.4

7. An organism that produces both eggs and sperm is called a(n) _____.

    ANS: hermaphrodite   DIF: I   OBJ: 35-1.4

8. A free-floating, gelatinous body form found in some cnidarians is called a(n) _____, while an attached body form in these animals is called a(n) _____.

    ANS: medusa, polyp   DIF: I   OBJ: 35-2.1

9. The two distinct body forms of cnidarians are the _____ and the _____.

    ANS: polyp, medusa   DIF: I   OBJ: 35-2.1

10. Cnidarians have two _____ layers.

    ANS: tissue   DIF: I   OBJ: 35-2.2

11. The Portuguese man-of-war is a complex colony containing both _____ and _____.

    ANS: medusae, polyps   DIF: I   OBJ: 35-2.3

12. Cnidarians that typically have a thick, stalk-like body crowned by tentacles that occur in groups of six belong to the class known as the _____.

    ANS: anthozoans   DIF: I   OBJ: 35-2.3

13. A coral is a member of the phylum _____.

    ANS: Cnidaria   DIF: I   OBJ: 35-2.3

14. Ctenophores are the largest organisms that move by means of the _____.

    ANS: beating of cilia   DIF: I   OBJ: 35-2.4

ESSAY

1. Like plants that show an alternation of generations, many cnidarians also exhibit two different body forms during their life cycles. Describe these two body forms and their role in cnidarian life cycles. Write your answer in the space below.

   ANS:
   Polyps are a form that lives attached to a hard surface. They reproduce asexually by budding, resulting in the production of either more polyp forms or, in some species, the medusa stage. Medusae (or jellyfish) are free-living organisms, swimming or floating in currents. They reproduce sexually, producing an embryo that develops into a larva, settles to the bottom of the body of water, and grows into a polyp.

   DIF: II   OBJ: 35-2.1

2. Sea anemones and corals belong to the same group of cnidarians, the class Anthozoa. Distinguish between these two groups of organisms. Write your answer in the space below.

   ANS:
   While both types of organisms exist only in polyp forms, their adult structures are different. Sea anemones are generally solitary, soft-bodied polyps. Corals, on the other hand, usually live in colonies that are surrounded by a calcium-rich skeleton.

   DIF: II   OBJ: 35-2.3

TRUE/FALSE

1. Planarians have a branched digestive tract with both a mouth and an anus.

    ANS: F   DIF: I   OBJ: 36-1.2

2. Most flatworms are not parasitic.

    ANS: F   DIF: I   OBJ: 36-1.3

3. Tapeworms absorb food from their host's intestine directly through their skin.

    ANS: T   DIF: I   OBJ: 36-1.5

4. Humans can avoid trichinosis by wearing shoes when they walk through fields.

    ANS: F   DIF: I   OBJ: 36-2.2

5. Rotifers have a distinct head end with a mouth and a distinct tail end that has an opening through which substances from the digestive, reproductive, and excretory systems exit the body.

    ANS: T   DIF: I   OBJ: 36-2.3

MULTIPLE CHOICE

1. Flatworms can reproduce asexually by
    a. fission.
    b. forming larvae.
    c. producing polyps.
    d. exchanging both sperm and eggs.

    ANS: A   DIF: I   OBJ: 36-1.1

2. Which of the following is *not* found in flatworms?
    a. a head
    b. a circulatory system
    c. bilateral symmetry
    d. a nervous system

    ANS: B   DIF: II   OBJ: 36-1.2

3. Flatworms have no need for circulatory and respiratory systems because
    a. the digestive system performs these functions.
    b. their cells are close to the animal's exterior surface.
    c. the spherical body shape allows diffusion of materials into tissues.
    d. the coelom is bathed in blood and oxygen.

    ANS: B   DIF: I   OBJ: 36-1.3

4. Schistosomiasis is a disease caused by a
   a. roundworm.
   b. trematode.
   c. cestode.
   d. planarian.

   ANS: B   DIF: I   OBJ: 36-1.4

5. turbellarians : free living ::
   a. planaria : parasitic
   b. tapeworms : free living
   c. cestodes : free living
   d. flukes : parasitic

   ANS: D   DIF: II   OBJ: 36-1.4

6. Which of the following statements about tapeworms is *false*?
   a. They can infect a person who eats improperly cooked beef.
   b. They belong to the genus *Schistosoma*.
   c. They can grow to be large in human intestines.
   d. These flatworms do not have a digestive system.

   ANS: B   DIF: I   OBJ: 36-1.5

7. To which phylum do roundworms belong?
   a. Annelida
   b. Nematoda
   c. Platyhelminthes
   d. Arthropoda

   ANS: B   DIF: I   OBJ: 36-2.1

8. Roundworms have a fluid-filled cavity between the gut and body wall called a
   a. coelom.
   b. pseudocoelom.
   c. digestive system.
   d. None of the above

   ANS: B   DIF: I   OBJ: 36-2.1

9. Pseudocoelomates
   a. must move rapidly to enhance diffusion of nutrients.
   b. must be very small or have body shapes with short distances between organs and the body surface.
   c. must have a circulatory system.
   d. All of the above

   ANS: B   DIF: I   OBJ: 36-2.1

10. The first organisms to develop an internal body cavity were the
    a. flatworms.
    b. nematodes.
    c. mollusks.
    d. arthropods.

    ANS: B   DIF: I   OBJ: 36-2.1

11. All of the following groups of invertebrates are coelomates, *except*
    a. annelids.
    b. echinoderms.
    c. mollusks.
    d. nematodes.

    ANS: D   DIF: I   OBJ: 36-2.1

12. The evolution of body cavities was important because
    a. fluids within the body cavity aid in circulation of materials from one part of the body to another.
    b. fluids in the cavity make the body rigid and offer resistance to muscles, aiding in movement.
    c. organs are better able to function if they can move freely within the body cavity.
    d. All of the above

    ANS: D   DIF: I   OBJ: 36-2.1

13. The nematode *Ascaris lumbricoides* infects humans, spending most of its adult life inside the intestines of its host. To be infected, a person must
    a. consume the nematode's eggs.   c. sit on an infested toilet seat.
    b. walk barefoot on infested soil.   d. All of the above

    ANS: A   DIF: I   OBJ: 36-2.2

14. A type of roundworm that lives a parasitic life is
    a. *Ascaris.*   c. *Trichinella.*
    b. *Necator.*   d. All of the above

    ANS: D   DIF: I   OBJ: 36-2.2

15. Rotifers eliminate excess water that they collect from their freshwater environment by
    a. diffusion.   c. flame cells and excretory tubules.
    b. kidneys.   d. a mastax.

    ANS: C   DIF: I   OBJ: 36-2.3

COMPLETION

1. A schistosome is a member of the phylum _____.

    ANS: Platyhelminthes   DIF: I   OBJ: 36-1.1

2. The ability of some animals, such as flatworms, to regrow lost parts of their bodies is called _____.

    ANS: regeneration   DIF: I   OBJ: 36-1.1

3. Flatworms take up oxygen and release carbon dioxide by the process of _____, which occurs across the _____ of the animals.

    ANS: diffusion; surface of the body   DIF: I   OBJ: 36-1.2

4. The _____ is a thick, protective cellular covering of the bodies of endoparasitic flukes that prevents them from being digested by their hosts.

    ANS: tegument   DIF: I   OBJ: 36-1.4

5. _____ are rectangular body sections of tapeworms.

    ANS: Proglottids   DIF: I   OBJ: 36-1.5

6. Roundworms are members of the phylum _____.

    ANS: Nematoda   DIF: I   OBJ: 36-2.1

7. Roundworms take in food through the mouth and eliminate wastes through an opening at the other end of the gut called the _____.

    ANS: anus   DIF: I   OBJ: 36-2.1

8. Organisms that feed by the use of sweeping cilia, resembling a rotating wheel, near their mouths are called _____.

    ANS: rotifers   DIF: I   OBJ: 36-2.3

ESSAY

1. A flatworm cannot eat when food is already in its gut. Why? Write your answer in the space below.

    ANS:
The guts of most flatworms have only one opening. Because they consume their food and excrete their wastes through the same opening, two-way movement of material occurs within their guts. A flatworm cannot eat when food is already in the gut, since newly consumed food would mix with partially digested food and wastes.

    DIF: II   OBJ: 36-1.1

2. Parasitic lifestyles have evolved independently among different phyla of worms. Using examples, discuss species of worms that are adapted to a parasitic lifestyle. Write your answer in the space below.

    ANS:
Among the Platyhelminthes, two parasitic worms are schistosomes, which inhabit blood vessels of their hosts, and tapeworms, which live in the intestinal tracts of their hosts. Parasitic nematodes include *Ascaris*, an intestinal parasite of humans and pigs, and *Wuchereria*, the cause of filariasis (elephantiasis) in humans. Leeches, blood-sucking worms of the phylum Annelida, can live off the blood of a variety of hosts.

    DIF: II   OBJ: 36-1.3

TRUE/FALSE

1. Mollusks and annelids are believed to be the first animals to develop a true coelom.

   ANS: T   DIF: I   OBJ: 37-1.1

2. Mollusks must eat constantly because the functioning of their nephridia causes the disposal of useful molecules as well as of waste products.

   ANS: F   DIF: I   OBJ: 37-1.1

3. All mollusk shells are lined with and secreted by a fleshy fold of tissue called the foot.

   ANS: F   DIF: I   OBJ: 37-1.4

4. Unlike arthropods, mollusks are unsegmented; instead, they are divided into three regions.

   ANS: T   DIF: I   OBJ: 37-1.4

5. Mollusks have four distinct body parts: a foot, a head, a visceral mass, and a tail.

   ANS: F   DIF: I   OBJ: 37-1.4

6. In terrestrial snails, the mantle cavity functions as a simple lung.

   ANS: T   DIF: I   OBJ: 37-1.4

7. Most bivalves have separate sexes, but some are hermaphroditic.

   ANS: T   DIF: I   OBJ: 37-1.4

8. Due to the presence of a shell, all gastropods are capable of living on land for at least a portion of their lives.

   ANS: F   DIF: I   OBJ: 37-1.4

9. Since cephalopods have tentacles, they have no need for a radula.

   ANS: F   DIF: I   OBJ: 37-1.4

10. Different regions of an annelid's body specialize for different functions.

    ANS: T   DIF: I   OBJ: 37-2.1

11. While all but one group of mollusks have open circulatory systems, all annelids possess a closed circulatory system.

    ANS: T   DIF: I   OBJ: 37-2.4

12. Some leeches have become specialized to a parasitic way of life by developing the ability to suck blood from the bodies of other organisms.

ANS: T   DIF: I   OBJ: 37-2.4

MULTIPLE CHOICE

1. All of the following are characteristics of mollusks *except* that they have
   a. a pseudocoelomate body plan.
   b. bilateral symmetry.
   c. a complete digestive tract.
   d. an open circulatory system.

ANS: A   DIF: I   OBJ: 37-1.1

2. Which of the following has a true coelom?
   a. flatworm
   b. roundworm
   c. rotifer
   d. mollusk

ANS: D   DIF: I   OBJ: 37-1.1

3. The evolution of a coelom was significant because
   a. more food could be stored within it.
   b. more wastes could be stored before excretion.
   c. it enabled development of more complex organ systems.
   d. it eliminated the need for a circulatory system.

ANS: C   DIF: I   OBJ: 37-1.1

4. mollusks : a mantle ::
   a. pseudocoelomate animals : true body cavities
   b. solid worms : a gut with one opening
   c. solid worms : coelom
   d. mollusks : a coelom

ANS: D   DIF: II   OBJ: 37-1.1

5. The cilia of a trochophore larva
   a. allow attachment to the ocean bottom.
   b. create currents for drawing in food.
   c. cover the entire larval body.
   d. are necessary for reproduction.

ANS: B   DIF: I   OBJ: 37-1.2

6. Trochophore larvae
   a. are found in molluscan life cycles.
   b. possess a belt of cilia around their bodies.
   c. occur in annelid life cycles.
   d. All of the above

ANS: D   DIF: I   OBJ: 37-1.2

7. A characteristic structure found in many mollusks is the radula, which is involved in
   a. jet propulsion.
   b. opening and closing of the shells.
   c. eating.
   d. reproduction.

   ANS: C   DIF: I   OBJ: 37-1.3

8. Which of the following is correctly paired?
   a. phylum Platyhelminthes—hydra
   b. phylum Nematoda—planaria
   c. phylum Mollusca—octopus
   d. phylum Annelida—roundworm

   ANS: C   DIF: I   OBJ: 37-1.4

9. All of the animal phyla that evolved after the mollusks
   a. are vertebrates.
   b. are prokaryotes.
   c. have a coelom.
   d. lack mesoderm.

   ANS: C   DIF: I   OBJ: 37-1.4

10. All of the following are classes of the phylum Mollusca *except*
    a. bivalves.
    b. cephalopods.
    c. gastropods.
    d. pseudopods.

    ANS: D   DIF: I   OBJ: 37-1.4

11. The only mollusks that have a closed circulatory system are
    a. bivalves.
    b. cephalopods.
    c. chitons.
    d. gastropods.

    ANS: B   DIF: I   OBJ: 37-1.4

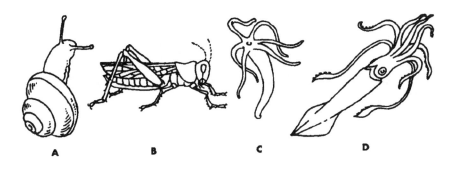

12. Refer to the illustration above. Which two organisms in the diagrams possess mantles?
    a. Organisms "A" and "C"
    b. Organisms "B" and "C"
    c. Organisms "A" and "D"
    d. Organisms "B" and "D"

    ANS: C   DIF: II   OBJ: 37-1.4

13. "Jet propulsion" is the usual means of locomotion in water for
    a. arthropods.
    b. echinoderms.
    c. cephalopods.
    d. annelids.

    ANS: C   DIF: I   OBJ: 37-1.4

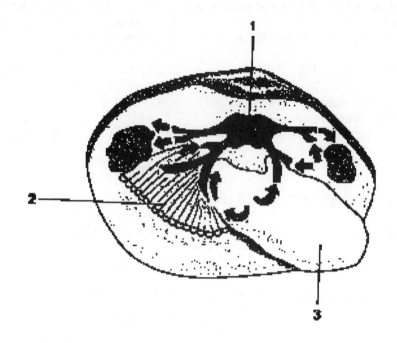

14. Refer to the illustration above. The organism shown in this diagram is a
   a. bivalve.
   b. cephalopod.
   c. chiton.
   d. gastropod.

   ANS: A   DIF: II   OBJ: 37-1.4

15. Refer to the illustration above. This organism possesses a(n)
   a. simple lung.
   b. closed circulatory system.
   c. internal beak.
   d. open circulatory system.

   ANS: D   DIF: II   OBJ: 37-1.4

16. Refer to the illustration above. Movement of this organism is dependent upon the structure labeled
   a. "1."
   b. "2."
   c. "3."
   d. None of the above

   ANS: C   DIF: II   OBJ: 37-1.4

17. Shells of mollusks
   a. may consist of one or more pieces.
   b. provide protection.
   c. allow for the attachment of muscles.
   d. All of the above

   ANS: D   DIF: I   OBJ: 37-1.4

18. Adductor muscles are responsible for
   a. moving the valves of bivalves.
   b. extending the feet of mollusks.
   c. pumping the hearts of mollusks.
   d. fanning the gills of aquatic mollusks.

   ANS: A   DIF: I   OBJ: 37-1.4

19. In an open circulatory system,
    a. water is drawn into the mantle cavity to provide oxygen to body tissues.
    b. lungs branch into small tubules to provide oxygen to tissues.
    c. wastes are eliminated directly to the environment from the tissues.
    d. body tissues are bathed directly in blood.

    ANS: D   DIF: I   OBJ: 37-1.4

20. The foot of the mollusk performs all the following functions *except*
    a. locomotion.
    b. scraping particles of food off the sea bottom.
    c. burrowing into the sand.
    d. capturing prey.

    ANS: B   DIF: I   OBJ: 37-1.4

21. The gills of bivalves are covered with a sticky mucus
    a. because bivalves live in polluted waters.
    b. in order to trap small organisms consumed as food.
    c. to protect them from irritation.
    d. in order to cause water to pass over them more rapidly.

    ANS: B   DIF: I   OBJ: 37-1.4

22. During reproduction in bivalves, fertilization
    a. occurs internally.
    b. occurs externally.
    c. takes place in the mantle cavity.
    d. does not occur, since bivalves are hermaphroditic.

    ANS: B   DIF: I   OBJ: 37-1.4

23. Twisting of the visceral mass of gastropods is called
    a. extension.   c. torsion.
    b. inversion.   d. conversion.

    ANS: C   DIF: I   OBJ: 37-1.4

24. Among the various species of gastropods, respiration may take place
    a. with gills.   c. with lungs.
    b. through the skin.   d. All of the above

    ANS: D   DIF: I   OBJ: 37-1.4

25. All of the cephalopods
    a. have eight tentacles.   c. possess protective shells.
    b. are active predators.   d. are filter feeders.

    ANS: B   DIF: I   OBJ: 37-1.4

26. Jet propulsion in an octopus or squid is the result of
    a. rapid closing of the organism's shell.
    b. strong contractions of the tentacles.
    c. high-pressure "spitting" of fluid from the organism's mouth.
    d. forcefully squeezing water from the siphon.

    ANS: D   DIF: I   OBJ: 37-1.4

27. The only cephalopod that has retained its external shell is the
    a. cuttlefish.   c. octopus.
    b. nautilus.   d. squid.

    ANS: B   DIF: I   OBJ: 37-1.4

28. Segmented worms are known as
    a. nematodes.   c. planarians.
    b. annelids.   d. arthropods.

    ANS: B   DIF: I   OBJ: 37-2.1

29. Each segment of an annelid
    a. is capable of reproduction.   c. has a pseudocoelom.
    b. has a well-developed brain.   d. has a complete set of digestive organs.

    ANS: D   DIF: I   OBJ: 37-2.1

30. An example of segmentation in humans is the
    a. digestive system.   c. vertebral column.
    b. skin.   d. brain.

    ANS: C   DIF: I   OBJ: 37-2.1

31. The evolution of tremendous diversity in the phylum Annelida is due primarily to
    a. gills.   c. cephalization.
    b. specialized reproductive organs.   d. segmented bodies.

    ANS: D   DIF: I   OBJ: 37-2.1

32. The most significant evolutionary advancement of annelids over mollusks is believed to be
    a. the ability to burrow.   c. segmentation.
    b. the existence of a true coelom.   d. cephalization.

    ANS: C   DIF: I   OBJ: 37-2.1

33. A similarity between annelids and arthropods is that they both have
    a. exoskeletons made of chitin.   c. segmented body patterns.
    b. the ability to fly.   d. well-developed lungs for respiration.

    ANS: C   DIF: I   OBJ: 37-2.1

34. Segmented worms are known as
    a. nematodes.
    b. annelids.
    c. planarians.
    d. arthropods.

ANS: B   DIF: I   OBJ: 37-2.1

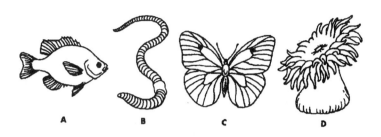

35. Refer to the illustration above. Which two organisms in the diagrams have segmented body plans?
    a. Organisms "A" and "C"
    b. Organisms "B" and "D"
    c. Organisms "A" and "D"
    d. Organisms "B" and "C"

ANS: D   DIF: II   OBJ: 37-2.1

36. true coelom : mollusks and annelids ::
    a. tentacle : annelids
    b. siphon : annelids
    c. valve : annelids
    d. segmentation : annelids

ANS: D   DIF: II   OBJ: 37-2.1

37. Coordinated movements of an annelid's body segments are possible because of the
    a. development of an advanced brain.
    b. ventral nerve cord and paired segmental ganglia.
    c. presence of a true coelom in the annelid body.
    d. existence of a complete digestive system.

ANS: B   DIF: I   OBJ: 37-2.2

38. Of the four basic types of tissue, the tissue that is specialized to transmit and receive messages in the body is
    a. epithelial tissue.
    b. connective tissue.
    c. muscle tissue.
    d. nerve tissue.

ANS: D   DIF: I   OBJ: 37-2.2

39. earthworm movement : circular muscles and setae ::
    a. earthworm digestion : circular muscles and setae
    b. earthworm digestion : sperm receptacles
    c. earthworm reproduction : pharynx
    d. earthworm respiration : skin

ANS: D   DIF: II   OBJ: 37-2.2

40. Small tubules that collect wastes from the coelom of mollusks and discharge them from the body are called
    a. nephridia.   c. bivalves.
    b. radulae.   d. spicules.

    ANS: A   DIF: I   OBJ: 37-2.3

41. The digestive tube of annelids is divided into three regions. Which of the following is *not* among these regions?
    a. crop   c. radula
    b. intestine   d. stomach

    ANS: C   DIF: I   OBJ: 37-2.3

42. The advantage of a closed circulatory system over an open circulatory system is that
    a. blood moves more efficiently through the tubes of a closed circulatory system.
    b. a closed circulatory system prevents blood from leaking out of the body.
    c. blood is able to be pumped by a muscular heart in a closed circulatory system.
    d. lungs are able to function in animals with a closed circulatory system.

    ANS: A   DIF: I   OBJ: 37-2.3

43. Of the following organs, the one that does *not* exist in annelids is the
    a. heart.   c. nephridia.
    b. gills.   d. stomach.

    ANS: B   DIF: I   OBJ: 37-2.3

44. The clitellum of an earthworm
    a. contains the heart.   c. acts as a primitive respiratory system.
    b. is associated with reproduction.   d. is necessary for movement.

    ANS: B   DIF: I   OBJ: 37-2.3

45. Earthworms are considered to be beneficial to the environment because
    a. their castings contain nutrients.
    b. they aerate the soil as they move through it.
    c. they break up the soil in which they live.
    d. All of the above

    ANS: D   DIF: I   OBJ: 37-2.3

46. cephalopod motion : siphon ::
    a. annelid motion : siphon
    b. annelid breathing : nephridia
    c. annelid circulation : closed circulatory system
    d. annelid motion : tentacles

    ANS: C   DIF: II   OBJ: 37-2.3

47. The basic body plan of an annelid
    a. consists of joined legs.
    b. is similar to a long tube.
    c. is a tube within a tube.
    d. can be compared to a corkscrew.

    ANS: C   DIF: I   OBJ: 37-2.4

48. The body of the water leech
    a. has suckers on the front and back.
    b. is somewhat flattened.
    c. is segmented.
    d. All of the above

    ANS: D   DIF: I   OBJ: 37-2.4

49. Parapodia are involved in all of the following *except*
    a. swimming.
    b. gas exchange.
    c. burrowing.
    d. reproduction.

    ANS: D   DIF: I   OBJ: 37-2.4

50. Leeches
    a. use suckers to aid in movement.
    b. may be parasitic.
    c. are segmented.
    d. All of the above

    ANS: D   DIF: I   OBJ: 37-2.4

51. leeches : blood ::
    a. earthworms : small animals
    b. earthworms : blood
    c. marine worms : small animals
    d. marine worms : blood

    ANS: C   DIF: II   OBJ: 37-2.4

COMPLETION

1. The _____ larva is a distinguishing characteristic of mollusks and annelids.

    ANS: trochophore   DIF: I   OBJ: 37-1.2

2. Constant beating of _____ in the mantle cavity of mollusks causes a continuous stream of water to pass over the gills.

    ANS: cilia   DIF: I   OBJ: 37-1.2

3. A tonguelike scraping organ used by gastropods in feeding is called a(n) _____.

    ANS: radula   DIF: I   OBJ: 37-1.3

4. An organ known as the _____ is a rasping, tonguelike structure found in some mollusks.

    ANS: radula   DIF: I   OBJ: 37-1.3

5. A snail can pull its head into its mantle cavity because the cavity has been moved to the anterior of the animal during a twisting process called _____ that occurs during development.

ANS: torsion   DIF: I   OBJ: 37-1.4

6. Water is drawn into the bodies of bivalves through tubes called _____.

ANS: siphons   DIF: I   OBJ: 37-1.4

7. A clam's shells close when the pair of _____ contract.

ANS: adductor muscles   DIF: I   OBJ: 37-1.4

8. Structures in mollusks that function as simple kidneys are called _____.

ANS: nephridia   DIF: I   OBJ: 37-1.4

9. The only living cephalopod that has retained its external shell is the _____.

ANS: nautilus   DIF: I   OBJ: 37-1.4

10. The foot of cephalopods has been divided into numerous _____.

ANS: tentacles   DIF: I   OBJ: 37-1.4

11. Snails and slugs belong to the molluscan class _____.

ANS: Gastropoda   DIF: I   OBJ: 37-1.4

12. Of the major classes of mollusks, the one that contains sessile filter-feeders is the _____.

ANS: bivalves   DIF: I   OBJ: 37-1.4

13. A feature of annelids that allowed the development of specialized functions in different parts of the body is _____.

ANS: segmentation   DIF: I   OBJ: 37-2.1

14. Annelids, arthropods, echinoderms, and chordates all have _____ bodies.

ANS: segmented   DIF: I   OBJ: 37-2.1

15. Earthworms belong to the phylum _____.

ANS: Annelida   DIF: I   OBJ: 37-2.2

16. A(n) _____ is a collection of different tissues that work together as a unit to perform a particular function.

    ANS: organ   DIF: I   OBJ: 37-2.3

17. A group of different tissues that are dedicated to one function is called a(an) _____.

    ANS: organ   DIF: I   OBJ: 37-2.3

18. Refer to the illustration above. The structure labeled "A" in the diagram is the ventral _____ cord.

    ANS: nerve   DIF: II   OBJ: 37-2.3

19. In one anterior segment of annelids there is a(n) _____, which is the brain of these organisms.

    ANS: cerebral ganglion   DIF: I   OBJ: 37-2.3

20. A muscular portion of the annelid digestive system that grinds up organic material is called the _____.

    ANS: gizzard   DIF: I   OBJ: 37-2.3

21. A mucus cocoon that will contain the eggs and sperm and allow development of an earthworm's offspring is produced by the _____.

    ANS: clitellum   DIF: I   OBJ: 37-2.3

22. Bristles that exist along the sides of an annelid are called _____.

    ANS: setae   DIF: I   OBJ: 37-2.4

23. Leeches are _____ annelids because they feed on the blood of other animals.

    ANS: parasitic   DIF: I   OBJ: 37-2.4

24. The _____ are annelids that are marine and that have many setae and parapodia.

ANS: polychaetes   DIF: I   OBJ: 37-2.4

PROBLEM

1. You are given an unknown animal to identify. You find that it has a coelom, a one-way digestive tract, and an open circulatory system. Write your answers to the following in the space below.
   a. Which two phyla of animals could this animal possibly belong in?
   b. What kind of information would you need in order to determine which phylum this animal belongs in?

ANS:
a. Mollusca or Arthropoda
b. The presence of a single large foot would indicate that the animal is a mollusk. The presence of six jointed legs would indicate that the animal is an arthropod. If the digestive tract were found to have undergone torsion during development (so that the anus ended up above the mouth), this would indicate that the animal is a mollusk. Arthropods do not undergo such torsion. If the animal were found to respire by means of tracheae, this would indicate that the animal is an arthropod. There are no mollusks that have tracheae. If the animal were found to have a heavy, mineralized shell, this would indicate that the animal is a mollusk. If the exoskeleton is less hard and mineralized, this would indicate that the animal is an arthropod. If the animal were found to have three body parts, a foot, a head, and a visceral mass, this would indicate that the animal is a mollusk. If the animal were found to have three body parts, a head, a thorax, and an abdomen, this would indicate that the animal is an arthropod.

DIF: III   OBJ: 37-1.2

ESSAY

1. From a developmental point of view, what is the advantage of the coelomate body plan over the pseudocoelomate body plan? Write your answer in the space below.

ANS:
The development of the coelom totally within the mesoderm allows contact between the mesoderm and the endoderm. Such contact permits primary induction, physical and chemical contact between the cells of the two germ layers, to occur. This results in the development of organ systems more complex than those in pseudocoelomate organisms.

DIF: II   OBJ: 37-1.1

2. Describe the function of molluscan nephridia. Write your answer in the space below.

ANS:
The movement of cilia draws coelomic fluid into the nephridia. Useful molecules in this fluid are reabsorbed into the mollusk's body tissues. Wastes then pass out of the nephridia through a pore that leads into the mantle cavity. The wastes then leave the body.

DIF: II   OBJ: 37-1.4

3. How is it possible for a snail to pull its head into its mantle cavity in times of danger? Write your answer in the space below.

ANS:
Snails are able to protect themselves when threatened by pulling their head into their mantle cavity. This is possible because the mantle cavity of snails moves to the anterior end of the body during development. Such movement is brought about by a process called torsion, in which the visceral mass of the organism twists 180°, bringing the mantle cavity to the front in a position just over and behind the head.

DIF: II   OBJ: 37-1.4

4. Explain the advantage of internal digestion. Write your answer in the space below.

ANS:
Internal digestion allows animals to eat organisms larger than themselves by taking pieces of those organisms into the body to be digested. The gut of a cnidarian allows this process to take place. A sponge has no gut and is able to consume only organisms small enough to be absorbed by the cells lining its internal cavity.

DIF: II   OBJ: 37-2.3

5. In what ways do the three major phyla of worms differ? In what ways are they alike? Write your answer in the space below.

ANS:
The three phyla of worms have different body plans: Flatworms have a digestive cavity with only one opening and lack a coelom; roundworms have a tubular digestive system open at both ends and a pseudocoelom; segmented worms have an efficient digestive and circulatory system and a true coelom. The worms are similar in that they have tubelike, highly flexible bodies, bilateral symmetry, and three tissue layers.

DIF: II   OBJ: 37-2.4

6. Distinguish among the three classes of annelids. Write your answer in the space below.

ANS:
The phylum Annelida is divided into three classes: polychaetes, oligochaetes, and hirudineans. The polychaetes, believed to be the most ancient of the three classes, have many setae and parapodia on each body segment. Oligochaetes have fewer setae per segment and completely lack parapodia. Hirudineans, the leeches, have neither setae nor parapodia.

DIF: II   OBJ: 37-2.4

CHAPTER 38—ARTHROPODS

TRUE/FALSE

1. Arthropods evolved from insects.

   ANS: F   DIF: I   OBJ: 38-1.1

2. Humans are more closely related to the arthropods than to the echinoderms.

   ANS: F   DIF: I   OBJ: 38-1.1

3. Arthropods may have either an open or a closed circulatory system.

   ANS: F   DIF: I   OBJ: 38-1.1

4. Arthropods have an exoskeleton made of chitin.

   ANS: T   DIF: I   OBJ: 38-1.2

5. The bodies of arthropods are encased in a shell-like exoskeleton.

   ANS: T   DIF: I   OBJ: 38-1.2

6. The outer layer of the arthropod exoskeleton is shed during molting, but products of the breakdown of the exoskeleton inner layer are used to make a new exoskeleton.

   ANS: T   DIF: I   OBJ: 38-1.3

7. Most crustaceans are aquatic.

   ANS: T   DIF: I   OBJ: 38-2.1

8. Crustaceans range in size from microscopic forms to huge lobsters.

   ANS: T   DIF: I   OBJ: 38-2.1

9. Despite the high concentrations often found in the sea, copepods play a very small role in the ocean's food web.

   ANS: F   DIF: I   OBJ: 38-2.2

10. The barnacle is an example of a crustacean that is sessile as an adult.

    ANS: T   DIF: I   OBJ: 38-2.2

11. The swimmerets of lobsters and crayfish are attached to their thorax.

    ANS: F   DIF: I   OBJ: 38-2.3

12. The anatomy of spiders and insects is essentially identical.

ANS: F   DIF: I   OBJ: 38-3.1

13. Female spiders use silk to entrap a prospective mate as part of the mating ritual.

ANS: F   DIF: I   OBJ: 38-3.2

14. Except for the number of legs, millipedes and centipedes are basically the same in structure and diet.

ANS: F   DIF: I   OBJ: 38-3.4

MULTIPLE CHOICE

1. The first animals to invade the land were the
   a. amphibians.
   b. arthropods.
   c. insects.
   d. monerans.

ANS: B   DIF: I   OBJ: 38-1.1

2. The appendages of arthropods
   a. may serve as walking legs.
   b. may be modified into antennae.
   c. may be modified into large pincers.
   d. All of the above

ANS: D   DIF: I   OBJ: 38-1.1

3. The exoskeleton of arthropods and the skin of vertebrates both
   a. are waterproof coatings of the bodies.
   b. are necessary for sensing sound vibrations.
   c. have joints that allow movement to occur.
   d. provide physical support to the body.

ANS: A   DIF: I   OBJ: 38-1.1

4. A similarity between annelids and arthropods is that they both have
   a. exoskeletons made of chitin.
   b. the ability to fly.
   c. segmented body patterns.
   d. well-developed lungs for respiration.

ANS: C   DIF: I   OBJ: 38-1.1

5. Jointed appendages of arthropods may
   a. become specialized for particular functions.
   b. function in locomotion.
   c. function in feeding.
   d. All of the above

ANS: D   DIF: I   OBJ: 38-1.1

6. Characteristics of the arthropods include
   a. segmentation.
   b. a chitinous exoskeleton.
   c. jointed appendages.
   d. All of the above

   ANS: D   DIF: I   OBJ: 38-1.1

7. All of the following are arthropods *except*
   a. spiders.
   b. clam worms.
   c. crabs.
   d. centipedes.

   ANS: B   DIF: I   OBJ: 38-1.1

8. evolutionary origin of arthropod circulatory system : mollusks ::
   a. annelid evolution : arthropods
   b. annelid evolution : trilobite
   c. evolution of arthropod segmentation : annelids
   d. evolution of arthropod segmentation : mollusks

   ANS: C   DIF: II   OBJ: 38-1.1

9. The exoskeleton of arthropods is
   a. moist and thin.
   b. a stiff, watertight outer coat composed of chitin.
   c. an internal structure made up of bones and cartilage.
   d. None of the above

   ANS: B   DIF: I   OBJ: 38-1.2

10. The exoskeleton of arthropods is made of a material called
    a. spongin.
    b. mesoglea.
    c. chitin.
    d. None of the above

    ANS: C   DIF: I   OBJ: 38-1.2

11. Arthropods have a hard outer skeleton and
    a. a backbone.
    b. hair.
    c. a four-chambered heart.
    d. jointed appendages.

    ANS: D   DIF: I   OBJ: 38-1.2

12. arthropod exoskeletons : muscle attachment ::
    a. antennae : walking or flying
    b. mouthparts : flying or walking
    c. arthropod appendages : walking or chewing
    d. arthropod muscles : impeding water loss

    ANS: C   DIF: II   OBJ: 38-1.2

13. Molting in arthropods occurs in response to
    a. enzyme action.
    b. hormonal action.
    c. pressure.
    d. All of the above

    ANS: D   DIF: I   OBJ: 38-1.3

14. Lobsters, insects, and spiders are all examples of
    a. amphibians.
    b. vertebrates.
    c. arthropods.
    d. monerans.

ANS: C   DIF: I   OBJ: 38-1.4

15. Members of the subphylum Uniramia differ from members of other subphyla of arthropods in that
    a. they lack antennae.
    b. their appendages are unbranched.
    c. they have mandibles instead of chelicerae.
    d. they are aquatic.

ANS: B   DIF: I   OBJ: 38-1.4

16. In what way are lobsters similar to spiders?
    a. They have jointed appendages.
    b. They have exoskeletons.
    c. They have segmented bodies.
    d. All of the above

ANS: D   DIF: I   OBJ: 38-2.1

17. Crabs, lobsters, shrimp, and barnacles are members of the subphylum
    a. Diptera.
    b. Centipeda.
    c. Crustacea.
    d. Arachnida.

ANS: C   DIF: I   OBJ: 38-2.1

18. If all copepods died,
    a. bubonic plague would cease to be a problem.
    b. predators that depend on them would quickly find substitute food sources in the sea and fresh water.
    c. our sources of food from the ocean would disappear.
    d. nothing would change.

ANS: C   DIF: I   OBJ: 38-2.2

19. Shrimps, lobsters, and crabs are examples of
    a. uropods.
    b. copepods.
    c. hemipods.
    d. decapods.

ANS: D   DIF: I   OBJ: 38-2.2

20. spiders : subphylum Chelicerata ::
    a. scorpions : class Crustacea
    b. millipedes : class Crustacea
    c. centipedes : class Crustacea
    d. lobsters : class Crustacea

ANS: D   DIF: II   OBJ: 38-2.2

21. crayfish : swimmerets for swimming and reproduction ::
    a. lobsters : uropods for reproduction
    b. shrimp : telson for chewing
    c. crabs : telson for eating
    d. crustaceans : gills for breathing

ANS: D   DIF: II   OBJ: 38-2.3

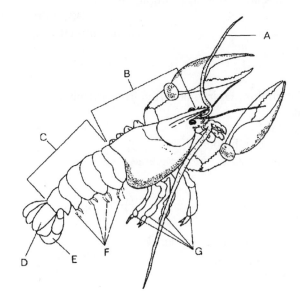

22. Refer to the illustration above. "A flattened, paddle-like appendage" best describes the structure labeled
    a. "D."   c. "F."
    b. "E."   d. "G."

    ANS: B   DIF: II   OBJ: 38-2.3

23. Refer to the illustration above. The organism shown is
    a. an insect.   c. a crustacean.
    b. a chelicerate.   d. a nymph.

    ANS: C   DIF: II   OBJ: 38-2.3

24. Refer to the illustration above. The structure labeled "C" is the
    a. cephalothorax.   c. abdomen.
    b. tail.   d. gill case.

    ANS: C   DIF: II   OBJ: 38-2.4

25. Refer to the illustration above. The structure labeled "B" is covered on top by a shield called the
    a. nauplius.   c. thorax.
    b. carapace.   d. ossicle.

    ANS: B   DIF: II   OBJ: 38-2.4

26. Spiders, scorpions, and mites belong to the subphylum
    a. Arthropoda.   c. Chordata.
    b. Crustacea.   d. Chelicerata.

    ANS: D   DIF: I   OBJ: 38-3.1

27. Spiders, scorpions, and ticks belong to the class
    a. Isoptera.
    b. Crustacea.
    c. Chordata.
    d. Arachnida.

    ANS: D   DIF: I   OBJ: 38-3.1

28. Directly behind the chelicerae, spiders have a pair of appendages called the
    a. antennae.
    b. walking legs.
    c. pedipalps.
    d. spinnerets.

    ANS: C   DIF: I   OBJ: 38-3.2

29. Spiders use silk to
    a. trap their prey.
    b. line their nests.
    c. encase captured prey.
    d. All of the above

    ANS: D   DIF: I   OBJ: 38-3.2

30. Spiders typically have
    a. three body segments and six legs.
    b. two body segments and four legs.
    c. two body segments and eight legs.
    d. None of the above

    ANS: C   DIF: I   OBJ: 38-3.2

31. The small nozzle-like structures used by spiders to produce silk are called
    a. mouthparts.
    b. pedipalps.
    c. spinnerets.
    d. silk nozzles.

    ANS: C   DIF: I   OBJ: 38-3.2

32. arachnid's second pair of appendages : palps ::
    a. arachnid's legs : pincers
    b. arachnid's first pair of appendages : walking legs
    c. spider's first pair of appendages : chelicerae
    d. spider's fangs : palps

    ANS: C   DIF: II   OBJ: 38-3.2

33. The appendages that scorpions and spiders use to capture and handle their prey are called
    a. diptera.
    b. walking legs.
    c. palps.
    d. uropods.

    ANS: C   DIF: I   OBJ: 38-3.3

34. Mites and ticks differ from other arthropods in that
    a. they have pedipalps.
    b. they are parasitic.
    c. their cephalothorax and abdominal regions are fused together.
    d. they are very small.

    ANS: C   DIF: I   OBJ: 38-3.3

35. Millipedes feed mainly on
    a. decayed plants.
    b. other insects.
    c. crustaceans.
    d. wood products.

    ANS: A   DIF: I   OBJ: 38-3.4

36. Centipedes
    a. have one pair of legs per segment and eat decaying matter.
    b. have two pairs of legs per segment and are predators.
    c. have two pairs of legs per segment and eat decaying matter.
    d. have one pair of legs per segment and are predators.

    ANS: D   DIF: I   OBJ: 38-3.4

37. The name *millipede* means
    a. "thousand feet."
    b. "hundred feet."
    c. "one foot per millimeter."
    d. None of the above

    ANS: A   DIF: I   OBJ: 38-3.4

COMPLETION

1. Bees, spiders, shrimp, and lobsters are all members of the phylum
   _____.

   ANS: Arthropoda   DIF: I   OBJ: 38-1.1

2. A lobster is a member of the phylum _____.

   ANS: Arthropoda   DIF: II   OBJ: 38-1.1

3. Arthropods have an external skeleton called the _____.

   ANS: exoskeleton   DIF: I   OBJ: 38-1.2

4. An arthropod's exoskeleton is softest when it _____.

   ANS: is first formed   DIF: I   OBJ: 38-1.3

5. Arthropods that have jaws, such as centipedes, are called _____.

   ANS: mandibulates   DIF: I   OBJ: 38-1.4

6. Insects, millipedes, and centipedes belong to the subphylum _____.

   ANS: Uniramia   DIF: I   OBJ: 38-1.4

7. _____ are the only arthropods with two pairs of antennae.

   ANS: Crustaceans   DIF: I   OBJ: 38-2.1

8. _____ are very important crustaceans that link the ocean's photosynthetic life to the rest of the ocean's food web.

ANS: Copepods   DIF: I   OBJ: 38-2.2

9. Crustaceans breathe with the aid of _____.

ANS: gills   DIF: I   OBJ: 38-2.2

10. Some decapods have a tail spine called a(n) _____.

ANS: telson   DIF: I   OBJ: 38-2.3

11. The gills of the crayfish are located _____.

ANS: inside the crayfish's exoskeleton   DIF: I   OBJ: 38-2.4

12. The structures at the end of a spider's abdomen that direct the flow of silk from silk-producing glands are called _____.

ANS: spinnerets   DIF: I   OBJ: 38-3.2

Respiratory Structure of Some Arthropods

13. Refer to the illustration above. Structure "B," which is an opening through which air enters some arthropods, is called a(n) _____.

ANS: spiracle   DIF: II   OBJ: 38-3.2

14. Refer to the illustration above. Structure "A," which is known as a(n) _____, carries air from the outside to the tissues of some arthropods.

ANS: trachea   DIF: II   OBJ: 38-3.2

15. Scorpions are distinguished from other arthropods by the presence of a
_____ on the abdomen.

    ANS: stinger   DIF: I   OBJ: 38-3.3

16. The name _____ means "hundred feet."

    ANS: centipede   DIF: I   OBJ: 38-3.4

ESSAY

1. If a mutation occurred during a crustacean's embryonic development that prevented it from molting, how might the crustacean be affected? Write your answer in the space below.

    ANS:
Because crustaceans must molt in order to grow, the crustacean would be unable to grow larger than the size it attained before emerging from the egg.

    DIF: II   OBJ: 38-2.1

2. Why have crustaceans been less successful than insects in invading the land? Write your answer in the space below.

    ANS:
The exoskeleton of crustaceans is heavier and less waterproof than that of insects. Insects have efficient excretory and water-balance organs that help them get rid of wastes while conserving water. In addition, crustaceans have gills that are efficient underwater but collapse in air.

    DIF: II   OBJ: 38-2.2

3. Describe the uses of spider silk. Write your answer in the space below.

    ANS:
Spider silk is used as a safety line, to protect the young, to line burrows, and to trap food.

    DIF: II   OBJ: 38-3.2

CHAPTER 39—INSECTS

TRUE/FALSE

1. A flying insect carries pollen from one flower to pollinate other flowers of different species.

   ANS: F   DIF: I   OBJ: 39-1.1

2. Insects comprise the only group of invertebrates whose members are primarily terrestrial.

   ANS: T   DIF: II   OBJ: 39-1.1

3. Insects were the first animals to evolve wings.

   ANS: T   DIF: I   OBJ: 39-1.2

4. Flight enabled insects to search Earth's surface for food, mates, and nesting sites.

   ANS: T   DIF: I   OBJ: 39-1.2

5. A major factor in the evolutionary success of insects is their ability to move to and survive in new environments.

   ANS: T   DIF: I   OBJ: 39-1.2

6. Insects destroy not only crops but also wood buildings and clothing.

   ANS: T   DIF: I   OBJ: 39-1.3

7. Butterflies undergo incomplete metamorphosis.

   ANS: F   DIF: I   OBJ: 39-1.5

8. Insects use pheromones, sounds, and light to attract mates.

   ANS: T   DIF: I   OBJ: 39-2.1

9. The honeybee's round dance gives complete location information about a food source.

   ANS: F   DIF: I   OBJ: 39-2.3

MULTIPLE CHOICE

1. Most insects
   a. have two pairs of wings and two pairs of legs.
   b. have one set of wings and six pairs of legs.
   c. cannot fly.
   d. have two wings and three pairs of legs.

   ANS: D   DIF: I   OBJ: 39-1.1

2. From fossils, we know that insects were the first animals to evolve
   a. pincers on their front legs.   c. jointed legs.
   b. stingers at the end of their tails.   d. wings.

   ANS: D   DIF: I   OBJ: 39-1.1

3. The most diverse group of animals on Earth are the
   a. reptiles.   c. insects.
   b. mammals.   d. amphibians.

   ANS: C   DIF: I   OBJ: 39-1.1

4. Flying insects feed on flowering plants and
   a. pollinate other plants of the same species.
   b. pollinate other plants of different species.
   c. carry pollen home to the young insects that can't yet fly.
   d. then, because of their body weight, are unable to fly away.

   ANS: A   DIF: I   OBJ: 39-1.1

5. Which of the following is *not* a characteristic of most insects?
   a. wings   c. small size
   b. three body regions   d. abdomen with three pairs of legs

   ANS: D   DIF: I   OBJ: 39-1.1

6. Insects have been very successful because
   a. they reproduce in large numbers.
   b. they evolved the ability to fly.
   c. some of them can feed on flower nectar.
   d. All of the above

   ANS: D   DIF: I   OBJ: 39-1.2

7. The exoskeleton of an insect
   a. does not have any muscles attached to it.
   b. is moved by muscles that are attached to the outside of the exoskeleton.
   c. may be modified into large pincers.
   d. is moved only by muscles attached to the wings.

   ANS: C   DIF: I   OBJ: 39-1.2

8. Flying insects were able to use the ability to fly to do everything listed below *except*
   a. patrol the entire surface of Earth.
   b. search for food, mates, or nesting sites.
   c. develop a mutualistic relationship with fungi.
   d. transport objects long distances.

   ANS: C   DIF: I   OBJ: 39-1.2

9. arthropods : live on land ::
   a. plants : absorb minerals from rocks
   b. fungi : make food
   c. scorpions : fly
   d. insects : fly

   ANS: D   DIF: II   OBJ: 39-1.2

10. While insects destroy crops grown for human consumption, they also contribute to crop production by
   a. serving as food for many animals.
   b. pollinating crop plants.
   c. dying in the soil, and leaving behind nutrients.
   d. stimulating crop plants to grow faster.

   ANS: B   DIF: I   OBJ: 39-1.3

11. Insects transmit diseases caused by
   a. bacteria.
   b. viruses.
   c. protozoa.
   d. All of the above

   ANS: D   DIF: II   OBJ: 39-1.3

12. Malpighian tubules in insects
   a. remove wastes.
   b. carry blood.
   c. carry Malpighian fluid.
   d. are important in respiration.

   ANS: A   DIF: I   OBJ: 39-1.4

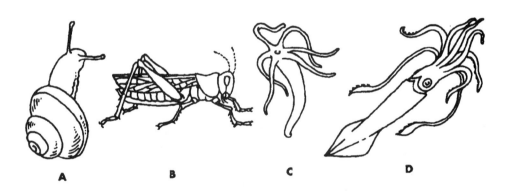

A   B   C   D

13. Refer to the illustration above. Which of the organisms in the diagrams has a chitinous exoskeleton?
   a. Organism "A"
   b. Organism "B"
   c. Organism "C"
   d. Organism "D"

   ANS: B   DIF: II   OBJ: 39-1.4

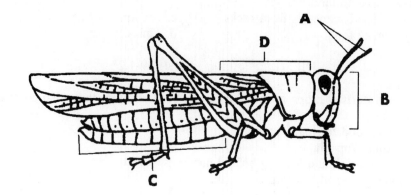

14. Refer to the illustration above. The structures labeled "A" are
    a. similar to structures found on spiders.
    b. used to take in air and water.
    c. specialized for sensing the environment.
    d. reproductive organs.

    ANS: C   DIF: II   OBJ: 39-1.4

15. Refer to the illustration above. Mandibles are attached to the structure labeled
    a. "A."   c. "C."
    b. "B."   d. "D."

    ANS: B   DIF: II   OBJ: 39-1.4

16. Refer to the illustration above. The structure labeled "C" is called the
    a. diptera.   c. boll.
    b. thorax.   d. abdomen.

    ANS: D   DIF: II   OBJ: 39-1.4

17. Refer to the illustration above. The structure labeled "D" is called the
    a. abdomen.   c. thorax.
    b. orthopterus.   d. cuticle.

    ANS: C   DIF: II   OBJ: 39-1.4

18. Pheromones are used by ants to
    a. guide members of a colony back to their own nest.
    b. determine which ants will become queens of future colonies.
    c. ensure that females mate with only one male.
    d. warn members of a colony of adverse environmental conditions.

    ANS: A   DIF: II   OBJ: 39-2.1

Life Cycle of a Butterfly

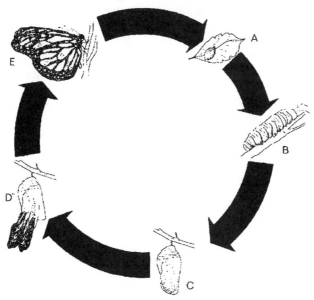

19. Refer to the illustration above. The life cycle shown is an example of
    a. direct development.
    b. complete metamorphosis.
    c. seasonal development.
    d. incomplete metamorphosis.

    ANS: B   DIF: II   OBJ: 39-1.5

20. Refer to the illustration above. The developmental stage shown in diagram "C" is known as the
    a. larva.
    b. caterpillar.
    c. nymph.
    d. chrysalis.

    ANS: D   DIF: II   OBJ: 39-1.5

21. Refer to the illustration above. A larva is shown in diagram
    a. "A."
    b. "B."
    c. "C."
    d. "E."

    ANS: B   DIF: II   OBJ: 39-1.5

22. The behaviors exhibited by honey bees are
    a. learned.
    b. taught.
    c. genetically programmed.
    d. All of the above

    ANS: C   DIF: I   OBJ: 39-2.2

23. Which of the following are the reproductive members of a honeybee colony?
    a. drones
    b. queen
    c. workers
    d. a and b

    ANS: D   DIF: I   OBJ: 39-2.2

24. Which of the following is the accepted explanation for the existence of sterile female worker bees?
    a. Because they are sterile, they do not have to use energy to produce eggs and therefore can use energy to collect food for other bees.
    b. Workers become sterile when they leave the nest to obtain food and are exposed to toxic substances.
    c. Workers pass on a lot of their own genes by helping their fertile sisters to survive and reproduce.
    d. Workers can become fertile females if they are fed queen factor.

ANS: C   DIF: I   OBJ: 39-2.2

COMPLETION

1. Flying insects carry _____ from a flowering plant to other flowers of the same species.

    ANS: pollen   DIF: I   OBJ: 39-1.1

2. The first terrestrial organisms that were able to fly were the _____.

    ANS: insects   DIF: I   OBJ: 39-1.2

3. _____ were the first flying animals.

    ANS: Insects   DIF: I   OBJ: 39-1.2

4. Insects that undergo _____ metamorphosis go through a larval and pupal stage.

    ANS: complete   DIF: I   OBJ: 39-1.5

5. The _____ produced by crickets more readily identify species than do physical characteristics.

    ANS: sounds   DIF: I   OBJ: 39-2.1

6. Young females in a honeybee colony can become queens if they are fed _____.

    ANS: queen factor   DIF: I   OBJ: 39-2.2

7. The angle of a honeybee's dance gives information about the _____, and the duration of the dance gives information about the _____.

    ANS: direction of food; distance of food   DIF: I   OBJ: 39-2.3

PROBLEM

1. Insects have a relatively hard outer covering, called an exoskeleton, that helps protect against excessive water loss and provides structural support. As an insect grows, it periodically sheds its exoskeleton and replaces it with a larger exoskeleton. This process is called molting. Molting is regulated by at least two hormones. One of these, molting hormone, determines when a molt occurs. A sudden, large production of molting hormone will induce an insect to molt. A second hormone, juvenile hormone, determines the nature of a molt. When juvenile hormone levels are high, an insect molts into another juvenile, or larval, stage. When juvenile hormone levels are low, an insect molts into a pupa or an adult. In the space below, draw a graph showing relative levels of molting and juvenile hormones over the life span of an insect that hatches from an egg, has four larval molts, a pupal stage, and an adult stage. Indicate on the time axis when molts occur.

ANS:
The students' graphs should look something like the following:

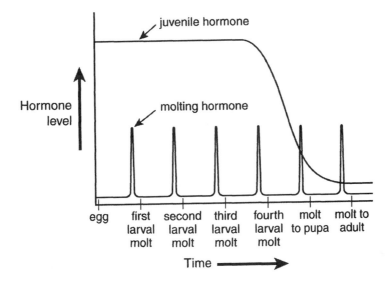

DIF: III   OBJ: 39-1.5

ESSAY

1. Insect larvae typically spend most of their time eating. What do you think might be the purpose of this behavior? Write your answer in the space below.

ANS:
Larvae eat to store energy for the pupa stage, during which metamorphosis takes place.

DIF: II   OBJ: 39-1.5

CHAPTER 40—ECHINODERMS AND INVERTEBRATE CHORDATES

TRUE/FALSE

1. Chordates and echinoderms have a common ancestor.

   ANS: T   DIF: I   OBJ: 40-1.1

2. None of the echinoderms living in the oceans today is sessile.

   ANS: F   DIF: I   OBJ: 40-1.1

3. In addition to radial symmetry, echinoderms have a water-vascular system.

   ANS: T   DIF: I   OBJ: 40-1.2

4. The hard, spiny skin of an echinoderm is called an exoskeleton.

   ANS: F   DIF: I   OBJ: 40-1.2

5. All echinoderms except the sand dollar display a five-part radial symmetry.

   ANS: F   DIF: I   OBJ: 40-1.2

6. The adult form of all echinoderms exhibits radial symmetry.

   ANS: T   DIF: I   OBJ: 40-1.2

7. Sea stars are carnivores and are among the most important predators in many marine ecosystems.

   ANS: T   DIF: I   OBJ: 40-1.3

8. In some echinoderms, respiration and waste removal are performed by skin gills.

   ANS: T   DIF: I   OBJ: 40-1.4

9. A separated piece of a sea star can regenerate the rest of its body as long as the piece contains part of the central region of the animal.

   ANS: T   DIF: I   OBJ: 40-1.5

MULTIPLE CHOICE

1. Embryological evidence suggests that the echinoderms are closely related to the
   a. vertebrates.
   b. arthropods.
   c. annelids.
   d. arachnids.

   ANS: A   DIF: I   OBJ: 40-1.1

2. The first organisms to develop a hardened endoskeleton were the
   a. echinoderms.
   b. annelids.
   c. arthropods.
   d. chordates.

   ANS: A   DIF: I   OBJ: 40-1.1

3. Echinoderms
   a. are radially symmetrical as larvae and as adults.
   b. have an exoskeleton as adults.
   c. are bilaterally symmetrical as larvae and radially symmetrical as adults.
   d. are radially symmetrical as larvae and bilaterally symmetrical as adults.

   ANS: C   DIF: I   OBJ: 40-1.2

4. The symmetry exhibited by echinoderms is
   a. bilateral.
   b. spherical.
   c. radial.
   d. mirror image.

   ANS: C   DIF: I   OBJ: 40-1.2

5. Echinoderms are restricted to marine habitats because they
   a. have no circulatory system.
   b. reproduce externally.
   c. have gills.
   d. have no excretory organs.

   ANS: D   DIF: I   OBJ: 40-1.2

6. In echinoderms and chordates, all the cells of the early embryo
   a. are controlled by molecules within the egg.
   b. form the "first mouth."
   c. fall into four different categories.
   d. are identical.

   ANS: D   DIF: I   OBJ: 40-1.2

7. The skeleton of an echinoderm is composed of individual plates called
   a. ocelli.
   b. ossicles.
   c. odonata.
   d. isopods.

   ANS: B   DIF: I   OBJ: 40-1.2

8. Which of the following are echinoderms?
   a. sea stars
   b. sand dollars
   c. sea urchins
   d. All of the above

   ANS: D   DIF: I   OBJ: 40-1.3

9. Which of the following are sessile echinoderms?
   a. feather stars
   b. sand dollars
   c. sea urchins
   d. sea lilies

   ANS: D   DIF: I   OBJ: 40-1.3

10. Which of the following is *not* a food source for sea stars?
    a. clams
    b. cnidarians
    c. oysters
    d. sponges

    ANS: D   DIF: I   OBJ: 40-1.3

11. sea cucumbers : a fused skeleton ::
    a. sea urchins : a five-part body plan
    b. sea urchins : distinct arms
    c. sand dollars : endoskeletons
    d. sea urchins : endoskeletons

    ANS: B   DIF: II   OBJ: 40-1.3

12. Sea stars can reproduce asexually by
    a. growing longer and longer arms that eventually break off and form new individuals.
    b. growing an extra arm that separates from the parent and forms a new individual.
    c. dividing in half; each half regenerating the missing half, and forming two new individuals.
    d. All of the above

    ANS: C   DIF: I   OBJ: 40-1.5

13. The subphylum Vertebrata includes all of the following *except*
    a. fish.
    b. lancelets.
    c. reptiles.
    d. birds.

    ANS: B   DIF: I   OBJ: 40-2.1

14. Vertebrates, tunicates, and lancelets
    a. are all members of the phylum Chordata.
    b. all have a backbone in the adult stage.
    c. are all marine fish.
    d. are all terrestrial heterotrophs.

    ANS: A   DIF: I   OBJ: 40-2.1

15. Lancelets
    a. are animals that live near the ocean surface.
    b. filter food from water that enters the mouth.
    c. have chordate features only in the larvae stage.
    d. are the first animals that evolved backbones.

    ANS: B   DIF: I   OBJ: 40-2.2

16. Which embryonic chordate characteristics do lancelets retain as adults?
    a. notochord
    b. notochord and dorsal nerve cord
    c. notochord, dorsal nerve cord, and postanal tail
    d. notochord, dorsal nerve cord, postanal tail, and pharyngeal pouches

    ANS: D   DIF: I   OBJ: 40-2.2

17. tunicates : in shallow- and deep-water environments ::
    a. lancelets : buried in mud or sand
    b. lancelets : swimming near the water's surface
    c. tentacles : in sea urchin mouths
    d. ossicles : in lancelets

    ANS: A   DIF: II   OBJ: 40-2.3

18. Some scientists have hypothesized that the first vertebrates, which were fish, may have evolved from an ancestral tunicate that became sexually mature in the larval form. They suggest that these reproducing larvae were successful and natural selection reinforced the absence of metamorphosis to the adult. Which of the following statements does *not* support the hypothesis that vertebrates evolved from a sexually mature larval tunicate?
    a. Many invertebrates, tunicate larvae and adults, and the earliest vertebrates are or were filter feeders.
    b. Adult tunicates are sessile and larval tunicates are free-swimming.
    c. The vertebral column of adult vertebrates replaces the notochord present in embryonic vertebrates.
    d. Some living urochordates exist only as free-swimming larvae.

    ANS: A   DIF: III   OBJ: 40-2.3

COMPLETION

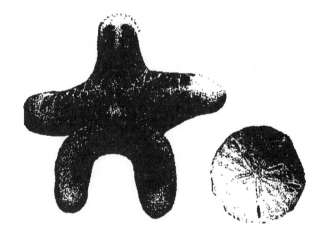

1. Refer to the illustration above. The animals shown are members of the phylum _____.

    ANS: Echinodermata   DIF: II   OBJ: 40-1.2

2. Sea cucumbers belong to the phylum _____.

    ANS: Echinodermata   DIF: I   OBJ: 40-1.3

3. A sand dollar is a member of the phylum _____.

    ANS: Echinodermata   DIF: II   OBJ: 40-1.3

4. The system of interconnected canals and tube feet in echinoderms is called a(n) _____ system.

    ANS: water-vascular   DIF: I   OBJ: 40-1.4

5. Water enters the water-vascular system of echinoderms through small pores in the _____, a sievelike plate on the arboral surface.

    ANS: madreporite   DIF: I   OBJ: 40-1.4

6. Sexual reproduction in most echinoderms occurs as follows: a sperm and an egg fuse to form a zygote, the zygote develops into a swimming larva called a _____, which is _____ symmetrical, and then the larva develops into a _____ symmetrical adult.

    ANS: bipinnaria; radially; pentaradially   DIF: I   OBJ: 40-1.5

7. Adult tunicates have a tough sac made out of _____ that surrounds their bodies.

    ANS: cellulose   DIF: I   OBJ: 40-2.3

ESSAY

1. The phylum Chordata is divided into three subphyla. Briefly describe each of these groups of organisms, and explain why animals in each group are considered chordates. Write your answer in the space below.

    ANS:
All these subphyla exhibit the three typical chordate features (notochord, dorsal hollow nerve cord, pharyngeal gill slits) at some time during their life cycle. The Urochordata (tunicates) have larvae that show these characteristics, but the adults do not. Members of Cephalochordata show the three features as adults. Members of the subphylum Vertebrata have all the stages throughout the life cycle, but are distinguished from members of the other two subphyla by the possession of a vertebral column (backbone) as well.

    DIF: II   OBJ: 40-2.1

2. While lancelets and humans do not resemble each other in appearance, they are both members of the same phylum. Why? Write your answer in the space below.

    ANS:
Lancelets and humans are chordates. All chordates have a dorsal hollow nerve chord, a notochord, and slits in the pharynx that connect the pharynx to the outside.

    DIF: II   OBJ: 40-2.2

3. Compare and contrast tunicates and lancelets. How are they alike and how are they different from vertebrates? Write your answer in the space below.

ANS:
Tunicates and lancelets are both members of the phylum Chordata, which also includes vertebrates. The tunicates lack a notochord in their adult stage but possess one in their free-swimming, larval state. Tunicates and lancelets differ from vertebrates in several ways. Tunicates are sessile, filter-feeding marine animals and have a plantlike substance, cellulose, in their outer body layer. Tunicates lose the ability to swim once they become adults, and they maintain only one chordate feature, the pharyngeal slit. Lancelets are tiny marine animals that live in shallow water. Lancelets can swim, but they spend most of their time burrowed in the mud or sand. Lancelets retain all four chordate features throughout their lifetime.

DIF: II   OBJ: 40-2.3

4. Why are tunicates classified in the phylum Chordata? Write your answer in the space below.

ANS:
Tunicate larvae have a body cavity, nerve cord, and notochord. These are all characteristics possessed by chordates.

DIF: II   OBJ: 40-2.3

CHAPTER 41—FISHES

TRUE/FALSE

1. Lobe-finned fishes were the ancestors of amphibians.

    ANS: T   DIF: I   OBJ: 41-1.2

2. A land animal needs stronger bones and muscles than an aquatic animal does because of the increased pull of gravity on terrestrial body structures.

    ANS: T   DIF: I   OBJ: 41-1.2

3. Small, jawed fishes are the first vertebrates for which there is fossil evidence.

    ANS: F   DIF: I   OBJ: 41-1.3

4. Fishes and amphibians first appeared on Earth during the Cambrian period, about 550 million years ago.

    ANS: F   DIF: I   OBJ: 41-1.3

5. Jawless fishes were the first vertebrates to evolve.

    ANS: T   DIF: I   OBJ: 41-1.3

6. A fish's gills would collapse on land.

    ANS: T   DIF: I   OBJ: 41-2.1

7. Since they live in salt water, marine fishes do not have a problem maintaining the proper balance of water and salt in their body.

    ANS: F   DIF: I   OBJ: 41-2.1

8. The first fishes that appeared in the ancient seas were jawless and toothless.

    ANS: T   DIF: I   OBJ: 41-2.3

9. The first fishes to develop jaws were called spiny fishes, members of the class Acanthodia.

    ANS: T   DIF: I   OBJ: 41-2.3

10. Both sharks and bony fishes evolved in the ancient seas.

    ANS: F   DIF: I   OBJ: 41-2.3

11. Sharks have good vision and can detect electromagnetic fields coming from prey animals.

    ANS: T   DIF: I   OBJ: 41-2.4

12. Sharks and rays have skeletons of bone.

ANS: F   DIF: I   OBJ: 41-3.1

13. Members of the class Osteichthyes have skeletons of cartilage.

ANS: F   DIF: I   OBJ: 41-3.1

14. In fishes, oxygenated blood passes from the gills to the heart and then to the rest of the body.

ANS: F   DIF: I   OBJ: 41-3.4

15. Bony fishes have a swim bladder.

ANS: T   DIF: I   OBJ: 41-3.5

16. In order to fill their swim bladders, bony fishes have to come to the surface to gulp air.

ANS: F   DIF: I   OBJ: 41-3.5

MULTIPLE CHOICE

1. Which of the following would *not* be an advantage of the endoskeleton found in all vertebrates?
   a. It protects internal body structures.
   b. It aids in movement.
   c. It helps prevent desiccation in terrestrial vertebrates.
   d. It provides structural support in terrestrial vertebrates.

ANS: C   DIF: II   OBJ: 41-1.1

2. Which of the following is *not* found in all vertebrates?
   a. jaws   c. endoskeleton
   b. cranium   d. vertebral column

ANS: A   DIF: I   OBJ: 41-1.1

3. The first stage in the evolution of the animal body occurred
   a. over millions of years in the sea.
   b. relatively recently, once organisms emerged from the sea.
   c. among free-floating algae in ancient seas.
   d. on dry land, several hundred million years ago.

ANS: A   DIF: I   OBJ: 41-1.3

4. The first fishes to have paired fins and jaws were
   a. sharks.   c. bony fishes.
   b. rays.   d. acanthodians.

ANS: D   DIF: I   OBJ: 41-1.4

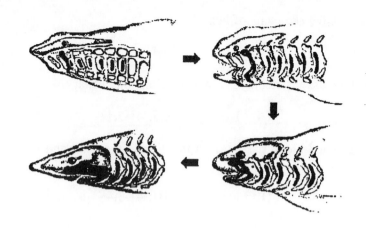

5. Refer to the illustration above. The diagrams show
   a. how a lamprey feeds.
   b. the evolution of gills.
   c. the evolution of jaws.
   d. the evolution of bony skeletons.

   ANS: C   DIF: II   OBJ: 41-1.4

6. Jaws probably evolved from the
   a. pectoral fins of jawless fishes.
   b. gills slits of sharks and rays.
   c. paired pelvic fins of jawless fishes.
   d. gill arches of jawless fishes.

   ANS: D   DIF: I   OBJ: 41-1.4

7. The concentration of the urine an animal produces depends primarily on
   a. the time of the year.
   b. the size of the organism.
   c. the animal's environment.
   d. the diet of the organism.

   ANS: C   DIF: I   OBJ: 41-2.1

8. The structure of a fish that filters dissolved chemical wastes from the blood is a(n)
   a. lung.
   b. heart.
   c. amnion.
   d. kidney.

   ANS: D   DIF: II   OBJ: 41-2.1

9. The urinary bladder and kidneys make up the _____ of a fish.
   a. respiratory system.
   b. digestive system.
   c. excretory system.
   d. circulatory system.

   ANS: C   DIF: II   OBJ: 41-2.1

10. Substances that are useful to the body, but filtered out of the blood by kidneys,
    a. are lost and must be constantly replaced through the animal's diet.
    b. would prove poisonous if allowed to remain in the blood.
    c. are converted to feces to be disposed of.
    d. are selectively reabsorbed back into the blood.

    ANS: D   DIF: I   OBJ: 41-2.1

11. Lampreys and hagfishes have
    a. jaws.
    b. paired fins.
    c. a rigid skeleton.
    d. a notochord through all stages of their life cycle.

    ANS: D   DIF: I   OBJ: 41-2.2

12. The word *agnatha* means
    a. "bony fishes."
    b. "without jaws."

    c. "without vertebral column."
    d. "early fish."

    ANS: B   DIF: I   OBJ: 41-2.2

Three Types of Fish

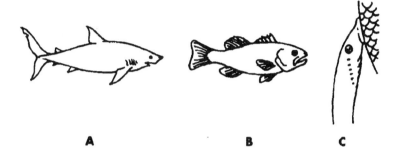

A   B   C

13. Refer to the illustration above. Fish "C" in the diagram
    a. has skin covered by overlapping structures called scales.
    b. has many small scales embedded in the skin.
    c. feeds parasitically on other fish.
    d. does not have a lateral line system.

    ANS: C   DIF: II   OBJ: 41-2.2

14. Refer to the illustration above. Fish "A" in the diagram
    a. has skin covered by overlapping structures called scales.
    b. has many small scales embedded in the skin.
    c. feeds parasitically on other fish.
    d. does not have a lateral line system.

    ANS: B   DIF: II   OBJ: 41-2.3

15. Refer to the illustration above. Fish "B" in the diagram
    a. has skin covered by overlapping structures called scales.
    b. has many small scales embedded in the skin.
    c. feeds parasitically on other fish.
    d. does not have a lateral line system.

    ANS: A   DIF: II   OBJ: 41-3.1

16. The first vertebrates
    a. were jawless fishes.
    b. had thick, bony plates that covered their bodies.
    c. had no well-developed vertebral column.
    d. All of the above

    ANS: D   DIF: I   OBJ: 41-2.2

17. The living agnathans are the
    a. lampreys and sharks.   c. hagfishes and coelacanths.
    b. sharks and rays.   d. lampreys and hagfishes.

    ANS: D   DIF: I   OBJ: 41-2.2

18. Lampreys are
    a. autotrophs.   c. parasites.
    b. mutualistic organisms.   d. amphibians.

    ANS: C   DIF: I   OBJ: 41-2.2

19. jaws : lampreys ::
    a. cartilage : shark   c. teeth : jaws
    b. fins : jawed fishes   d. paired fins : jawless fishes

    ANS: D   DIF: II   OBJ: 41-2.2

20. The ion concentration in the body of a shark
    a. changes constantly as the shark swims at different depths.
    b. is higher than that in the surrounding sea water.
    c. is lower than that in the surrounding sea water.
    d. is the same as that in the surrounding sea water.

    ANS: D   DIF: I   OBJ: 41-2.3

21. The word *chondrichthyes* means
    a. bony fish.   c. big fish.
    b. gilled fish.   d. cartilage fish.

    ANS: D   DIF: I   OBJ: 41-2.3

22. Cartilaginous fishes have all of the following *except*
    a. spiracles.   c. a swim bladder.
    b. internal fertilization.   d. gill slits.

    ANS: C   DIF: I   OBJ: 41-2.3

23. placoderms : armor ::
    a. bony fishes : cartilaginous skeleton
    b. sharks : no teeth
    c. lampreys : jaws
    d. sharks and bony fishes : streamlined bodies

    ANS: D   DIF: II   OBJ: 41-2.3

24. bony fishes : stronger muscles ::
    a. bony fishes : lungs   c. sharks : ray fins
    b. sharks : bony skeleton   d. sharks : rows of teeth

    ANS: D   DIF: II   OBJ: 41-2.3

Structures of the Lateral Line of a Fish

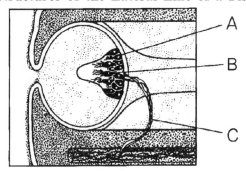

25. Refer to the illustration above. The structure labeled "C" is a
    a. cilium.   c. supporting cell.
    b. scale.   d. nerve.

    ANS: D   DIF: II   OBJ: 41-2.3

26. Which of the following senses is *not* used by sharks to detect prey?
    a. olfaction   c. lateral-line system
    b. vision   d. touch

    ANS: D   DIF: I   OBJ: 41-2.4

27. The eggs of sharks
    a. all develop externally.
    b. are fertilized internally.
    c. are fertilized externally.
    d. have shells like those of chicken eggs.

    ANS: B   DIF: I   OBJ: 41-2.5

28. The eggs of many species of sharks
    a. are released from the mother's body before fertilization.
    b. are released from the mother's body after fertilization.
    c. are released from the mother's body after developing into young embryos.
    d. hatch inside the mother's body, where the young sharks continue to grow.

    ANS: D   DIF: I   OBJ: 41-2.5

29. Members of the class Osteichthyes
    a. have skeletons made of bone.   c. include the rays and skates.
    b. do not have jaws.   d. All of the above

    ANS: A   DIF: I   OBJ: 41-3.1

Modern Biology Assessment Item Listing
379

30. lateral line : motion detector ::
   a. swim bladder : roof on a house
   b. operculum : wheel
   c. operculum : water pump
   d. fin : microwave oven

   ANS: C   DIF: II   OBJ: 41-3.1

External Structure of a Bony Fish

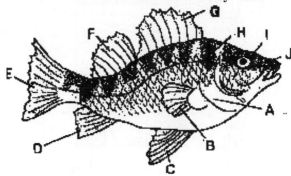

31. Refer to the illustration above. In order to move forward, the fish uses the fin(s) labeled
   a. "B."
   b. "C."
   c. "E."
   d. "F."

   ANS: C   DIF: II   OBJ: 41-3.1

32. Refer to the illustration above. The structure labeled "A," which draws water into the mouth of the fish, is the
   a. pharynx.
   b. esophagus.
   c. gills.
   d. operculum.

   ANS: D   DIF: II   OBJ: 41-3.4

33. Lungfishes
   a. may live in water with a low oxygen content.
   b. are lobe-finned fishes.
   c. can breathe air.
   d. All of the above

   ANS: D   DIF: I   OBJ: 41-3.2

34. The two major groups of bony fishes are the lobe-finned fishes and the
   a. lungfishes.
   b. ray-finned fishes.
   c. coelacanths.
   d. placoderms.

   ANS: B   DIF: I   OBJ: 41-3.2

35. The coelacanth is a
   a. lungfish.
   b. cartilaginous fish.
   c. ray-finned fish.
   d. lobe-finned fish.

   ANS: D   DIF: I   OBJ: 41-3.2

36. A collection chamber that reduces the resistance of blood flow into the heart of a fish is called the
a. sinus venosus.
b. ventricle.
c. conus arteriosus.
d. atrium.

ANS: A   DIF: I   OBJ: 41-3.3

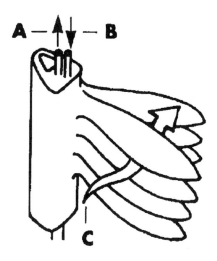

37. Refer to the illustration above. The structure shown in the diagram is a
a. lung.
b. lateral line.
c. gill.
d. trachea.

ANS: C   DIF: II   OBJ: 41-3.4

38. Refer to the illustration above. In the diagram, which arrow indicates the direction of water flow?
a. Arrow "A"
b. Arrow "B"
c. Arrow "C"
d. None of the above

ANS: C   DIF: II   OBJ: 41-3.4

39. Refer to the illustration above. In which of the following organisms might you expect to find the structure illustrated in the diagram?
a. frog
b. spider
c. bird
d. goldfish

ANS: D   DIF: II   OBJ: 41-3.4

40. Refer to the illustration above. Which arrow(s) in the diagram indicate(s) the direction of oxygen-poor blood flow?
a. Arrow "A"
b. Arrow "B"
c. Arrow "C"
d. Arrows "A" and "B"

ANS: B   DIF: II   OBJ: 41-3.4

41. The countercurrent flow of water and blood found in the gills of fishes
    a. allows blood and water to flow in the same direction.
    b. ensures that oxygen diffuses into the blood over the whole length of the blood vessels in the gills.
    c. results in an uneven supply of oxygen reaching the blood vessels in the gills.
    d. hampers the diffusion of oxygen and carbon dioxide between the blood and the water.

    ANS: B   DIF: I   OBJ: 41-3.4

42. The operculum
    a. is part of the skeletal system.   c. covers the gill chamber.
    b. is an adaptation for rapid swimming.   d. None of the above

    ANS: C   DIF: I   OBJ: 41-3.4

43. The gills of bony fishes
    a. give them buoyancy.
    b. are found in a single chamber behind the operculum.
    c. are composed of scales.
    d. are housed in chambers on each side of the head.

    ANS: D   DIF: I   OBJ: 41-3.4

44. folds : lung ::
    a. fish : gill filaments   c. oxygen : atmosphere
    b. gill filaments : gills   d. lung : fish

    ANS: B   DIF: II   OBJ: 41-3.4

45. freshwater fish kidney : dilute urine ::
    a. nephron : kidney   c. milk : kitten
    b. car : exhaust   d. salt water intake : absorption

    ANS: B   DIF: II   OBJ: 41-3.4

46. The swim bladder
    a. stores air for breathing.
    b. contains antibodies.
    c. is found in all amphibians.
    d. allows fishes to become more buoyant.

    ANS: D   DIF: I   OBJ: 41-3.5

47. A critical difference between bony fishes and sharks is
    a. the presence of a swim bladder in most bony fishes.
    b. the presence of a lateral line system in sharks.
    c. that most sharks have color vision.
    d. All of the above

    ANS: A   DIF: I   OBJ: 41-3.5

48. External fertilization is not common on land because
    a. both the sperm and egg run the risk of drying out.
    b. sexual reproduction takes place more readily in rivers, lakes, and oceans.
    c. most of Earth's surface area is covered by water.
    d. All of the above

    ANS: A   DIF: I   OBJ: 41-3.6

49. In most bony fishes,
    a. internal fertilization takes place.   c. internal development takes place.
    b. external fertilization takes place.   d. All of the above

    ANS: B   DIF: I   OBJ: 41-3.6

COMPLETION

1. Frogs, toads, and salamanders belong to class _____.

    ANS: Amphibia   DIF: I   OBJ: 41-1.2

Cross Section of the Head of a Jawless Fish

2. Refer to the illustration above. The arrow labeled "C" is pointing to the
    _____.

    ANS: gill slits   DIF: II   OBJ: 41-1.4

3. Refer to the illustration above. The arrow labeled "B" is pointing to the
    _____.

    ANS: gill arches   DIF: II   OBJ: 41-1.4

4. Shark nostrils have specialized nerve cells that connect with the _____.

    ANS: olfactory bulbs   DIF: II   OBJ: 41-2.4

5. Jawless fishes lay eggs _____ fertilization, while sharks' eggs are
    fertilized _____.

    ANS: before; internally   DIF: I   OBJ: 41-2.5

6. Lobe-finned fishes evolved _____, which let them extract oxygen from the air.

ANS: lungs   DIF: I   OBJ: 41-3.2

Three Vertebrate Hearts

7. Refer to the illustration above. Diagram I represents the heart of a(n) _____.

ANS: fish   DIF: II   OBJ: 41-3.3

8. Refer to the illustration above. The structure labeled "A" is a(n) _____.

ANS: atrium   DIF: II   OBJ: 41-3.3

9. The process of _____ is responsible for the exchange of gases across respiratory membranes.

ANS: diffusion   DIF: I   OBJ: 41-3.4

10. Each gill in a fish is made up of two rows of gill _____ that are stacked on top of one another.

ANS: filaments   DIF: I   OBJ: 41-3.4

11. Marine bony fishes lose water continuously by _____ to the saltier water in which they swim.

ANS: osmosis   DIF: I   OBJ: 41-3.4

12. The _____ gives most bony fishes buoyancy.

ANS: swim bladder   DIF: I   OBJ: 41-3.5

PROBLEM

1. The word *cord* means "a string or other structure that connects two points." From this definition, what can you infer that the notochord of the vertebrate embryo develops into in the adult? Write your answer in the space below.

ANS: The vertebral column   DIF: III   OBJ: 41-1.1

ESSAY

1. Describe how jaws are thought to have evolved. Write your answer in the space below.

   ANS:
   Scientists think that jaws evolved from one or more of the gill arches that support the pharynx in agnathans.

   DIF: II   OBJ: 41-1.4

2. Why must a shark constantly swim through the water? Write your answer in the space below.

   ANS:
   A shark must constantly swim through the water because it has no swim bladder and its body is denser than water.

   DIF: II   OBJ: 41-2.3

3. How is the body design of bony fishes and sharks better adapted for swimming than the body design of primitive fishes? Write your answer in the space below.

   ANS:
   Most bony fishes and sharks have streamlined bodies that are well adapted for movement through the water. The head acts as a wedge that cleaves the water, and the body tapers back to the tail, allowing the fish to slip through the water with minimal resistance. In addition, sharks and bony fishes have an assortment of movable fins that aid their swimming.

   DIF: II   OBJ: 41-3.1

4. Explain the importance of the swim bladder in a bony fish. Write your answer in the space below.

   ANS:
   The swim bladder is a gas-filled sac that gives the fish buoyancy. By regulating the amount of gas in the swim bladder, a fish can remain at different depths without expending energy through swimming.

   DIF: II   OBJ: 41-3.5

5. Why isn't external fertilization an effective way to reproduce on dry land? Write your answer in the space below.

   ANS:
   External fertilization takes place outside the body of either parent. This form of fertilization is less common on dry land because both the egg and sperm run the risk of drying out and dying.

   DIF: II   OBJ: 41-3.6

CHAPTER 42—AMPHIBIANS

TRUE/FALSE

1. Some fossil amphibians had bony plates and armor covering their bodies.

   ANS: T   DIF: I   OBJ: 42-1.2

2. The earliest known amphibian fossil is that of an extinct amphibian called Ichthyostega.

   ANS: T   DIF: I   OBJ: 42-1.2

3. In most amphibians, fertilization takes place externally.

   ANS: T   DIF: I   OBJ: 42-1.3

4. Caecilians are tropical amphibians with four legs and a tail.

   ANS: F   DIF: I   OBJ: 42-1.4

5. Because their skins are watertight, amphibians can live anywhere on dry land.

   ANS: F   DIF: I   OBJ: 42-2.1

6. Waterproof skin is a reptilian adaptation to life on land.

   ANS: T   DIF: I   OBJ: 42-2.2

7. In amphibians, the blood that is pumped from the heart to the body is completely oxygenated.

   ANS: F   DIF: I   OBJ: 42-2.3

8. In amphibians, reproductive cells and wastes exit the body through the cloacal opening.

   ANS: T   DIF: I   OBJ: 42-2.5

9. Frog eggs must be laid in a wet or moist environment.

   ANS: T   DIF: I   OBJ: 42-3.1

10. Some frog larvae undergo metamorphosis in the stomach of their mother.

   ANS: T   DIF: I   OBJ: 42-3.3

MULTIPLE CHOICE

1. The word *amphibian* is derived from Greek words meaning
   a. "fishlike."
   b. "froglike."
   c. "double life."
   d. "first lunged."

   ANS: C   DIF: I   OBJ: 42-1.1

2. Which of the following does *not* indicate that amphibians evolved from a lobe-finned fish?
   a. The limb bones of amphibians are similar in shape and position to those of lobe-finned fishes.
   b. Amphibians' limb bones are used to support the body.
   c. Amphibians are still alive, while lobe-finned fishes are extinct.
   d. Both amphibians and lobe-finned fishes have a skull and a vertebral column.

   ANS: C   DIF: I   OBJ: 42-1.1

3. The earliest known land vertebrate
   a. was a coelacanth.   c. lacked bones in its legs.
   b. was an amphibian.   d. was a now-extinct reptile.

   ANS: B   DIF: I   OBJ: 42-1.2

4. In amphibians, gases are exchanged through lung breathing and through the
   a. heart.   c. lateral line system.
   b. air bladder.   d. skin.

   ANS: D   DIF: I   OBJ: 42-1.3

5. Toads, like frogs,
   a. must live in moist areas.   c. have long tails as adults.
   b. return to the water to reproduce.   d. belong to the order Urodela.

   ANS: B   DIF: I   OBJ: 42-1.3

6. Amphibians without tails are classified in the order
   a. Apoda.   c. Urodela.
   b. Anura.   d. Hydrodela.

   ANS: B   DIF: I   OBJ: 42-1.4

7. Newts and salamanders are amphibians of the order
   a. Apoda.   c. Urodela.
   b. Anura.   d. Gymnophiona.

   ANS: C   DIF: I   OBJ: 42-1.4

8. Amphibians that have slender bodies and no limbs are classified as
   a. anurans.   c. salamanders.
   b. caecilians.   d. newts.

   ANS: B   DIF: I   OBJ: 42-1.4

9. amphi : "double" ::
   a. external : inside
   b. internal : outside   c. anura : "no tail"
                                    d. bios : "water"

   ANS: C   DIF: II   OBJ: 42-1.4

10. Amphibians must have thin, moist skin
    a. to allow easier gas exchange.
    b. because thin, moist skin cannot be eaten by a predator.
    c. so that they can slip easily into tight places.
    d. to resist water loss.

    ANS: A   DIF: I   OBJ: 42-2.1

11. In amphibians, gases are exchanged through lung breathing and through the
    a. heart.   c. tracheids.
    b. air bladder.   d. skin.

    ANS: D   DIF: I   OBJ: 42-2.1

12. reptile : dry ::
    a. amphibian : watertight   c. swim bladder : active
    b. terrestrial : moist   d. amphibian : moist

    ANS: D   DIF: II   OBJ: 42-2.1

13. Some type of skeletal support
    a. exists in all animals, whether they are aquatic or terrestrial.
    b. was necessary for animals to leave aquatic environments.
    c. is present primarily in land vertebrates.
    d. evolved first in reptiles.

    ANS: B   DIF: I   OBJ: 42-2.2

14. Which of the following characteristics of the skeletons of frogs are adaptations for
    jumping?
    a. forelimbs attached to a pectoral girdle and hindlimbs attached to a pelvic girdle
    b. fusion of bones of the hind limbs and of the vertebral column
    c. cervical vertebrae
    d. bony vertebral column

    ANS: B   DIF: I   OBJ: 42-2.2

15. All terrestrial vertebrates
    a. must stay near water in order to reproduce.
    b. have thin, moist skin for gas exchange.
    c. have tracheal systems for delivering oxygen to cells.
    d. have a double-loop circulatory system.

    ANS: D   DIF: I   OBJ: 42-2.3

16. The amphibian heart
    a. pumps only deoxygenated blood.
    b. has four chambers.
    c. pumps only oxygenated blood.
    d. pumps both deoxygenated and oxygenated blood.

    ANS: D   DIF: I   OBJ: 42-2.3

17. Pulmonary veins carry blood from the
    a. body to the heart.
    b. heart to the lungs.
    c. lungs to the heart.
    d. heart to the body.

    ANS: C   DIF: I   OBJ: 42-2.3

18. The amphibian heart
    a. pumps only deoxygenated blood.
    b. has four chambers.
    c. pumps only oxygenated blood.
    d. pumps both deoxygenated and oxygenated blood.

    ANS: D   DIF: I   OBJ: 42-2.3

19. The amount of oxygen a lung can absorb depends primarily on
    a. its thickness.
    b. its position in the body of an animal.
    c. its internal surface area.
    d. the diameter of the bronchioles in the lung.

    ANS: C   DIF: I   OBJ: 42-2.4

20. Frogs breathe by
    a. changing the volume and pressure in their chest cavity.
    b. allowing air currents they encounter as they move to inflate their lungs.
    c. changing the volume and pressure of air in their mouth.
    d. expanding and contracting the muscles of the rib cage.

    ANS: C   DIF: I   OBJ: 42-2.4

21. Adult frogs, like other amphibians, are
    a. herbivores.
    b. omnivores.
    c. parasites.
    d. carnivores.

    ANS: D   DIF: I   OBJ: 42-2.5

22. tympanic membrane : hearing ::
    a. frog tongue : catching prey
    b. frog teeth : chewing food
    c. skin : balance
    d. frog tongue : vocalization

    ANS: A   DIF: II   OBJ: 42-2.5

23. Which of the following senses is *not* more developed in amphibians than in bony fishes?
    a. lateral line system
    b. vision
    c. smell
    d. hearing

    ANS: A   DIF: I   OBJ: 42-2.6

24. Although adapted to land, toads must have access to a watery environment in order to
    a. obtain food and oxygen.
    b. excrete wastes.
    c. reproduce.
    d. All of the above

    ANS: C   DIF: I   OBJ: 42-3.1

25. Amphibians must reproduce in water or moist places because their eggs
    a. are fertilized externally.
    b. have a jelly-like coating that is freely permeable to water.
    c. will dry out if removed from moisture.
    d. All of the above

    ANS: D   DIF: I   OBJ: 42-3.1

26. The series of changes in the life cycle of a frog is called
    a. amniocentesis.   c. evolution.
    b. metamorphosis.   d. synapsis.

    ANS: B   DIF: II   OBJ: 42-3.2

27. During metamorphosis in frogs,
    a. lungs replace gills.   c. the tail disappears.
    b. limbs develop.   d. All of the above

    ANS: D   DIF: I   OBJ: 42-3.2

28. Pulmonary veins carry blood from the
    a. body to the heart.   c. lungs to the heart.
    b. heart to the lungs.   d. heart to the body.

    ANS: C   DIF: I   OBJ: 42-3.3

29. Which of the following is *not* a method used by at least some frogs for caring for
    fertilized eggs as they develop?
    a. gastric-brooding   c. sitting on eggs (nest-brooding)
    b. vocal-chord brooding   d. mouth-brooding

    ANS: D   DIF: I   OBJ: 42-3.3

COMPLETION

1. Amphibians differ from lobe-finned fishes and most other fishes in that they take in
   oxygen through _____.

   ANS: lungs   DIF: I   OBJ: 42-1.1

2. Salamanders and _____ are amphibians with a distinct head, tail, and
   limbs.

   ANS: newts   DIF: I   OBJ: 42-1.3

3. Frogs and toads are amphibians of the class _____.

   ANS: Anura   DIF: I   OBJ: 42-1.4

4. Amphibians supplement the use of their lungs by respiring directly through their skin. This "skin breathing" is known as _____ respiration.

    ANS: cutaneous   DIF: I   OBJ: 42-2.1

5. Amphibians achieve more efficient circulation than fishes because of their _____ circulatory system.

    ANS: double-loop   DIF: I   OBJ: 42-2.3

6. In amphibians, the blood vessels that go from the lungs to the heart are called the _____ veins.

    ANS: pulmonary   DIF: I   OBJ: 42-2.3

7. Young frogs respire using _____ while adult frogs respire using _____.

    ANS: gills; lungs and skin   DIF: I   OBJ: 42-2.4

8. In frogs, the eardrum is called the _____.

    ANS: tympanic membrane   DIF: I   OBJ: 42-2.6

9. Amphibians receive sound waves in their _____, which then causes vibrations that transfer to the _____, which transfers movement to the _____ and finally to the _____.

    ANS: tympanic membrane; columella; inner ear; brain

    DIF: I   OBJ: 42-2.6

10. The changes that transform a tadpole into an adult frog are called _____.

    ANS: metamorphosis   DIF: I   OBJ: 42-3.2

11. Some frogs protect their young until the eggs _____; some protect them all the way through _____.

    ANS: hatch; metamorphosis   DIF: I   OBJ: 42-3.3

ESSAY

1. Why are amphibians found near water? Write your answer in the space below.

    ANS:
Most amphibians pass through a larval stage in water before moving to land, and most amphibians return to water to lay their eggs. Also, the lack of a watertight skin limits many amphibians to a moist environment.

    DIF: II   OBJ: 42-3.1

TRUE/FALSE

1. The embryos of reptiles are surrounded by a watertight protective membrane called the chorion.

    ANS: T   DIF: I   OBJ: 43-1.1

2. Lizards and snakes are found on every continent of the Earth.

    ANS: F   DIF: I   OBJ: 43-1.1

3. The dominant land animals from the middle of the Permian era until the middle of the Triassic era were the therapsids.

    ANS: T   DIF: I   OBJ: 43-1.1

4. Though most dinosaurs became extinct 65 million years ago, a few species still live in remote areas.

    ANS: F   DIF: I   OBJ: 43-1.2

5. The embryos of reptiles are surrounded by a watertight protective membrane called the allantois.

    ANS: F   DIF: I   OBJ: 43-1.3

6. Reptiles must return to the water in order to reproduce.

    ANS: F   DIF: I   OBJ: 43-1.3

7. Modern reptiles are classified by the number of membranes found in their eggs.

    ANS: F   DIF: I   OBJ: 43-1.3

8. Reptiles have dry, largely watertight skin and lay watertight eggs.

    ANS: T   DIF: I   OBJ: 43-1.4

9. Because reptiles have well developed senses of smell and heat detection, sight is of little importance in prey detection.

    ANS: F   DIF: I   OBJ: 43-2.3

10. Animals in which body temperature is largely determined by the environment are called endothermic.

    ANS: F   DIF: I   OBJ: 43-2.4

11. Reptiles are endotherms.

    ANS: F   DIF: I   OBJ: 43-2.4

12. Many reptiles regulate their temperature by their behavior.

    ANS: T   DIF: I   OBJ: 43-2.4

13. Like reptiles, monotremes are oviparous.

    ANS: T   DIF: I   OBJ: 43-2.5

14. Ovoviviparous reptiles carry their eggs in their bodies throughout development, and their young are born alive.

    ANS: T   DIF: I   OBJ: 43-2.5

15. The majority of reptiles are oviparous.

    ANS: T   DIF: I   OBJ: 43-2.5

16. Turtles generally live on land, while tortoises generally live in the water.

    ANS: F   DIF: I   OBJ: 43-3.1

17. Crocodiles have undergone enormous changes since they first appeared 200 million years ago.

    ANS: F   DIF: I   OBJ: 43-3.2

18. Lizards appeared in the late Permian period, about 250 million years ago.

    ANS: T   DIF: I   OBJ: 43-3.3

19. Even though reptiles are ectothermic, rapid movement is important in avoiding capture by predators.

    ANS: T   DIF: I   OBJ: 43-3.3

20. The age of a rattlesnake can be accurately determined by counting the number of rings on its rattle.

    ANS: F   DIF: I   OBJ: 43-3.4

21. Like snakes, tuataras lack legs and move by gliding along the ground.

    ANS: F   DIF: I   OBJ: 43-3.5

MULTIPLE CHOICE

Reptilian Skulls

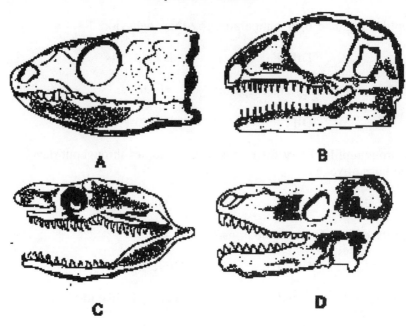

1. Refer to the illustration above. Which diagram shows the type of skull that would most probably have been found on an early reptile?
   a. "A"
   b. "B"
   c. "C"
   d. "D"

   ANS: A   DIF: II   OBJ: 43-1.1

2. Refer to the illustration above. The skull in diagram "C" is most likely the skull of a
   a. turtle.
   b. rhynchocephalian.
   c. snake.
   d. crocodile.

   ANS: C   DIF: II   OBJ: 43-3.4

3. The most widely accepted hypothesis to explain the mass extinction of dinosaurs proposes
   a. a massive volcanic eruption.
   b. sunspots that disrupted the earth's weather.
   c. that Earth cooled in an ice age 65 million years ago.
   d. that Earth was struck by a meteorite that caused thick dust clouds.

   ANS: D   DIF: I   OBJ: 43-1.2

4. dust cloud from meteorite : sun ::
   a. hole in a wall : a wall
   b. window shade : sunlight
   c. road : forest
   d. window : view

   ANS: B   DIF: II   OBJ: 43-1.2

5. The chorion and amnion are
   a. species of primitive fish believed to have been ancestors of modern-day amphibians.
   b. protective membranes in reptile and bird eggs.
   c. protective jelly-like coatings that surround amphibian eggs once they have been fertilized.
   d. chemical forms of nitrogen-containing waste found in aquatic and terrestrial animals, respectively.

   ANS: B   DIF: I   OBJ: 43-1.3

6. Which of the following is a reptilian adaptation to living on land?
   a. external fertilization   c. respiration through gills
   b. endothermic temperature regulation   d. the amniotic egg

   ANS: D   DIF: I   OBJ: 43-1.3

7. The eggs of reptiles, birds, and mammals are surrounded by
   a. the placenta.   c. the yolk.
   b. watertight membranes.   d. a jelly-like, permeable coating.

   ANS: B   DIF: I   OBJ: 43-1.3

8. The outermost membrane of a reptilian egg is the
   a. allantois.   c. mitotic membrane.
   b. yolk sac.   d. chorion.

   ANS: D   DIF: I   OBJ: 43-1.3

9. The skin of reptiles is
   a. moist and watertight.   c. dry and nearly watertight.
   b. moist and thin.   d. dry and watertight.

   ANS: D   DIF: I   OBJ: 43-1.4

10. Evaporation of body water can be limited by
    a. mucus on amphibians.   c. reptilian scales.
    b. a waxy coating on spiders.   d. All of the above

    ANS: D   DIF: I   OBJ: 43-1.4

11. amphibian : moist ::
    a. ball : square   c. reptile : scaly
    b. oxygen : liquid   d. lung : primitive

    ANS: C   DIF: II   OBJ: 43-1.4

12. Reptiles, except for alligators and crocodiles, have a heart that has
    a. two atria and two ventricles.
    b. two atria and one partially divided ventricle.
    c. one atrium and two partially divided ventricles.
    d. two atria and two partially divided ventricles.

    ANS: B   DIF: I   OBJ: 43-2.1

13. oxygen delivery : pulmonary blood vessels ::
    a. lungs : gills
    b. blood separation : septum
    c. oxygen-rich : oxygen-poor
    d. heart : amphibian

    ANS: B   DIF: II   OBJ: 43-2.1

14. While frogs breathe by changing the air pressure in their mouths, reptiles breathe by
    a. expanding and contracting the muscles of their lungs.
    b. sucking air into their lungs.
    c. changing the air pressure in their thorax.
    d. taking in air they encounter in currents or as they move.

    ANS: C   DIF: I   OBJ: 43-2.2

15. rattlesnake pit organ : heat ::
    a. camera light meter : vibrations
    b. cat's whisker : light
    c. crocodile eye : heat
    d. human ear : sound

    ANS: D (detects)   DIF: II   OBJ: 43-2.3

16. Reptiles are
    a. ectothermic.
    b. endothermic.
    c. ergothermic.
    d. None of the above

    ANS: A   DIF: I   OBJ: 43-2.4

17. Endothermic animals
    a. have bodies whose metabolisms maintain a constant internal temperature.
    b. have body temperatures that are not stable.
    c. are found among the reptiles.
    d. are coldblooded.

    ANS: A   DIF: I   OBJ: 43-2.4

18. A four-chambered heart is a characteristic of
    a. ectotherms.
    b. reptiles.
    c. amphibians.
    d. endotherms.

    ANS: D   DIF: I   OBJ: 43-2.4

19. One disadvantage of endothermy is that it
    a. limits the size of an organism.
    b. requires a relatively greater amount of food.
    c. impedes circulation.
    d. limits the organism to temperate climates.

    ANS: B   DIF: I   OBJ: 43-2.4

20. Unlike other living reptiles, crocodilians
    a. are viviparous.
    b. have a three-chambered heart.
    c. care for their young after hatching.
    d. have a synapsid skull.

    ANS: C   DIF: I   OBJ: 43-2.5

21. Some animals are oviparous. This means that their young
    a. are nourished by a placenta.
    b. are born live from eggs that hatch within the mother's body.
    c. hatch from eggs laid outside the mother's body.
    d. continue to develop in the mother's pouch.

    ANS: C   DIF: I   OBJ: 43-2.5

22. The most ancient surviving group of reptiles are the
    a. rhynchocephalians.   c. lizards.
    b. snakes.   d. turtles.

    ANS: D   DIF: I   OBJ: 43-3.1

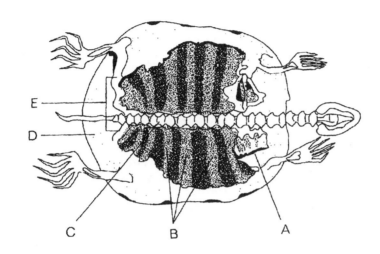

23. Refer to the illustration above. Structure "D" is called the
    a. carapace.   c. cervical cape.
    b. lumbar cover.   d. therapsid.

    ANS: A   DIF: II   OBJ: 43-3.1

24. Refer to the illustration above. The pectoral girdle is labeled
    a. "A."   c. "C."
    b. "B."   d. "D."

    ANS: A   DIF: II   OBJ: 43-3.1

25. Refer to the illustration above. In a turtle, the
    a. ribs are reduced or missing.   c. vertebrae are fused to the ventral shell.
    b. shells are made of calcified cartilage.   d. None of the above

    ANS: D   DIF: I   OBJ: 43-3.1

26. Unlike other reptiles, turtles and tortoises
    a. live only in water.   c. are endangered.
    b. are prehistoric.   d. do not have teeth.

    ANS: D   DIF: I   OBJ: 43-3.1

27. Crocodilians are
    a. herbivorous.
    b. carnivorous.
    c. omnivorous.
    d. carnivorous during the winter months and herbivorous during the summer months.

    ANS: B   DIF: I   OBJ: 43-3.2

28. Autotomy in lizards and other animals is the ability to
    a. maintain warm body temperature by basking in sunlight.
    b. capture enough prey to meet survival needs.
    c. lay eggs that hatch without requiring incubation by a parent's body.
    d. detach a limb when attacked by a predator.

    ANS: D   DIF: II   OBJ: 43-3.3

29. Snakes are reptiles of the order
    a. Squamata.
    b. Saurischia.
    c. Testudines.
    d. Ichthysauria.

    ANS: A   DIF: I   OBJ: 43-3.4

30. Which of the following is true of snakes?
    a. They lack limbs.
    b. They lack movable eyelids.
    c. They lack external ears.
    d. All of the above

    ANS: D   DIF: I   OBJ: 43-3.4

31. The heat-sensing organs between the eyes and nostril on each side of the head of a rattlesnake are the
    a. tracheal organs.
    b. Jacobson's organs.
    c. thermal organs.
    d. pit organs.

    ANS: D   DIF: I   OBJ: 43-3.4

32. The tuatara
    a. represents the last species of reptiles to have evolved.
    b. has a four-chambered heart.
    c. represents the last surviving species of a group of reptiles that appeared more than 225 million years ago.
    d. is found throughout the world except in the Antarctic.

    ANS: C   DIF: I   OBJ: 43-3.5

33. The tuataras are named for the
    a. spiny crest on their back.
    b. large size.
    c. the islands they inhabit.
    d. the prey they eat.

    ANS: A   DIF: I   OBJ: 43-3.5

COMPLETION

1. Shelled eggs with membranes that surround the embryo and provide an aquatic environment for the development of reptiles and birds are called _____.

ANS: amniotic eggs   DIF: I   OBJ: 43-1.3

2. Watertight eggs of terrestrial organisms contain a material called _____, which provides nutrition for the developing embryo.

ANS: yolk   DIF: I   OBJ: 43-1.3

3. The membrane in a reptilian egg that encloses the developing embryo within a fluid-filled cavity is called the _____.

ANS: amnion   DIF: I   OBJ: 43-1.3

4. The _____ is the food source in a reptilian egg.

ANS: yolk   DIF: I   OBJ: 43-1.3

5. Modern reptiles differ from amphibians in that they have a _____ skin.

ANS: watertight   DIF: I   OBJ: 43-1.4

6. Reptiles have dry, largely _____ skin.

ANS: watertight or waterproof   DIF: I   OBJ: 43-1.4

7. Refer to the illustration above. The structure labeled "B" is a(n) _____.

ANS: ventricle   DIF: II   OBJ: 43-2.1

8. The inner surface of reptile lungs consists of small chambers called _____.

ANS: alveoli   DIF: I   OBJ: 43-2.2

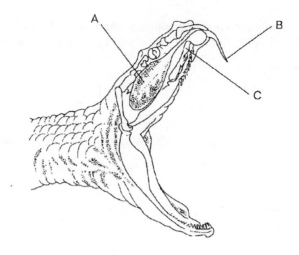

9. Refer to the illustration above. Structure "C," which is analogous to the taste buds found in other vertebrates, is called _____.

    ANS: Jacobson's organs   DIF: II   OBJ: 43-2.3

10. Refer to the illustration above. Structure "B" is a(n) _____.

    ANS: fang   DIF: II   OBJ: 43-3.4

11. Refer to the illustration above. Structure "A" is the _____ gland.

    ANS: venom   DIF: II   OBJ: 43-3.4

12. Fishes, amphibians, and reptiles, whose body temperatures change as the temperature of their surroundings changes, are _____.

    ANS: ectotherms   DIF: I   OBJ: 43-2.4

13. Reptiles, whose body temperature changes with the temperature of their surroundings, are known as _____.

    ANS: ectotherms   DIF: I   OBJ: 43-2.4

14. A reptile's body temperature is largely determined by the temperature of its _____.

    ANS: environment   DIF: I   OBJ: 43-2.4

15. The term used to describe mammals that give birth to live offspring that develop within the mother's body is _____.

    ANS: viviparous   DIF: I   OBJ: 43-2.5

16. Reptilian limbs are positioned to support _____ body weight than are the limbs of amphibians.

    ANS: more or greater   DIF: I   OBJ: 43-3.1

17. The lower (ventral) portion of a tortoise's shell is called the _____.

    ANS: plastron   DIF: I   OBJ: 43-3.1

18. Crocodilians don't get water in their lungs when they submerge themselves for capturing prey because they have a _____ that prevents water from entering their air passageway.

    ANS: valve at the back of their throat   DIF: I   OBJ: 43-3.2

ESSAY

1. What features of an amniotic egg are adaptations to life on land? Write your answer in the space below.

    ANS:
    Answers may include any of the following features: eggs have a series of protective membranes—amnion and chorion—and a shell that enclose the embryo in a watery environment; the membranes and shell are resistant to loss of water and allow for exchange of gases; eggs have a yolk sac for food storage.

    DIF: II   OBJ: 43-1.3

2. As reptiles evolved, many were able to leave water and become completely terrestrial animals. Amphibians, however, are not totally free of the aquatic environment. Explain two reasons why these statements are true. Write your answer in the space below.

    ANS:
    Amphibians must remain near water because they depend on a thin, moist skin for oxygen/carbon dioxide exchange. They also need a watery environment to keep their shell-less eggs moist and to enable sperm to swim to the eggs, which are fertilized externally. Reptiles, on the other hand, have evolved lungs and have a scaly skin that is impermeable to water, allowing them to follow a terrestrial existence. Also, reptiles have evolved internal fertilization and shelled eggs so that they can reproduce on land.

    DIF: II   OBJ: 43-2.2

3. What improvements in jaw design have contributed to the success of snakes and lizards as predators? Write your answer in the space below.

    ANS:
    The lower jaw of snakes and lizards is loosely connected to the skull. This loose connection allows the mouth to open to accommodate large prey. In addition, the loss of the lower arch of bone below the lower opening in the skull of lizards makes room for large muscles to move the jaws.

    DIF: II   OBJ: 43-3.4

CHAPTER 44—BIRDS

TRUE/FALSE

1. Modern birds have teeth.

    ANS: F   DIF: I   OBJ: 44-1.1

2. Some skeletons of fossil birds have teeth.

    ANS: T   DIF: I   OBJ: 44-1.3

3. Scientists do not agree on whether flight evolved first in tree-dwelling birds or in ground-dwelling birds.

    ANS: T   DIF: I   OBJ: 44-1.4

4. Birds have a three-chambered heart.

    ANS: F   DIF: I   OBJ: 44-2.4

5. Both reptiles and birds lay amniotic eggs.

    ANS: T   DIF: I   OBJ: 44-2.5

6. Most land animals reproduce by external fertilization.

    ANS: F   DIF: I   OBJ: 44-2.5

MULTIPLE CHOICE

1. Birds are different from reptiles in that they
    a. are endothermic.
    b. have feathers covering their bodies rather than scales.
    c. have four-chambered hearts.
    d. All of the above

    ANS: D   DIF: I   OBJ: 44-1.2

2. Scientific evidence suggests that birds arose from
    a. mammals.   c. reptiles.
    b. amphibians.   d. protozoa.

    ANS: C   DIF: I   OBJ: 44-1.2

3. Birds retain many reptilian features, including
    a. teeth.   c. scales on their feet and lower legs.
    b. a long, bony tail.   d. None of the above

    ANS: C   DIF: I   OBJ: 44-1.2

4. amphibian : reptile ::
   a. land : jaw
   b. feathers : scales
   c. reptile : bird
   d. mammal : bird

   ANS: C   DIF: II   OBJ: 44-1.2

5. Which of the following statements is *not* a true statement providing evidence for the hypothesis that birds evolved from a dinosaur ancestor?
   a. Some dinosaurs had feathers.
   b. Some dinosaurs were endothermic.
   c. The collarbone of certain dinosaurs is well developed, as it is in birds.
   d. The pubic bone of certain dinosaurs is directed towards the tail end of the animal, as it is in birds.

   ANS: C   DIF: III   OBJ: 44-1.2

6. Which of the following characteristics of birds is *not* found in *Archaeopteryx*?
   a. feathers
   b. wishbone
   c. beak
   d. ability to fly

   ANS: C   DIF: I   OBJ: 44-1.3

7. bird : hollow bones ::
   a. *Compsognathus* : feathers
   b. reptile : hollow bones
   c. *Archaeopteryx* : feathers
   d. bird : dinosaur forelimbs

   ANS: C   DIF: II   OBJ: 44-1.3

8. The earliest flying vertebrates were
   a. birds.
   b. squirrels.
   c. dinosaurs.
   d. mammals.

   ANS: C   DIF: I   OBJ: 44-1.4

9. The first wings appearing on animals are thought to have been used for
   a. movement on the ground or in the air.
   b. capture of prey.
   c. stabilization.
   d. All of the above

   ANS: D   DIF: I   OBJ: 44-1.4

10. Feathers
    a. evolved as a deterrent to insects.
    b. replaced fur as the body covering of birds.
    c. are found on all birds and some mammals.
    d. replaced scales as the body covering of birds.

    ANS: D   DIF: I   OBJ: 44-2.1

11. Which of the following is *not* a function of contour feathers?
    a. flight
    b. coloration
    c. food capture
    d. filtering dust

    ANS: C   DIF: I   OBJ: 44-2.1

12. Which of the following does a contour feather most closely resemble?
    a. a piece of paper
    b. a chain-linked fence
    c. the wing of an airplane
    d. a parachute

    ANS: B   DIF: I   OBJ: 44-2.1

13. The bones of birds
    a. are composed primarily of keratin.
    b. are solid.
    c. are found sparingly throughout the body.
    d. are thin and hollow.

    ANS: D   DIF: I   OBJ: 44-2.2

14. A bird's skeleton is
    a. composed of thin, hollow bones.
    b. more rigid than a reptile's.
    c. composed of many fused bones.
    d. All of the above

    ANS: D   DIF: I   OBJ: 44-2.2

15. A bird's crop
    a. temporarily stores food.
    b. is the first chamber of its stomach.
    c. is critical for flight.
    d. often contains small stones that the bird has swallowed.

    ANS: A   DIF: I   OBJ: 44-2.3

16. Birds excrete most of their nitrogenous wastes as
    a. urea.
    b. ammonia.
    c. uric acid.
    d. urine.

    ANS: C   DIF: I   OBJ: 44-2.3

17. Food taken into a bird's body is ground up in the
    a. mouth.
    b. crop.
    c. gizzard.
    d. small intestines.

    ANS: C   DIF: I   OBJ: 44-2.3

18. Gas exchange is necessary in all animals because
    a. oxygen is needed to break down food molecules.
    b. carbon dioxide is a waste product that must be eliminated.
    c. there is more oxygen in the environment than in animal bodies.
    d. All of the above

    ANS: D   DIF: I   OBJ: 44-2.4

19. Bird respiration is very efficient because
    a. bird lungs are small and hollow.
    b. only one lung functions at a time.
    c. of a special set of blood vessels.
    d. birds' system of air sacs permits air to flow in only one direction through the lungs.

    ANS: D   DIF: I   OBJ: 44-2.4

20. A bird's heart has
    a. one chamber.   c. three chambers.
    b. two chambers.   d. four chambers.

    ANS: D   DIF: I   OBJ: 44-2.4

21. Lungs and air sacs are structures of the respiratory system of a(n)
    a. fish.   c. reptile.
    b. amphibian.   d. bird.

    ANS: D   DIF: I   OBJ: 44-2.4

22. Talons would most likely be found among birds that
    a. eat seeds.   c. live in water.
    b. capture their prey.   d. drink the nectar of flowers.

    ANS: B   DIF: I   OBJ: 44-3.1

23. Large, flat feet would most likely be found on birds that
    a. are predators.   c. eat insects.
    b. fly.   d. cannot fly.

    ANS: D   DIF: II   OBJ: 44-3.1

24. Relationships among the families of modern birds are mostly inferred from studies of
    a. fossils.   c. feathers.
    b. bones.   d. DNA.

    ANS: D   DIF: I   OBJ: 44-3.2

25. Which of the following associations between a bird order and a member of the order is incorrect?
    a. The hummingbird is a member of the order Apodiformes.
    b. The turkey is a member of the order Galliformes.
    c. The penguin is a member of the order Struthioniformes.
    d. The parrot is a member of the order Psittaciformes.

    ANS: C   DIF: I   OBJ: 44-3.2

26. Melodious songs are characteristic of _____ songbirds.
    a. female   c. female and male
    b. male   d. young

    ANS: B   DIF: II   OBJ: 44-3.3

27. The syrinx of a bird functions in
  a. capturing prey.
  b. flight.
  c. producing songs.
  d. marking time.

  ANS: C   DIF: I   OBJ: 44-3.3

28. The syrinx is located in a bird's
  a. mouth.
  b. esophagus.
  c. trachea.
  d. lungs.

  ANS: C   DIF: I   OBJ: 44-3.3

COMPLETION

1. Feathers are modified _____ scales.

  ANS: reptilian   DIF: I   OBJ: 44-1.1

2. Birds, like mammals, are _____.

  ANS: endothermic   DIF: I   OBJ: 44-1.1

3. Refer to the illustration above. Structure "B" is called the _____, or keel of the _____.

  ANS: breastbone, sternum   DIF: II   OBJ: 44-2.2

4. Refer to the illustration above. Structure "A" is known as the wishbone or

  _____.

  ANS: collarbone   DIF: II   OBJ: 44-2.2

5. Long incubation times are associated with _____ young, who are relatively independent when they hatch, while short incubation times are associated with _____ young, who are dependent for some time after they hatch.

  ANS: precocial; altricial   DIF: I   OBJ: 44-2.5

Modern Biology Assessment Item Listing
406

6. Short, thick beaks would be found on birds that eat _____, while long, pointed, curved beaks would be found on birds that eat _____, and thin beaks would be found on birds that eat _____.

ANS: seeds; animals; nectar   DIF: I   OBJ: 44-3.1

7. The songbirds belong to the largest order of birds, the _____.

ANS: Passeriformes   DIF: I   OBJ: 44-3.2

ESSAY

1. Birds live in the Arctic, but reptiles do not. Offer an explanation for this fact. Write your answer in the space below.

ANS:
Reptiles are ectothermic and cannot survive extreme temperatures. Birds are endothermic and can adapt to some extremes.

DIF: II   OBJ: 44-1.1

2. Name three forms in which nitrogen-containing waste is eliminated in the animal kingdom, and use examples to describe why each has an advantage in certain situations. Write your answer in the space below.

ANS:
The breakdown of amino acids results in ammonia production. Ammonia is toxic and must be quickly eliminated in dilute form. Freshwater animals have plenty of water available to dilute ammonia quickly, so they excrete nitrogenous waste as ammonia. Terrestrial animals cannot afford to lose large amounts of body water. They must excrete nitrogenous waste in more concentrated form. Most mammals excrete urea, a nontoxic liquid that can be safely transported to the kidneys for disposal. Insects, birds, and reptiles excrete uric acid, a solid that is mixed with feces and disposed of with very little water loss.

DIF: II   OBJ: 44-1.1

3. Support the statement "Crocodiles resemble birds far more than they resemble living reptiles." Write your answer in the space below.

ANS:
Crocodiles are the only living reptiles that, like birds, care for their young. They are also the only living reptiles that have a four-chambered heart like that of birds. In many other anatomical features, crocodiles differ from all other living reptiles and resemble birds.

DIF: II   OBJ: 44-1.1

4. Flying requires a great amount of energy. What adaptations in the respiratory systems of birds allow them to meet their high energy needs? Write your answer in the space below.

ANS:
In order to release large amounts of energy, birds must have a constant supply of oxygen. Birds have a system of air sacs that maintain a constant one-way flow (and supply of oxygen) to the lungs. In addition, the network of lung capillaries is arranged across the air flow at a 90° angle. Blood leaving a bird's lung can contain more oxygen than exhaled air does.

DIF: II   OBJ: 44-2.4

5. The right and left sides of a bird's heart are completely separated, so oxygen-rich blood is never mixed with oxygen-poor blood. Why is this complete separation necessary for birds? Write your answer in the space below.

ANS:
Birds need blood with a high oxygen content because flight requires large amounts of energy and oxygen.

DIF: II   OBJ: 44-2.4

TRUE/FALSE

1. Birds, reptiles, and mammals minimize water loss by means of their watertight skins.

   ANS: T   DIF: I   OBJ: 45-1.1

2. Hair evolved from reptilian scales.

   ANS: F   DIF: I   OBJ: 45-1.1

3. Hair may serve as camouflage.

   ANS: T   DIF: I   OBJ: 45-1.1

4. Mammals have hair on their bodies and the ability to produce milk.

   ANS: T   DIF: I   OBJ: 45-1.1

5. Mammals have been the dominant land animals on Earth for over 500 million years.

   ANS: F   DIF: I   OBJ: 45-1.2

6. The first mammals to appear on Earth were about the size of a large dog.

   ANS: F   DIF: I   OBJ: 45-1.2

7. During the past few million years, the number of mammalian species on Earth has continued to increase.

   ANS: F   DIF: I   OBJ: 45-1.4

8. The geographic range of endothermic animals is greater than that of ectothermic animals because endothermic animals can survive in more extreme climates.

   ANS: T   DIF: I   OBJ: 45-2.1

9. The structure of a mammal's jaw and teeth usually reveals its diet.

   ANS: T   DIF: I   OBJ: 45-2.3

10. Marsupials are egg-laying mammals.

    ANS: F   DIF: I   OBJ: 45-2.4

11. Egg-laying mammals nourish their young after birth with milk.

    ANS: T   DIF: I   OBJ: 45-2.4

12. During its development, the embryo of a placental mammal is nourished by the mother through a unique structure called the placenta.

ANS: T   DIF: I   OBJ: 45-2.4

13. The offspring of placental mammals receive nourishment through the placenta throughout development.

ANS: T   DIF: I   OBJ: 45-2.4

14. The gestation period in marsupials is far shorter than the gestation period in placental mammals.

ANS: T   DIF: I   OBJ: 45-2.4

15. Most species of mammals are placental.

ANS: T   DIF: I   OBJ: 45-3.1

16. Because they can fly, bats are no longer classified as mammals.

ANS: F   DIF: I   OBJ: 45-3.1

17. Animals of the order Cetacea are the only mammals that live entirely in the water.

ANS: T   DIF: I   OBJ: 45-3.1

18. Monotremes are mammals that carry their young in pouches.

ANS: F   DIF: I   OBJ: 45-3.2

19. Unlike most other animals, ungulates produce enzymes that aid in the digestion of cellulose.

ANS: F   DIF: II   OBJ: 45-3.3

MULTIPLE CHOICE

1. Mammals, as well as birds, have
   a. teeth.   c. air sacs.
   b. a four-chambered heart.   d. All of the above

ANS: B   DIF: I   OBJ: 45-1.1

2. The large eye sockets on the early mammals suggest that the mammals
   a. could see in the back of their heads.
   b. did not have to turn their heads to see to the side.
   c. were active at night.
   d. lived in caves.

ANS: C   DIF: I   OBJ: 45-1.1

3. One of the main ways to distinguish the skull of a mammal from the skull of a therapsid is that mammals have
   a. a variety of teeth.
   b. eye sockets.
   c. a single jawbone.
   d. None of the above

   ANS: C   DIF: I   OBJ: 45-1.1

4. Hair may
   a. serve as insulation.
   b. have a sensory function.
   c. be a defensive weapon.
   d. All of the above

   ANS: D   DIF: I   OBJ: 45-1.1

5. Half of the energy in milk comes from
   a. keratin.
   b. carbohydrates.
   c. protein.
   d. fat.

   ANS: D   DIF: I   OBJ: 45-1.1

6. All of the following evolved from early reptiles *except*
   a. fish.
   b. birds.
   c. dinosaurs.
   d. mammals.

   ANS: A   DIF: I   OBJ: 45-1.2

7. Mammals evolved
   a. from reptiles earlier in history than did birds.
   b. from reptiles well after birds appeared on Earth.
   c. at the same time as birds.
   d. directly from birds.

   ANS: A   DIF: I   OBJ: 45-1.2

8. breathing and eating simultaneously: secondary palate ::
   a. higher body temperature : large synapsid opening
   b. better sensory functions : complex teeth
   c. bigger jaw muscles : mammalian hair
   d. bigger jaw muscles : large synapsid opening

   ANS: D   DIF: II   OBJ: 45-1.2

9. What adaptations did therapsids and mammals share?
   a. complex teeth
   b. a secondary palate
   c. large synapsid openings
   d. All of the above

   ANS: D   DIF: I   OBJ: 45-1.3

10. Pelycosaurs evolved into the
    a. dinosaurs.
    b. Pinnipedia.
    c. lizards.
    d. therapsids.

    ANS: D   DIF: I   OBJ: 45-1.3

11. Mammals arose from early reptiles called
    a. mesosaurs.
    b. ichthyosaurs.
    c. therapsids.
    d. pterosaurs.

    ANS: C   DIF: I   OBJ: 45-1.3

12. Mammals reached their maximal diversity during the
    a. Jurassic period.
    b. Permian period.
    c. Triassic period.
    d. Tertiary period.

    ANS: D   DIF: I   OBJ: 45-1.4

13. Which of the following statements about the earliest mammals is true?
    a. They first appeared after the extinction of the dinosaurs.
    b. They outcompeted dinosaurs for food and other resources, resulting in the dinosaurs' extinction.
    c. They were large and preyed on many small dinosaurs.
    d. They coexisted with dinosaurs but did not compete with them for food and other resources.

    ANS: D   DIF: II   OBJ: 45-1.4

14. Which of the following processes is responsible for the greatest amount of daily water loss in humans?
    a. exhalation of water vapor
    b. sweating
    c. urination
    d. None of the above

    ANS: C   DIF: I   OBJ: 45-2.1

15. The sheet of muscle at the bottom of the rib cage of mammals is called the
    a. secondary palate.
    b. metabolic sheet.
    c. diaphragm.
    d. placenta.

    ANS: C   DIF: I   OBJ: 45-2.2

16. gills : fish ::
    a. skin : reptile
    b. blood vessels : circulation
    c. tree : plant
    d. lungs : mammal

    ANS: D   DIF: II   OBJ: 45-2.2

17. hair : insulation ::
    a. endothermy : keeping mammals cool
    b. synapsid opening : swallowing
    c. diaphragm : drawing air into lungs
    d. complex teeth : breathing

    ANS: C   DIF: II   OBJ: 45-2.2

18. The sheet of bone that separates the mouth cavity from the nasal cavity in mammals is called the
    a. nasal septum.
    b. secondary palate.
    c. osseous plate.
    d. oral palate.

    ANS: B   DIF: I   OBJ: 45-2.3

Coyote's Skull

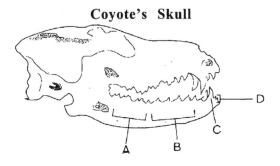

19. Refer to the illustration above. The teeth labeled "A" are called
    a. premolars.
    b. incisors.
    c. molars.
    d. canines.

    ANS: C   DIF: II   OBJ: 45-2.3

20. Refer to the illustration above. The teeth labeled "C" are called
    a. premolars.
    b. incisors.
    c. molars.
    d. canines.

    ANS: D   DIF: II   OBJ: 45-2.3

21. Refer to the illustration above. The teeth primarily used for biting and cutting are labeled
    a. "A."
    b. "B."
    c. "C."
    d. "D."

    ANS: D   DIF: II   OBJ: 45-2.3

22. Refer to the illustration above. The fact that the coyote is a predator can be inferred from
    a. the shape of the skull.
    b. the position of the eye sockets.
    c. the length of the jawbone.
    d. the shape of the teeth.

    ANS: D   DIF: II   OBJ: 45-2.3

23. Carnivorous mammals have
    a. large, flat molars.
    b. short, square canine teeth.
    c. long, sharp canine teeth.
    d. poor vision.

    ANS: C   DIF: I   OBJ: 45-2.3

24. Which of the following is usually characteristic of reproduction in a terrestrial environment?
    a. external fertilization
    b. internal fertilization
    c. shell-less, water-permeable eggs
    d. None of the above

    ANS: B   DIF: I   OBJ: 45-2.4

25. During internal fertilization,
    a. a sperm is deposited directly inside an egg that is floating in a pond.
    b. males and females need not be present at the site of fertilization at the same time.
    c. a male deposits sperm directly into the female.
    d. a female deposits eggs into a nest and the male covers them with sperm.

    ANS: C   DIF: I   OBJ: 45-2.4

26. Which of the following is *not* an advantage of the eggs of placental mammals over those of reptiles?
    a. protection from predators
    b. protection from overheating or freezing
    c. a protective shell forms around the egg
    d. further nourishment can be provided to the offspring

    ANS: C   DIF: I   OBJ: 45-2.4

27. The function of the placenta in certain mammals is to
    a. hold the embryo in place, preventing premature loss.
    b. carry nutrition to and remove wastes from the embryo during development.
    c. surround and protect the embryo like a shell.
    d. maintain a constant internal temperature.

    ANS: B   DIF: I   OBJ: 45-2.4

28. The major difference between marsupials and placentals is
    a. their ability to maintain a steady body temperature.
    b. their teeth.
    c. their pattern of embryonic development.
    d. the size of their eggs.

    ANS: C   DIF: I   OBJ: 45-2.4

29. Offspring remain inside the mother until development is essentially complete in
    a. placental mammals.   c. marsupials.
    b. monotremes.   d. All of the above

    ANS: A   DIF: I   OBJ: 45-2.4

30. Unlike reptiles, mammalian young are dependent on parental care for
    a. food.   c. learning.
    b. protection.   d. All of the above

    ANS: D   DIF: I   OBJ: 45-2.4

31. Mammals whose offspring remain inside the mother until development is complete are called
    a. placental mammals.   c. marsupials.
    b. monotremes.   d. All of the above

    ANS: A   DIF: I   OBJ: 45-2.4

32. The placental mammals are animals that
    a. nurse their young with milk.
    b. have body hair.
    c. give birth to live young.
    d. All of the above

    ANS: D   DIF: I   OBJ: 45-2.4

33. Mammals that lay eggs are
    a. placental mammals.
    b. pouched mammals.
    c. monotremes.
    d. semi-pouched mammals.

    ANS: C   DIF: I   OBJ: 45-2.4

34. Egg-laying mammals are
    a. oviparous.
    b. viviparous.
    c. ovoviviparous.
    d. None of the above

    ANS: A   DIF: I   OBJ: 45-2.4

35. The duckbill platypus and two species of echidnas are the only living
    a. monotremes.
    b. marsupials.
    c. placental mammals.
    d. reptiles.

    ANS: A   DIF: I   OBJ: 45-3.1

36. Kangaroos and opossums are
    a. marsupials.
    b. monotremes.
    c. macroscelidea.
    d. placentals.

    ANS: A   DIF: I   OBJ: 45-3.1

37. The largest animal that ever lived is
    a. a cetacean.
    b. the blue whale.
    c. a filter feeder.
    d. All of the above

    ANS: D   DIF: I   OBJ: 45-3.1

38. A dog is a member of the order
    a. Rodentia.
    b. Insectivora.
    c. Carnivora.
    d. Cetacea.

    ANS: C   DIF: I   OBJ: 45-3.1

39. Bat wings
    a. are covered with feathers.
    b. can be used only for gliding.
    c. are leathery membranes of skin.
    d. are modified hind limbs.

    ANS: C   DIF: I   OBJ: 45-3.1

40. Bats
    a. are all exclusively carnivores.
    b. fly only by gliding.
    c. always emerge only at night.
    d. use sound to help them navigate.

    ANS: D   DIF: I   OBJ: 45-3.1

41. The sounds that bats emit
    a. help them navigate.
    b. help them capture their prey.
    c. are too high pitched to be heard by humans.
    d. All of the above

    ANS: D   DIF: I   OBJ: 45-3.1

42. Which of the following characteristics is *not* associated with marsupial mammals?
    a. pouch   c. milk-fed young
    b. shelled egg   d. internal fertilization

    ANS: B   DIF: I   OBJ: 45-3.2

43. The offspring of marsupial mammals
    a. hatch from eggs.
    b. remain inside their mother until development is complete.
    c. are born early and complete their development in their mother's pouch.
    d. All of the above

    ANS: C   DIF: I   OBJ: 45-3.2

44. Today all monotremes and most marsupials live in Australia and New Guinea. This
    limited distribution is due to
    a. predation by other mammals.
    b. continental drift.
    c. inability of these animals to survive in cold climates.
    d. All of the above

    ANS: B   DIF: I   OBJ: 45-3.2

45. A deer has
    a. long, sharp canine teeth.
    b. large, flat molars with ridged surfaces.
    c. small, sharp molars.
    d. All of the above

    ANS: B   DIF: I   OBJ: 45-3.3

46. Dugongs and sea cows are
    a. toothless mammals.   c. sirenians.
    b. hoofed mammals.   d. marine hunters.

    ANS: C   DIF: I   OBJ: 45-3.4

47. The forelimbs of ____ are modified into flippers and are used to help these animals move
    through water.
    a. proboscideans   c. monotremes
    b. cetaceans   d. edentatans

    ANS: B   DIF: I   OBJ: 45-3.4

48. cetaceans : oceans ::
    a. edentates : South and Central America
    b. native carnivores : Australia
    c. placental mammals : Antarctica
    d. manatees : terrestrial areas

    ANS: A   DIF: II   OBJ: 45-3.4

COMPLETION

1. Female mammals have _____ that secrete milk.

    ANS: mammary glands   DIF: I   OBJ: 45-1.1

2. A synapsid skull has a single _____ behind each eye socket.

    ANS: opening   DIF: I   OBJ: 45-1.2

3. The _____ are the direct ancestors of the mammals.

    ANS: therapsids   DIF: I   OBJ: 45-1.3

4. Scientists think that therapsids may have declined in numbers because of competition
   from _____.

    ANS: thecodonts   DIF: I   OBJ: 45-1.3

5. An animal that maintains a high, nearly constant body temperature through metabolism
   is said to be _____.

    ANS: endothermic   DIF: I   OBJ: 45-2.1

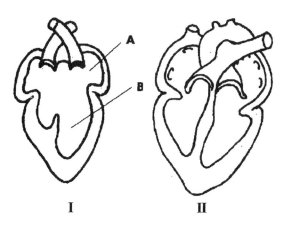

I   II

6. Refer to the illustration above. Diagram II represents the heart of a
   _____.

    ANS: mammal or bird   DIF: II   OBJ: 45-2.2

7. Refer to the illustration above. The structure labeled "B" is a(n) _____.

ANS: ventricle   DIF: II   OBJ: 45-2.2

8. Over the course of vertebrate evolution, the _____ has become reduced in size. It has become the pacemaker in the hearts of birds and mammals.

ANS: sinus venosus   DIF: I   OBJ: 45-2.2

9. An animal with a secondary palate can _____ and chew at the same time.

ANS: breathe   DIF: I   OBJ: 45-2.2

10. _____ fertilization reduces the risk that gametes will dry out.

ANS: Internal   DIF: I   OBJ: 45-2.4

11. The period of time between fertilization and birth in placentals and marsupials is known as the _____.

ANS: gestation period   DIF: I   OBJ: 45-2.4

12. Mice and humans belong to a group of mammals in which the young receive nutrition from the mother through a structure called a(n) _____.

ANS: placenta   DIF: I   OBJ: 45-3.1

13. The only prototherians surviving today are the _____.

ANS: monotremes   DIF: I   OBJ: 45-3.1

14. The only mammals with binocular vision are the _____.

ANS: primates   DIF: I   OBJ: 45-3.1

15. _____ are the only mammals capable of powered flight.

ANS: Bats   DIF: I   OBJ: 45-3.1

16. Marsupial animals complete their development in the mother's _____.

ANS: pouch   DIF: I   OBJ: 45-3.2

17. Scientists think that _____ are more closely related to the early mammals than are any other living mammals.

ANS: monotremes   DIF: I   OBJ: 45-3.2

18. Perissodactyls have _____ numbers of toes, while artiodactyls have _____ numbers of toes.

ANS: odd; even   DIF: I   OBJ: 45-3.3

ESSAY

1. List the unique characteristics of mammals. Write your answer in the space below.

   ANS:
   Mammals have hair and are endothermic. Female mammals have mammary glands that produce milk to nourish their young until the offspring are able to feed on their own.

   DIF: II   OBJ: 45-1.1

2. While no living therapsids have ever been found, scientists are fairly certain they were endothermic. Why? Write your answer in the space below.

   ANS:
   Therapsid adaptations for efficient feeding suggest that they had a high demand for energy. In addition, therapsid fossils have been found in areas that had cold winters, and there is some evidence that they had fur to insulate their bodies.

   DIF: I   OBJ: 45-1.3

3. Why do scientists think monotremes are more closely related to the early mammals than are any other living mammals? Write your answer in the space below.

   ANS:
   Monotremes, like reptiles, lay eggs and have a cloaca. In addition, monotreme shoulders and forelimbs resemble those of reptiles.

   DIF: I   OBJ: 45-3.1

TRUE/FALSE

1. The four tissue types in the body are epithelial, muscle, nervous, and connective.

    ANS: T   DIF: I   OBJ: 46-1.1

2. Glandular tissue is a type of connective tissue.

    ANS: F   DIF: I   OBJ: 46-1.1

3. The smooth muscle that is found in the stomach walls is an example of a voluntary muscle.

    ANS: F   DIF: I   OBJ: 46-1.1

4. Organs working together form an organ system.

    ANS: T   DIF: I   OBJ: 46-1.2

5. The heart is located in the thoracic cavity.

    ANS: T   DIF: I   OBJ: 46-1.4

6. The majority of the bones of the skeleton are part of the axial skeleton.

    ANS: F   DIF: I   OBJ: 46-2.1

7. Yellow bone marrow is contained in the shaft of the long bones.

    ANS: T   DIF: I   OBJ: 46-2.2

8. The Haversian canals of long bones are filled with yellow marrow.

    ANS: F   DIF: I   OBJ: 46-2.2

9. Bone is living tissue made of cells that deposit minerals.

    ANS: T   DIF: I   OBJ: 46-2.2

10. You can tell the relative age of a person by the amount of cartilage present at the epiphyseal plates of his or her long bones.

    ANS: T   DIF: III   OBJ: 46-2.3

11. The bones of the knee are connected by semimovable joints.

    ANS: F   DIF: I   OBJ: 46-2.4

12. The shoulder joint is an example of a ball-and socket joint.

ANS: T   DIF: I   OBJ: 46-2.4

13. The three basic types of muscle are skeletal muscle, smooth muscle, and cardiac muscle.

ANS: T   DIF: I   OBJ: 46-3.1

14. A sarcomere is composed of filaments called myofibrils.

ANS: F   DIF: I   OBJ: 46-3.2

15. Extensor muscles cause bones to bend at a joint, while flexors cause them to straighten.

ANS: F   DIF: I   OBJ: 46-3.4

16. Moving a muscle requires three sets of muscles working in opposition.

ANS: F   DIF: I   OBJ: 46-3.4

17. The dermis is the outer layer of the skin, made mostly of dead cells.

ANS: F   DIF: I   OBJ: 46-4.2

18. The distribution of melanin in the epidermis of the skin determines the color of an individual.

ANS: T   DIF: I   OBJ: 46-4.2

19. Most skin cancers result from mutations in the melanin-producing cells.

ANS: F   DIF: I   OBJ: 46-4.2

20. Acne is caused by excessive sweating.

ANS: F   DIF: I   OBJ: 46-4.4

MULTIPLE CHOICE

1. Tissue that is specialized to cover the inner and outer surfaces of the internal organs is called
   a. epithelial tissue.   c. muscle tissue.
   b. connective tissue.   d. nervous tissue.

ANS: A   DIF: I   OBJ: 46-1.1

2. Tightly connected cells that are arranged in flat sheets are characteristic of
   a. epithelial tissue.   c. muscle tissue.
   b. connective tissue.   d. nervous tissue.

ANS: A   DIF: I   OBJ: 46-1.1

3. Blood, bone, and cartilage are examples of
   a. three different tissue types found in the body.
   b. connective tissue.
   c. epithelial tissue.
   d. organs of the body.

   ANS: B   DIF: I   OBJ: 46-1.1

4. Connective tissue consists of
   a. tendons that connect muscle to bone.
   b. the layer beneath your skin that connects the skin to muscle.
   c. fat.
   d. All of the above

   ANS: D   DIF: I   OBJ: 46-1.1

5. From the smallest functional units to the largest, the body is organized as follows:
   a. cell, system, organ, tissue, body.   c. system, organ, tissue, cell, body.
   b. organ, cell, tissue, system, body.   d. cell, tissue, organ, system, body.

   ANS: D   DIF: I   OBJ: 46-1.2

6. Organs that work together form
   a. connective tissues.   c. organ systems.
   b. tissue systems.   d. All of the above

   ANS: C   DIF: I   OBJ: 46-1.2

7. The heart and the blood vessels are separate organs that form the
   a. skeletal system.   c. reproductive system.
   b. circulatory system.   d. digestive system.

   ANS: B   DIF: I   OBJ: 46-1.3

8. Which of the following is a function of *both* the excretory system and the endocrine system?
   a. elimination of wastes   c. regulation of other organ systems
   b. water and mineral balance   d. transport of wastes out of the body

   ANS: B   DIF: I   OBJ: 46-1.3

9. The lungs are located in the
   a. cranial cavity.   c. thoracic cavity.
   b. abdominal cavity.   d. spinal cavity.

   ANS: C   DIF: I   OBJ: 46-1.4

10. Of the following, the structure that is *not* part of the axial skeleton is the
   a. backbone.   c. rib cage.
   b. pelvis.   d. skull.

   ANS: B   DIF: I   OBJ: 46-2.1

11. Osteocytes trapped within the spaces in the bone surrounding them
    a. are called marrow cells.
    b. are provided with food and oxygen by Haversian canals.
    c. receive nutrients directly from the cells of the surrounding cartilage.
    d. eventually become osteoblasts as the bone matures.

    ANS: B   DIF: I   OBJ: 46-2.2

12. Yellow marrow
    a. provides internal support to spongy bone.
    b. produces red blood cells.
    c. is found only in lower vertebrates.
    d. stores fat.

    ANS: D   DIF: I   OBJ: 46-2.2

13. The type of bone that provides the greatest strength for support is
    a. spongy bone.   c. compact bone.
    b. chitinous bone.   d. marrow bone.

    ANS: C   DIF: I   OBJ: 46-2.2

14. The periosteum is a section of the bone that contains
    a. blood vessels.   c. spongy bone.
    b. osteocytes.   d. red bone marrow.

    ANS: A   DIF: I   OBJ: 46-2.2

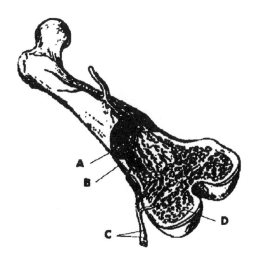

15. Refer to the illustration above. In the diagram, the compact bone is labeled
    a. "A."   c. "C."
    b. "B."   d. "D."

    ANS: B   DIF: I   OBJ: 46-2.2

16. Refer to the illustration above. In the diagram, the material labeled "A," which fills the center and spaces at ends and produces blood cells, is known as
    a. exocrine material.
    b. cartilage.
    c. marrow.
    d. spongy bone.

    ANS: C   DIF: I   OBJ: 46-2.2

17. Refer to the illustration above. The structure labeled "C" in the diagram is a
    a. nerve.
    b. blood vessel.
    c. muscle.
    d. ligament.

    ANS: B   DIF: I   OBJ: 46-2.2

18. The heart and lungs are protected by the
    a. pectoral girdle.
    b. pelvic girdle.
    c. rib cage.
    d. periosteum.

    ANS: C   DIF: I   OBJ: 46-2.2

19. A person with a broken pelvis would probably be unable to
    a. walk.
    b. turn his or her head.
    c. raise his or her arm.
    d. bend his or her wrist.

    ANS: A   DIF: I   OBJ: 46-2.2

20. compact bone : periosteum ::
    a. periosteum : compact bone
    b. compact bone : spongy bone
    c. spongy bone : compact bone
    d. marrow : compact bone

    ANS: D   DIF: II   OBJ: 46-2.2

21. human skeleton : internal organs ::
    a. spoon : fork
    b. construction worker's hard hat : a skull
    c. whiskbroom : dust
    d. turnstile : a ticket

    ANS: B   DIF: II   OBJ: 46-2.2

22. In an embryo, the skeleton is originally made of
    a. red and yellow marrow.
    b. calcium phosphate.
    c. cartilage.
    d. osteopores.

    ANS: C   DIF: I   OBJ: 46-2.3

23. What is the difference between cartilage and bone?
    a. Cartilage contains cells that can continue to divide and grow, while bone does not.
    b. Cartilage is found in the fetus, and bone is found in children and adults.
    c. Bone contains cells with significant mineral deposits between them, while cartilage does not.
    d. Bone contains dead cells while cartilage contains living cells.

    ANS: C   DIF: I   OBJ: 46-2.3

24. Ligaments attach
   a. bone to bone.
   b. muscle to bone.
   c. muscle to muscle.
   d. cartilage to bone.

   ANS: A   DIF: I   OBJ: 46-2.4

25. The point where two or more bones meet is called a
   a. sprain.
   b. joint.
   c. point of intersection.
   d. growth region.

   ANS: B   DIF: I   OBJ: 46-2.4

A   **B**   **C**   **D**

26. Refer to the illustration above. The joint shown in diagram "A" is an example of a
   a. suture joint.
   b. ball-and-socket joint.
   c. pivot joint.
   d. plant joint.

   ANS: B   DIF: I   OBJ: 46-2.4

27. Refer to the illustration above. The joint shown in diagram "D" would most likely be found in the
   a. shoulder.
   b. elbow.
   c. knee.
   d. wrist.

   ANS: C   DIF: I   OBJ: 46-2.4

28. Refer to the illustration above. Which of the diagrams shows a joint that allows bones to "glide" over each other?
   a. "A."
   b. "B."
   c. "C."
   d. "D."

   ANS: C   DIF: I   OBJ: 46-2.4

29. Refer to the illustration above. The elbow is a pivot joint that allows your hand to turn over. It is shown in diagram
   a. "A."
   b. "B."
   c. "C."
   d. "D."

   ANS: B   DIF: I   OBJ: 46-2.4

30. Bone loss may be slowed by
    a. calcium.
    b. regular exercise.
    c. a balanced diet.
    d. All of the above

    ANS: D   DIF: I   OBJ: 46-2.5

31. Women are more susceptible than men to the effects of osteoporosis because
    a. their bones are smaller than those of men.
    b. they lose calcium during the child-bearing years.
    c. sex hormone production declines during menopause.
    d. All of the above

    ANS: D   DIF: I   OBJ: 46-2.5

32. Degeneration of cartilage causes
    a. menopause.
    b. bone replacement.
    c. bone fractures.
    d. osteoarthritis.

    ANS: D   DIF: I   OBJ: 46-2.5

33. The three types of muscles are
    a. skeletal, smooth, and cardiac.
    b. skeletal, voluntary, and cardiac.
    c. smooth, cardiac, and involuntary.
    d. skeletal, cardiac, and ridged.

    ANS: A   DIF: I   OBJ: 46-3.1

34. Smooth muscle
    a. can change the diameter of blood vessels.
    b. moves food through the digestive tract.
    c. is not under conscious control.
    d. All of the above

    ANS: D   DIF: I   OBJ: 46-3.1

35. Smooth muscles can be found
    a. attached to the skeleton.
    b. in the wrist bones.
    c. at the knee joint.
    d. in internal organs.

    ANS: D   DIF: I   OBJ: 46-3.1

36. The functional unit of muscle contraction is called the
    a. myofibril.
    b. sarcomere.
    c. muscle fiber.
    d. myosin filament.

    ANS: B   DIF: I   OBJ: 46-3.2

37. Actin and myosin
    a. are found in the sarcomeres.
    b. are proteins.
    c. interact during muscle contraction.
    d. All of the above

    ANS: D   DIF: I   OBJ: 46-3.2

38. Repeating units of myosin and actin filaments bound by two Z lines are
    a. muscles.
    b. myofibrils.
    c. sarcomeres.
    d. extensors.

    ANS: C   DIF: I   OBJ: 46-3.2

39. It has been known for a long time that muscle contraction requires ATP. Recently, scientists have discovered that ATP is required in order for the muscle filaments actin and myosin to slide past each other, resulting in muscle contraction. The ATP is specifically required to release the attachments between actin and myosin in the many cycles of attachment, release, and reattachment that result in sliding of these filaments past each other. Which of the following phenomena is explained by this specific role of ATP?
    a. muscle fatigue
    b. stiffening of a body after death (rigor mortis)
    c. opposing pairs of muscles functioning as flexors and extensors
    d. muscle sprain

    ANS: B   DIF: III   OBJ: 46-3.2

40. The total amount of force that a muscle can exert
    a. is determined by the strength of the nerve impulse that caused the contraction.
    b. depends on the total number of individual muscle fibers that have been stimulated.
    c. is dependent upon the weight of the object being moved.
    d. correlates to the number of Z lines contained within the sarcomeres of the muscle.

    ANS: B   DIF: I   OBJ: 46-3.3

41. Muscle tissue functions to move
    a. blood.
    b. food in the digestive tract.
    c. bones.
    d. All of the above

    ANS: D   DIF: I   OBJ: 46-3.4

42. Tendons connect
    a. bone to bone.
    b. muscle to bone.
    c. muscle to muscle.
    d. cartilage to bone.

    ANS: B   DIF: I   OBJ: 46-3.4

43. A muscle can
    a. push a bone.
    b. pull a bone.
    c. both push and pull a bone simultaneously.
    d. sometimes push and sometimes pull a bone.

    ANS: B   DIF: I   OBJ: 46-3.4

44. Muscles that function by bending joints, such as the biceps, are categorized as
    a. flexors.
    b. abductors.
    c. extensors.
    d. adductors.

    ANS: A   DIF: I   OBJ: 46-3.4

45. Muscle cells are able to exert force by
    a. converting ADP and organic phosphate into ATP.
    b. interfering with the forces of gravity and friction.
    c. rapidly relaxing the muscle fibers.
    d. pulling on surrounding tissues.

    ANS: D   DIF: I   OBJ: 46-3.4

46. A muscle's insertion
    a. is located on a bone that remains stationary when the muscle contracts.
    b. moves away from the origin during muscle contraction.
    c. is attached to the bone by a ligament.
    d. None of the above

    ANS: D   DIF: I   OBJ: 46-3.4

47. The origin of a muscle
    a. is at the opposite end of the muscle from the insertion.
    b. is located on a bone that remains stationary when the muscle contracts.
    c. does not move when the muscle contracts.
    d. All of the above

    ANS: D   DIF: I   OBJ: 46-3.4

48. flexors : bend ::
    a. immovable joints : bend
    b. slightly movable joints : be immovable
    c. extensors : straighten
    d. sutures : move a great deal

    ANS: C   DIF: II   OBJ: 46-3.4

49. The skin performs all of the following *except*
    a. protection.   c. control of body temperature.
    b. elimination of waste products.   d. production of chemical messengers.

    ANS: D   DIF: I   OBJ: 46-4.1

50. The functions of the skin include
    a. defense against microbes.   c. prevention of dehydration.
    b. regulation of body temperature.   d. All of the above

    ANS: D   DIF: I   OBJ: 46-4.1

51. The skin stores excess food for energy in
    a. fat cells.   c. keratin.
    b. nerve tissue.   d. lymph vessels.

    ANS: A   DIF: I   OBJ: 46-4.1

52. Overexposure to sunlight may cause all of the following *except*
    a. mutations in the skin cells.   c. acne.
    b. premature aging of the skin.   d. skin cancer.

    ANS: C   DIF: I   OBJ: 46-4.1

53. The most effective way(s) to reduce the risk of skin cancer include(s)
    a. always staying in water.
    b. increasing exposure to the sunlight gradually.
    c. minimizing exposure to sunlight and using a sunscreen.
    d. All of the above

    ANS: C   DIF: I   OBJ: 46-4.1

54. Keratin
    a. is a waterproof protein.   c. is a skin pigment.
    b. fills dead cells in the dermis.   d. All of the above

    ANS: A   DIF: I   OBJ: 46-4.2

55. The thin outer layer of the skin is
    a. the dermis.   c. the fatty layer.
    b. the epidermis.   d. connective skin.

    ANS: B   DIF: I   OBJ: 46-4.2

56. The dermis of the skin is
    a. composed of corneal and basal layers.   c. the location of melanocytes.
    b. the innermost layer of the skin.   d. involved in temperature regulation.

    ANS: D   DIF: I   OBJ: 46-4.2

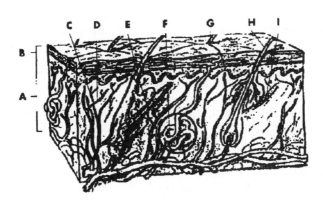

57. Refer to the illustration above. Skin receives nutrients, eliminates wastes, and helps regulate body temperature by using which of the following structures?
    a. "I."   c. "F."
    b. "G."   d. "D."

    ANS: B   DIF: I   OBJ: 46-4.2

58. Refer to the illustration above. Which of the structures in the diagram are composed mainly of dead cells?
    a. structures "A" and "F"
    b. structures "B" and "H"
    c. structures "C" and "D"
    d. None of the above

    ANS: B   DIF: I   OBJ: 46-4.2

59. Refer to the illustration above. The portion of the skin labeled "A" in the diagram is
    a. the dermis.
    b. sensitive to heat and cold.
    c. composed mainly of connective tissue.
    d. All of the above

    ANS: A   DIF: I   OBJ: 46-4.2

60. Refer to the illustration above. The structure labeled "E" in the diagram
    a. often is responsible for the formation of acne.
    b. is found in adults and teenagers.
    c. may be affected by high levels of sex hormones.
    d. All of the above

    ANS: D   DIF: I   OBJ: 46-4.4

61. Refer to the illustration above. The structure labeled "F" in the diagram
    a. is often responsible for the formation of acne.
    b. helps regulate the body temperature.
    c. is a reservoir for excess blood cells.
    d. is only found in teenagers.

    ANS: B   DIF: I   OBJ: 46-4.4

62. specialized epidermal cell : nails ::
    a. "half-moon area" : hair
    b. keratin : melanocytes
    c. melanocyte : hair
    d. hair follicle : hair

    ANS: D   DIF: II   OBJ: 46-4.3

63. Keratin
    a. is a strong, fibrous protein.
    b. fills dead cells in the dermis.
    c. is a skin pigment.
    d. All of the above

    ANS: A   DIF: I   OBJ: 46-4.3

64. Hair and nails are produced by the cells of the
    a. dermis.
    b. subcutaneous layer.
    c. subcutaneous glands.
    d. epidermis.

    ANS: D   DIF: I   OBJ: 46-4.3

65. A skin disorder caused by blockage of oil glands is called
    a. acne.
    b. carcinoma.
    c. osteoporosis.
    d. psoriasis.

    ANS: A   DIF: I   OBJ: 46-4.4

COMPLETION

1. _____ tissue joins, supports, and protects other types of tissue.

   ANS: Connective   DIF: I   OBJ: 46-1.1

2. All organs of the body contain epithelial, connective, muscle, and _____ tissues.

   ANS: nervous   DIF: I   OBJ: 46-1.1

3. The largest cavity in the human body is the _____ cavity.

   ANS: abdominal   DIF: I   OBJ: 46-1.4

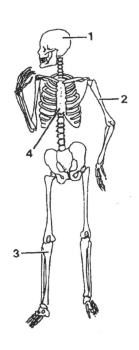

4. Refer to the illustration above. The bones labeled _____ and _____ are part of the appendicular skeleton.

   ANS: 2; 3   DIF: I   OBJ: 46-2.1

5. Refer to the illustration above. The bones labeled _____ and _____ are part of the axial skeleton.

   ANS: 1; 4   DIF: I   OBJ: 46-2.1

6. The bones of the skull and backbone are part of the _____ skeleton.

   ANS: axial   DIF: I   OBJ: 46-2.1

7. The bones of the arms, legs, and pelvis make up the _____ skeleton.

   ANS: appendicular   DIF: I   OBJ: 46-2.1

8. _____ is a membrane that surrounds individual bones.

   ANS: Periosteum   DIF: I   OBJ: 46-2.2

9. The _____ inside long bones is important in blood cell production and fat storage.

   ANS: marrow   DIF: I   OBJ: 46-2.2

10. _____ bone is dense—almost solid—and provides a great deal of support.

   ANS: Compact   DIF: I   OBJ: 46-2.2

11. The heart and lungs are protected by the _____.

   ANS: rib cage   DIF: I   OBJ: 46-2.2

12. The junction of two bones is called a(n) _____.

   ANS: joint   DIF: I   OBJ: 46-2.4

13. _____ is a painful degeneration of movable joints caused by attacks on the joints by cells of the immune system.

   ANS: Rheumatoid arthritis   DIF: I   OBJ: 46-2.5

14. _____ tissue can be smooth, skeletal, or cardiac.

   ANS: Muscle   DIF: I   OBJ: 46-3.1

15. _____ muscle is found in the walls of many internal organs.

   ANS: Smooth   DIF: I   OBJ: 46-3.1

16. The proteins actin and _____ in muscles enable the cells to contract.

   ANS: myosin   DIF: I   OBJ: 46-3.2

17. Repeating units of actin and myosin filaments are called _____.

   ANS: sarcomeres   DIF: I   OBJ: 46-3.2

18. _____ are muscles that cause bones to bend at a joint.

   ANS: Flexors   DIF: I   OBJ: 46-3.4

19. Moving a bone requires the cooperation of two sets of _____.

ANS: muscles   DIF: I   OBJ: 46-3.4

20. Muscles that function to straighten a joint are called _____.

ANS: extensors   DIF: I   OBJ: 46-3.4

21. Strips of dense connective tissue that attach muscles to bones are called
_____.

ANS: tendons   DIF: I   OBJ: 46-3.4

22. The brown pigment, _____, is responsible for most skin color.

ANS: melanin   DIF: I   OBJ: 46-4.1

23. Overexposure to _____ rays may result in the mutations in skin cells
that cause skin cancer.

ANS: ultraviolet   DIF: I   OBJ: 46-4.1

24. The outermost layer of the skin is called the _____.

ANS: epidermis   DIF: I   OBJ: 46-4.2

25. The outer layer of the skin that contains both living and nonliving cells is called the
_____.

ANS: epidermis   DIF: I   OBJ: 46-4.2

26. Hairs grow from specialized epidermal structures called hair _____.

ANS: follicles   DIF: I   OBJ: 46-4.3

27. Acne is caused by overactive _____ and hormones.

ANS: oil glands   DIF: I   OBJ: 46-4.4

PROBLEM

1. Connective tissue plays many different roles in the human body. It is crucial for
providing structural support for the body. It provides protection for internal organs. It
facilitates the movements of body parts. It functions in the transport of substances
throughout the body. It serves a storage function for certain kinds of molecules. It also
plays a vital role in enabling the body to defend itself against invading organisms or other
foreign substances.

In the space below or on a separate sheet of paper, write a short essay that first identifies
the connective cell types discussed in your text. Next, distinguish these cell types from
each other by their physical characteristics and by the type of matrix that is produced
between the cells. Finally, relate the physical characteristics and the type of intercellular
matrix to the specific function(s) that each of these cell types performs.

ANS: The students' essays should include the following information:
Bone is a kind of connective tissue that contains cells embedded in a matrix of collagen fibers that are coated with calcium salts. This makes bone fairly rigid and thus well-suited for providing structural support. It also provides protection of internal organs. For example, the skull protects the brain, the rib cage protects the heart and lungs, and the pelvic girdle protects organs of the reproductive, digestive, and excretory systems. Most of the human skeleton is composed of bone. Cartilage is a kind of connective tissue that contains cells embedded in a matrix of protein fibers. These fibers make cartilage strong yet flexible. Cartilage provides some structural support, particularly in young humans and at stress points between adjacent bones. Ligaments and tendons are both kinds of connective tissue that contain cells embedded in a matrix of collagen fibers. Ligaments connect bones to each other at joints and tendons attach muscles to bones. Both thus help the body make skeletal movements. Blood is a kind of connective tissue that contains cells embedded in a matrix of water. Blood is the medium in which oxygen, nutrients, wastes, hormones, antibodies, and many other chemicals are transported to and from the cells of the body. Some of the blood cells function as part of the immune system and other cells that defend our bodies against invading organisms and foreign substances. Some of these cells, such as macrophages, ingest and destroy any such harmful agent. Others of these cells, many of the lymphocytes, are involved in attacks against specific harmful agents. Adipose tissue is a kind of connective tissue that contains cells that store fat as an energy reserve.

DIF: III   OBJ: 46-3.1

ESSAY

1. Give an example of each of the following types of tissue, and briefly describe its functions: epithelial tissue, muscle tissue, connective tissue, and nervous tissue. Write your answer in the space below.

ANS:
Epithelial tissues, such as skin, are generally flat sheets of cells that protect from damage and control water loss in the tissues that they cover. Muscle tissue moves the body (skeletal muscle) and moves materials through the body (heart, smooth muscle of digestive tract). Connective tissue defends the body from invaders (white blood cells), sequesters materials (fat, melanin), and supports the body (bone and cartilage). Nervous tissues (brain, spinal cord, nerves) carry information in the form of electrical impulses.

DIF: I   OBJ: 46-1.1

2. Both glucose and oxygen are required for cells to carry out aerobic respiration and produce the ATP needed for cellular activities. How do glucose and oxygen enter the body and then all of the body's cells? Write your answer in the space below.

ANS:
Glucose is taken into the body in food, usually as part of larger carbohydrate molecules that are broken down in the digestive system to yield glucose. Glucose is absorbed across the walls of the digestive system and enters the circulatory system. The circulatory system transports glucose to all the cells of the body. Oxygen is taken into the body through the respiratory system. It is absorbed across the walls of the alveoli of the lungs and enters the circulatory system, which transports oxygen to all the cells of the body.

DIF: II   OBJ: 46-1.3

3. List five types of freely movable joints in your body, and give a location for each. Write your answer in the space below.

ANS:
A ball-and-socket joint is found in the shoulder and hip. A pivot joint enables your hand to turn over and is found in the elbow. A plane joint is found in your hand. A saddle joint functions at the thumb. The knee provides an example of a hinge joint.

DIF: I   OBJ: 46-2.4

4. Using examples, describe the three basic types of joints and their primary functions. Write your answer in the space below.

ANS:
Fixed joints are very tight joints that hold adjacent bones together, permitting little or no movement. The cranial bones of the skull are held together by fixed joints. Limited mobility is permitted by semi-movable joints, the second basic type of joint. In these joints, a bridge of cartilage joins two bones together, as in the joints between the vertebrae of the spine. The third type of joint is the freely movable joint. These joints allow the greatest degree of movement; they are found between bones that are held together by ligaments.

DIF: I   OBJ: 46-2.4

5. What is a ligament? Write your answer in the space below.

ANS:
A ligament is a tough connective tissue that joins one bone to another.

DIF: I   OBJ: 46-2.4

6. List the three types of muscle tissue, and give the function of each. Write your answer in the space below.

ANS:
The three types of muscle are skeletal muscle, cardiac muscle, and smooth muscle. Skeletal muscle moves bones, and cardiac muscle pumps blood through the body. Smooth muscle moves food through the body and performs other internal functions including changing blood vessel diameter, opening and closing bronchioles, and causing uterine contractions during labor.

DIF: I   OBJ: 46-3.1

7. Describe the contraction of muscle according to the sliding filament theory. Write your answer in the space below.

ANS:
Myosin and actin filaments lie in parallel lines along the length of a myofibril in units called sarcomeres. The myosin heads touch the adjacent actin filaments. When a muscle contracts, the myosin heads attach to the actin filaments, and when the heads bend inward, they pull the actin filaments along with them toward each other. This bending of the myosin head requires the use of an ATP molecule. As the actin filaments move toward each other along the myosin filament, they pull their Z lines with them, thus shortening the sarcomere. As sarcomeres are shortened along the entire muscle fiber, the entire muscle contracts.

DIF: II   OBJ: 46-3.3

8. How does the skin help regulate body temperature? Write your answer in the space below.

ANS:
Nerves in the skin sense heat, providing stimuli that dilate or constrict blood vessels. When the temperature in the environment is high, blood vessels dilate, allowing body heat to escape. Also, the skin produces sweat through its sweat glands, and the evaporation of sweat has a cooling effect on the body. When the temperature of the environment is low, blood vessels in the skin contract, reducing heat loss.

DIF: I   OBJ: 46-4.1

9. What are three functions of the blood vessels in the dermis? Explain. Write your answer in the space below.

ANS:
Blood vessels provide nutrient-rich blood to nourish skin cells, to carry away cellular waste products, and to regulate body temperature. Blood radiates heat into the air as it passes near the surface of the skin. If the body becomes too hot, these blood vessels enlarge, allowing more blood to flow through the dermis near the body surface.

DIF: I   OBJ: 46-4.2

10. What causes acne? Can it be prevented or controlled? Write your answer in the space below.

ANS:
Acne is caused by hormones and an increase in oil production by glands during adolescence. Excessive oil production can clog the oil glands, causing a buildup of oil. While acne cannot be prevented, the conditions associated with it may be controlled with proper skin care.

DIF: I   OBJ: 46-4.4

CHAPTER 47—CIRCULATORY AND RESPIRATORY SYSTEMS

TRUE/FALSE

1. The upper chambers of the heart are called the ventricles.

   ANS: F   DIF: I   OBJ: 47-1.1

2. The superior vena cava drains blood from the head and neck.

   ANS: T   DIF: I   OBJ: 47-1.2

3. Blood from the left ventricle flows into the aorta.

   ANS: T   DIF: I   OBJ: 47-1.2

4. Arteries contain valves that prevent the backward flow of blood.

   ANS: F   DIF: I   OBJ: 47-1.3

5. The innermost layer of an artery is a layer of elastic, smooth muscle tissue.

   ANS: F   DIF: I   OBJ: 47-1.3

6. Blood vessels in the body include arteries, veins, and capillaries.

   ANS: T   DIF: I   OBJ: 47-1.3

7. The systolic pressure tells how much pressure is exerted when the heart relaxes.

   ANS: F   DIF: I   OBJ: 47-1.3

8. Systemic circulation carries blood from the heart to the rest of the body.

   ANS: T   DIF: I   OBJ: 47-1.4

9. The lymphatic system returns fluids from around cells back to the blood vessels.

   ANS: T   DIF: I   OBJ: 47-1.5

10. Blood plasma is composed primarily of water.

    ANS: T   DIF: I   OBJ: 47-2.1

11. New red blood cells are produced by root cells in the bone marrow.

    ANS: F   DIF: I   OBJ: 47-2.2

12. Erythrocytes are responsible for the production of antibodies.

    ANS: F   DIF: I   OBJ: 47-2.2

13. When a platelet encounters a damaged blood vessel, it releases fibrin, which causes a clot to form.

    ANS: F   DIF: I   OBJ: 47-2.3

14. A person with type AB blood can donate blood to a person with any blood type.

    ANS: F   DIF: I   OBJ: 47-2.4

15. Type O blood contains neither A nor B antigens.

    ANS: T   DIF: I   OBJ: 47-2.4

16. When the diaphragm and the rib muscles contract, expiration occurs.

    ANS: F   DIF: I   OBJ: 47-3.4

17. Breathing is regulated mainly by response to the level of carbon dioxide detected in blood.

    ANS: T   DIF: I   OBJ: 47-3.5

MULTIPLE CHOICE

1. The ventricles are
   a. the upper chambers of the heart.
   b. the chambers of the heart that pump blood to the lungs and to the rest of the body.
   c. the chambers of the heart that receive blood from the lungs and the rest of the body.
   d. lower chambers of the heart that contract separately.

    ANS: B   DIF: I   OBJ: 47-1.1

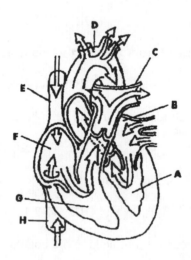

2. Refer to the illustration above. The chamber in the diagram indicated by "F" is
   a. the right atrium.   c. the right ventricle.
   b. the left atrium.   d. the left ventricle.

    ANS: A   DIF: I   OBJ: 47-1.1

3. Refer to the illustration above. In the diagram, the aorta is indicated by
   a. "C."
   b. "D."
   c. "G."
   d. "H."

   ANS: B   DIF: I   OBJ: 47-1.1

4. Refer to the illustration above. The vessels indicated by "C" in the diagram carry deoxygenated blood. The vessels are
   a. the pulmonary arteries.
   b. the pulmonary veins.
   c. parts of the aorta.
   d. part of the atria.

   ANS: A   DIF: I   OBJ: 47-1.2

5. Refer to the illustration above. In the diagram, blood in chamber "A"
   a. is full of oxygen.
   b. is returning from the lungs.
   c. is oxygen poor.
   d. has very little plasma.

   ANS: A   DIF: I   OBJ: 47-1.2

6. Vessels that carry blood away from the heart are called
   a. veins.
   b. capillaries.
   c. arteries.
   d. venules.

   ANS: C   DIF: I   OBJ: 47-1.2

7. The heart chamber that receives blood from the venae cavae is the
   a. left atrium.
   b. right atrium.
   c. left ventricle.
   d. right ventricle.

   ANS: B   DIF: I   OBJ: 47-1.2

8. Blood entering the right atrium
   a. is full of oxygen.
   b. is returning from the lungs.
   c. is deoxygenated.
   d. is low in plasma and platelets.

   ANS: C   DIF: I   OBJ: 47-1.2

9. Oxygenated blood from the lungs is received by the
   a. left ventricle.
   b. right atrium.
   c. left atrium.
   d. right ventricle.

   ANS: C   DIF: I   OBJ: 47-1.2

10. Which type of blood vessel is both strong and elastic?
    a. capillary
    b. artery
    c. vein
    d. venule

    ANS: B   DIF: I   OBJ: 47-1.3

11. An artery has a much thicker muscle layer than
    a. a vein.
    b. a capillary.
    c. a venule.
    d. All of the above

    ANS: D   DIF: I   OBJ: 47-1.3

12. The smallest and most numerous blood vessels in the body are the
    a. venules.
    b. veins.
    c. arteries.
    d. capillaries.

    ANS: D   DIF: I   OBJ: 47-1.3

13. An artery
    a. usually carries oxygen-rich blood.
    b. has thin, slightly elastic walls.
    c. has valves that prevent blood from flowing backward.
    d. All of the above

    ANS: A   DIF: I   OBJ: 47-1.3

14. If a blood vessel has valves, it probably
    a. is a vein.
    b. is an artery.
    c. is a venule.
    d. is part of the lymphatic system.

    ANS: A   DIF: I   OBJ: 47-1.3

15. The force exerted against the arterial walls when the heart contracts is called
    a. hypertension.
    b. systolic pressure.
    c. diastolic pressure.
    d. arterial relaxation.

    ANS: B   DIF: I   OBJ: 47-1.3

16. Normal blood pressure in millimeters of mercury is
    a. 145/95.
    b. 130/100.
    c. 120/80.
    d. 100/50.

    ANS: C   DIF: I   OBJ: 47-1.3

17. The pressure exerted on the inner walls of the arteries when the heart relaxes between beats is the ____ pressure.
    a. systolic.
    b. diastolic.
    c. barometric.
    d. residual.

    ANS: B   DIF: I   OBJ: 47-1.3

18. Pulmonary circulation flows to and from the
    a. stomach.
    b. liver.
    c. intestines.
    d. lungs.

    ANS: D   DIF: I   OBJ: 47-1.4

19. A condition known as atherosclerosis results in
    a. increased circulation to the heart.
    b. larger muscles.
    c. a narrowing of the inner walls of blood vessels.
    d. a widening of inner walls of blood vessels.

    ANS: C   DIF: I   OBJ: 47-1.4

20. cholesterol buildup : atherosclerosis ::
    a. iron buildup : atherosclerosis
    b. arteriosclerosis : the heart to work more easily
    c. low intake of saturated fats : heart attacks
    d. atherosclerosis : heart attacks

    ANS: D   DIF: II   OBJ: 47-1.4

21. Intercellular fluids are transported to the bloodstream by the
    a. renal circulation.   c. respiratory system.
    b. hepatic portal circulation.   d. lymphatic system.

    ANS: D   DIF: I   OBJ: 47-1.5

22. The iron-containing molecule in red blood cells is called
    a. plasma.   c. hemoglobin.
    b. ferric oxide.   d. carbonic acid.

    ANS: C   DIF: I   OBJ: 47-2.1

23. Mature red blood cells
    a. can live for about a year.   c. promote clotting.
    b. are the largest cells in the blood. d. do not have a nucleus.

    ANS: D   DIF: I   OBJ: 47-2.2

24. Infections generally result in an increase in the number of
    a. leukocytes.   c. platelets.
    b. erythrocytes.   d. alveoli.

    ANS: A   DIF: I   OBJ: 47-2.2

25. Red blood cells
    a. transport respiratory gases.   c. destroy viruses.
    b. combat bacterial infection.   d. transport cholesterol.

    ANS: A   DIF: I   OBJ: 47-2.2

26. Defending the body against bacterial infection and invasion by foreign substances is a
    function of
    a. red blood cells.   c. platelets.
    b. plasma.   d. white blood cells.

    ANS: D   DIF: I   OBJ: 47-2.2

27. Refer to the illustration above. The cells shown in the diagram are
    a. filled with plasma.   c. red blood cells.
    b. platelets.   d. white blood cells.

    ANS: C   DIF: I   OBJ: 47-2.2

28. Refer to the illustration above. The cells shown in the diagram
    a. can live for at least a year.
    b. are the largest cells in the circulatory system.
    c. promote clotting.
    d. contain hemoglobin.

    ANS: D   DIF: I   OBJ: 47-2.2

29. vitamins, salts, and proteins : plasma solutes ::
    a. arteries and veins : lymphatic vessels
    b. erythrocytes and leukocytes : blood cells
    c. platelets and megakaryocytes : leukocytes
    d. lymphocytes and macrophages : erythrocytes

    ANS: B   DIF: II   OBJ: 47-2.2

30. An abnormality involving the platelets would probably affect the process of
    a. breathing.   c. fighting bacterial infections.
    b. locomotion.   d. blood clotting.

    ANS: D   DIF: I   OBJ: 47-2.3

31. Which of the following is *not* involved in the formation of blood clots?
    a. platelet congregation at the site of rupture of a blood vessel
    b. release of clotting factors from platelets
    c. production of fibrin, a protein
    d. formation of fibrin–red blood cell complexes that circulate in the blood and are too
    large to move through ruptured blood-vessel walls

    ANS: D   DIF: I   OBJ: 47-2.3

32. A person with antigen A on their red blood cells can give blood to someone with blood type(s)
   a. A and AB.
   b. B and AB.
   c. only AB
   d. only O

   ANS: A   DIF: I   OBJ: 47-2.4

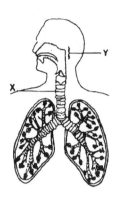

33. Refer to the illustration above. The structure labeled "X" is the
   a. epiglottis.
   b. pharynx.
   c. trachea.
   d. larynx.

   ANS: C   DIF: I   OBJ: 47-3.1

34. During swallowing, the air passage of the pharynx is covered by the
   a. larynx.
   b. epiglottis.
   c. trachea.
   d. bronchi.

   ANS: B   DIF: I   OBJ: 47-3.1

35. Alveoli in the lungs are connected to the bronchi by a network of tiny tubes called
   a. arterioles.
   b. venules.
   c. capillaries.
   d. bronchioles.

   ANS: D   DIF: I   OBJ: 47-3.1

36. bronchiole : alveoli ::
   a. alveoli : bronchi
   b. bronchi : larynx
   c. larynx : pharynx
   d. bronchi : bronchioles

   ANS: D   DIF: II   OBJ: 47-3.1

37. The actual exchange of gases occurs at the site of the
   a. trachea.
   b. nasal passageway.
   c. larynx.
   d. alveoli.

   ANS: D   DIF: I   OBJ: 47-3.2

38. Each alveolus
    a. contains many air sacs.
    b. attaches directly to the larynx.
    c. is surrounded by capillaries.
    d. is a large air sac.

    ANS: C   DIF: I   OBJ: 47-3.2

39. Gas exchange occurs when
    a. oxygen in the alveoli diffuses into the blood in the capillaries.
    b. oxygen binds with hemoglobin in the red blood cells.
    c. the red blood cells give up oxygen to the cells of the body tissues.
    d. All of the above

    ANS: D   DIF: I   OBJ: 47-3.2

40. carbon dioxide : lungs ::
    a. nutrients : kidneys
    b. nutrients : lungs
    c. nitrogenous waste : kidneys
    d. nitrogenous waste : lungs

    ANS: C   DIF: II   OBJ: 47-3.2

41. Carbon dioxide is transported in the blood in all of the following ways *except*
    a. dissolved in plasma.
    b. combined with hemoglobin.
    c. as bicarbonate ions.
    d. by white blood cells.

    ANS: D   DIF: I   OBJ: 47-3.3

42. When the diaphragm and rib cage muscles relax,
    a. the chest cavity enlarges.
    b. inspiration occurs.
    c. expiration occurs.
    d. it is impossible to breathe.

    ANS: C   DIF: I   OBJ: 47-3.4

43. The dome-shaped muscle below the chest cavity is called the
    a. soleus.
    b. biceps.
    c. diaphragm.
    d. popliteus.

    ANS: C   DIF: I   OBJ: 47-3.4

44. Which of the following occurs as air rushes into the lungs from the environment to equalize air pressure?
    a. inspiration
    b. contraction
    c. expiration
    d. None of the above

    ANS: A   DIF: I   OBJ: 47-3.4

45. The breathing center in the brain is *most* sensitive to the
    a. concentration of oxygen.
    b. concentration of carbon dioxide in the lungs.
    c. concentration of carbon dioxide in the blood.
    d. amount of oxygen in the cells.

    ANS: C   DIF: II   OBJ: 47-3.5

COMPLETION

1. The _____ system transports oxygen, carbon dioxide, food molecules, hormones, and other material to and from the cells of the body.

   ANS: circulatory   DIF: I   OBJ: 47-1.1

2. The _____ valve prevents blood from going from the left ventricle to the left atrium.

   ANS: mitral   DIF: I   OBJ: 47-1.1

3. The _____ starts each contraction of the heart.

   ANS: pacemaker or sinoatrial (SA) node   DIF: I   OBJ: 47-1.2

4. Electrical impulses in the heart are relayed to the ventricles by the _____.

   ANS: atrioventricular node   DIF: I   OBJ: 47-1.2

5. Blood flows from the right atrium to the right ventricle through the _____.

   ANS: tricuspid valve   DIF: I   OBJ: 47-1.2

6. The largest vein in the human body is the _____.

   ANS: vena cava   DIF: I   OBJ: 47-1.3

7. _____ are the blood vessels that connect the arteries to the veins.

   ANS: Capillaries   DIF: I   OBJ: 47-1.3

8. Systolic pressure is caused by contraction of the heart's _____.

   ANS: ventricles   DIF: I   OBJ: 47-1.3

9. The condition that results when blood pressure is consistently higher than normal is called _____.

   ANS: hypertension   DIF: I   OBJ: 47-1.3

10. The flow of blood from the heart to all parts of the body except the lungs is called _____ circulation.

    ANS: systemic   DIF: I   OBJ: 47-1.4

11. Excess fluids and proteins in the body are returned to the blood by a system of vessels called the _____ system.

    ANS: lymphatic   DIF: I   OBJ: 47-1.5

12. The major function of _____ is to assist in the blood clotting process.

ANS: platelets DIF: I OBJ: 47-2.1

13. The primary role of hemoglobin in the blood is to carry _____.

ANS: oxygen DIF: I OBJ: 47-2.1

14. Red blood cells are called _____.

ANS: erythrocytes DIF: I OBJ: 47-2.2

15. Defending the body against bacterial infection and invasion by other foreign substances is the function of _____ blood cells.

ANS: white DIF: I OBJ: 47-2.2

16. Antigens determining blood type are carried on the surface of _____.

ANS: erythrocytes or red blood cells DIF: I OBJ: 47-2.2

17. The _____ is a long, straight tube that carries air from the back of the throat to the lungs.

ANS: trachea DIF: I OBJ: 47-3.1

18. When you swallow, the _____ prevents food from entering the trachea.

ANS: epiglottis DIF: I OBJ: 47-3.1

19. Hemoglobin in red blood cells binds to both oxygen and _____.

ANS: carbon dioxide DIF: I OBJ: 47-3.3

20. When the diaphragm and the rib muscles contract, enlarging the chest cavity, _____ occurs.

ANS: inspiration DIF: I OBJ: 47-3.4

21. Breathing is regulated mainly by response to the level of _____ detected in the blood.

ANS: carbon dioxide DIF: I OBJ: 47-3.5

PROBLEM

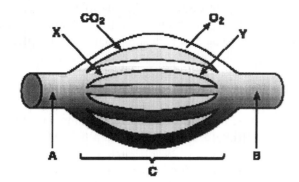

1. The diagram above shows two human blood vessels, "A" and "B," connected by a capillary bed, "C." Blood pressure is higher in vessel "B" than in vessel "A." The arrows indicate the direction of diffusion of O_2 and CO_2. Write your answers to the following in the spaces below.
   a. What type of blood vessel is vessel "A"?
   b. What type of blood vessel is vessel "B"?
   c. Does this diagram show part of the systemic circuit or part of the pulmonary circuit of the human circulatory system?
   d. In which location, "X" or "Y," will the concentration of O_2 in the blood be higher?
   e. Name one other substance typically found in blood that would move out of a capillary bed into body tissues along with the O_2 shown in the diagram.
   f. Name one other substance typically found in blood that would move into a capillary bed from body tissues along with the CO_2 shown in the diagram.

   ANS:
   a. vein
   b. artery
   c. systemic circuit
   d. "Y"
   e. possible answers: food molecule, water, vitamin, ion, hormone, or white blood cell
   f. possible answers: wastes or ammonia

   DIF: III   OBJ: 47-1.3

2. Every living cell in the human body must have an energy supply. Cells take up glucose or a related chemical and break it down inside the mitochondria to get ATP. ATP is the form of energy that cells use for their various activities. The breakdown of glucose occurs in the process of aerobic respiration. A summary of this process is shown in the following equation (note that this is not a balanced equation):

   $$C_6H_{12}O_6 + O_2 \leftrightarrow CO_2 + H_2O + ATP$$

   O_2, which is a gas, is consumed in this process and CO_2, also a gas, is produced. Trace the pathway of a molecule of O_2 from the location where it enters the human body, across any cell membranes it must pass, until it reaches a muscle cell in the right leg. Then, trace the pathway of a molecule of CO_2 from inside that muscle cell, where it is produced in aerobic respiration, until it leaves the body. Write your answer in the space below or on a separate sheet of paper.

ANS:
The O_2 molecule would enter the body through one of the nostrils, pass through the pharynx, the trachea, one of the two bronchi, and then enter a bronchiole in the lung. It would then move into an alveolus and then move across a cell membrane of the alveolus and enter the blood. Once in the blood, the O_2 would move across the cell membrane into a red blood cell. It would then be transported in the blood leaving the lungs in the pulmonary vein, which takes blood to the heart. The O_2 in blood would enter the heart in the left atrium, move to the left ventricle, and then be forced out of the heart into the aorta. The O_2 in blood would then be transported into smaller arteries, still smaller arterioles, and finally a capillary bed in the muscle in the right leg. The O_2 would then move out of the red blood cell, across its cell membrane, and across a cell membrane to enter a muscle cell. A CO_2 molecule produced by aerobic respiration in this muscle cell would leave the cell by moving across its cell membrane. It would then enter the blood. In the blood, it would most likely move across the cell membrane of a red blood cell and remain in its cytoplasm. The CO_2 in blood would then be transported into venules, and then into veins, until it returned to the vena cava. From the vena cava, it would reenter the heart. The CO_2 in blood would enter the right atrium of the heart, move to the right ventricle, and then be forced out of the heart into the pulmonary artery. From there, it would be transported to one of the lungs. In a lung, the CO_2 would move out of the red blood cell by moving across its cell membrane. It would then move across a cell membrane of an alveolus. From the alveolus, the CO_2 would pass through a bronchiole, a bronchus, the trachea, the pharynx, and then leave the body through one of the nostrils.

DIF: III   OBJ: 47-3.3

ESSAY

1. How does the circulatory system help the body maintain a constant temperature? Write your answer in the space below.

    ANS:
    The body maintains a relatively constant temperature by using metabolic energy to make heat. The circulatory system distributes the heat to all parts of the body. Passing just below the skin, the circulatory system absorbs the heat from a hot environment and gives off heat to a cold one. When it is cold outside, blood vessels constrict. In the opposite manner, the blood vessels under the skin dilate when it is hot outside, thereby delivering more blood to the surface and allowing more heat to escape.

    DIF: I   OBJ: 47-1.1

2. Do arteries carry oxygenated blood or deoxygenated blood? Explain. Write your answer in the space below.

    ANS:
    An artery is a blood vessel that carries blood away from the heart. Most arteries carry oxygenated blood, but some arteries carry deoxygenated blood. The pulmonary arteries, which carry blood from the heart to the lungs, carry deoxygenated blood that has been returned to the heart from the rest of the body. The arteries that carry blood from the heart to the rest of the body carry oxygenated blood that has been returned to the heart from the lungs.

    DIF: II   OBJ: 47-1.2

3. Describe the antibody-antigen interactions that take place when an Rh- person who has blood type B receives blood from an Rh+ person who has blood type AB. Write your answer in the space below.

ANS:
An Rh⁻ person who has blood type B has only blood antigen B. A person having this antigen would produce antibodies to antigens A and Rh. An Rh⁺ person who has blood type AB has blood antigens Rh, A, and B. When these antigens enter the recipient's blood, antibodies to the A and Rh will produce agglutination. The B antigen of the donor's blood will not cause agglutination because the recipient does not produce antibodies to this antigen.

DIF: II   OBJ: 47-2.2

4. Describe how oxygen is transported in the blood. Write your answer in the space below.

ANS:
Red blood cells are filled with hemoglobin, which is an iron-containing protein that gives blood its red color. Oxygen easily binds to the hemoglobin iron, making red blood cells efficient oxygen carriers that circulate throughout the body as they flow with the plasma.

DIF: I   OBJ: 47-3.3

5. Carbon dioxide (CO_2) dissolves poorly in plasma. While it can be carried by hemoglobin, the ability of red blood cells to transport it on hemoglobin is limited. Thus, seventy percent of the CO_2 that leaves the body is carried out in a third way. Explain what happens. Write your answer in the space below.

ANS:
With the help of an enzyme, this remaining 70 percent combines with water in the blood to form carbonic acid (H_2CO_3) inside red blood cells. Because carbonic acid is unstable, hydrogen (H^+) and bicarbonate (HCO_3^-) ions quickly form. When the blood reaches the lungs, chemical reactions that reverse the process occur, releasing carbon dioxide. The carbon dioxide diffuses from the blood into the alveoli in the lungs. It is then exhaled with water vapor.

DIF: II   OBJ: 47-3.3

6. How is air moved in and out of the lungs from the environment? Write your answer in the space below.

ANS:
When the diaphragm and rib muscles contract, the diaphragm moves downward and the rib cage moves up and outward. This expands the chest cavity, lowering the air pressure in the lungs and causing air to flow in. When the diaphragm and the rib muscles relax, the diaphragm moves upward and the rib cage moves down and inward. This reduces the size of the chest cavity, increasing the pressure of the air in the lungs and causing air to flow out.

DIF: I   OBJ: 47-3.4

TRUE/FALSE

1. In following Koch's postulates to determine whether a virus is the agent of a particular disease, it may not be possible to complete all of the steps because the viruses may not be able to be cultured.

   ANS: T   DIF: II   OBJ: 48-1.1

2. Koch's postulates can be used only for determining whether a bacterium is the agent of a disease.

   ANS: F   DIF: I   OBJ: 48-1.1

3. Most pathogens can readily pass through mucous membranes.

   ANS: F   DIF: I   OBJ: 48-1.2

4. Skin engages in chemical warfare.

   ANS: T   DIF: I   OBJ: 48-1.2

5. Secretions of sweat and oil glands make the skin extremely basic, allowing it to be an effective barrier to infection.

   ANS: F   DIF: I   OBJ: 48-1.2

6. When pathogens enter the body through a wound, they trigger an inflammatory response.

   ANS: T   DIF: I   OBJ: 48-1.3

7. During the inflammatory response, red blood cells engulf foreign substances.

   ANS: F   DIF: I   OBJ: 48-1.3

8. Natural killer cells attack cells that have been infected by microbes, but not the microbes themselves.

   ANS: T   DIF: I   OBJ: 48-1.4

9. Fevers above 103°F can have beneficial effects when the body is defending itself against pathogens.

   ANS: F   DIF: I   OBJ: 48-1.5

10. Helper T cells are a type of macrophage.

   ANS: F   DIF: I   OBJ: 48-2.2

11. The body possesses millions of different types of T cells, each of which bears unique receptor molecules that can recognize millions of different foreign proteins.

ANS: T DIF: I OBJ: 48-2.2

12. Cytotoxic T cells are able to recognize and attack virus-infected cells because the infected cells have been coated with a protein called interleukin-2 by helper T cells.

ANS: F DIF: I OBJ: 48-2.2

13. Cytotoxic T cells and B cells are activated by interleukin-2, which is secreted by helper T cells.

ANS: T DIF: I OBJ: 48-2.3

14. B cells function by attacking and destroying body cells that have been infected by viruses.

ANS: F DIF: I OBJ: 48-2.3

15. The first exposure to a pathogen results in a much faster immune response than the second exposure to the same pathogen.

ANS: F DIF: I OBJ: 48-2.4

16. If a pathogen that has already been defeated is encountered again, memory cells produce antibodies against it.

ANS: T DIF: I OBJ: 48-2.4

17. Type I diabetes is an autoimmune disease affecting the thyroid gland.

ANS: F DIF: I OBJ: 48-2.5

18. AIDS is a disorder of the immune system.

ANS: T DIF: I OBJ: 48-3.1

19. The AIDS virus may remain dormant for ten years or longer.

ANS: T DIF: I OBJ: 48-3.1

20. Any person who is HIV-positive has the disease called AIDS.

ANS: F DIF: I OBJ: 48-3.1

21. AIDS patients often succumb to infections or cancers that are rare in healthy individuals.

ANS: T DIF: I OBJ: 48-3.1

22. HIV can be transmitted through kissing.

ANS: F DIF: I OBJ: 48-3.2

23. Vaccines developed against HIV have been ineffective in preventing the disease because the surface proteins of the virus destroy the vaccines.

ANS: F   DIF: I   OBJ: 48-3.3

MULTIPLE CHOICE

1. Which of the following is the final step in using Koch's postulates to demonstrate that a particular agent causes a disease?
   a. A healthy animal inoculated with the disease agent contracts the disease.
   b. The disease agent is found in animals that have the disease but not in animals that are free of the disease.
   c. An animal infected with the disease agent obtained from an animal with the disease is found to have the disease agent in its tissues.
   d. The disease agent is collected and cultured in the laboratory.

ANS: C   DIF: I   OBJ: 48-1.1

2. Which of the following is true about the release of histamine from cells in nasal passages?
   a. It occurs during an allergic reaction.
   b. It causes nearby capillaries to swell.
   c. It may cause increased secretion by mucous membranes.
   d. All of the above

ANS: D   DIF: I   OBJ: 48-1.2

3. The body's first line of defense against infection includes all of the following *except*
   a. skin.   c. acids in the stomach.
   b. mucous membranes.   d. interleukin-1.

ANS: D   DIF: I   OBJ: 48-1.2

4. The skin repels pathogens by
   a. functioning as a barrier.   c. engaging in chemical warfare.
   b. producing antibodies.   d. Both a and c

ANS: D   DIF: I   OBJ: 48-1.2

5. Mucous membranes
   a. cover all the body's surfaces.
   b. line internal body surfaces that are in contact with the environment.
   c. produce antibodies to combat infection.
   d. secrete sweat, which has antibacterial enzymes.

ANS: B   DIF: I   OBJ: 48-1.2

6. Mucous membranes
   a. are moist epithelial layers that are impermeable to most pathogens.
   b. line the nasal passages, mouth, lungs, digestive tract, urethra, and vagina.
   c. contain glands that secrete mucus, a sticky fluid that traps pathogens.
   d. All of the above

ANS: D   DIF: I   OBJ: 48-1.2

7. The first line of defense against infection includes
   a. mucous membranes.
   b. neutrophils.
   c. cytotoxic T cells.
   d. antibodies.

   ANS: A   DIF: I   OBJ: 48-1.2

8. All of the following possess mucous membranes *except*
   a. the digestive tract.
   b. the surface of the skin.
   c. the nasal passages.
   d. the vagina.

   ANS: B   DIF: I   OBJ: 48-1.2

9. Mucus is produced by the cells lining the walls of the bronchi and bronchioles
   a. only when a person has a severe respiratory infection.
   b. to allow oxygen to diffuse into the blood more efficiently.
   c. as a lubricant for the expulsion of food that might go "down the wrong tube."
   d. to protect against microbes that might be inhaled.

   ANS: D   DIF: I   OBJ: 48-1.2

10. The stomach is involved in defense against infection by
    a. regurgitating any pathogen that might be swallowed.
    b. secreting mucus that is carried away by cilia.
    c. possessing acid that destroys potential pathogens that are swallowed.
    d. sending potential pathogens to the liver for destruction.

    ANS: C   DIF: I   OBJ: 48-1.2

11. Which of the following is a nonspecific defense against pathogens?
    a. B cells
    b. antibodies
    c. helper T cells
    d. the inflammatory response

    ANS: D   DIF: I   OBJ: 48-1.3

12. When the inflammatory response is triggered,
    a. damaged or infected cells release chemical alarm signals.
    b. more fluid than normal leaks from capillaries near the injury, and swelling results.
    c. white blood cells attack invading pathogens.
    d. All of the above

    ANS: D   DIF: I   OBJ: 48-1.3

13. When a puncture wound becomes infected,
    a. damaged cells release chemicals that promote the immune response.
    b. the temperature around the wound increases.
    c. white blood cells move into the injured area.
    d. All of the above

    ANS: D   DIF: I   OBJ: 48-1.3

14. The redness and swelling associated with an inflammatory response is caused by
    a. secretion of antibodies.
    b. expansion of local blood vessels.
    c. complement activity.
    d. natural killer cells destroying bacteria.

    ANS: B   DIF: I   OBJ: 48-1.3

15. Phagocytes, such as macrophages,
    a. produce strong antibiotics.
    b. secrete interferon.
    c. shut down immune responses.
    d. ingest and destroy pathogens.

    ANS: D   DIF: I   OBJ: 48-1.4

16. White blood cells that ingest invading microbes and cellular debris resulting from microbial attacks are called
    a. macrophages.
    b. neutrophils.
    c. natural killer cells.
    d. complement cells.

    ANS: A   DIF: I   OBJ: 48-1.4

17. Which of the following engulfs foreign cells?
    a. helper T cell
    b. B cell
    c. macrophage
    d. antibody

    ANS: C   DIF: I   OBJ: 48-1.4

18. Neutrophils are responsible for
    a. ingesting individual microbes.
    b. destroying viruses.
    c. secreting toxic chemicals that kill bacteria.
    d. producing antibodies.

    ANS: C   DIF: I   OBJ: 48-1.4

19. neutrophils : releasing chemicals ::
    a. macrophages : releasing chemicals
    b. natural killer cells : releasing chemicals
    c. natural killer cells : puncturing their membranes
    d. macrophages : puncturing their membranes

    ANS: C   DIF: II   OBJ: 48-1.4

20. Moderate fevers (below 103°F)
    a. damage essential proteins in your body.
    b. inhibit the growth of pathogens and stimulate macrophage action.
    c. occur late in the disease process after the pathogen is almost eliminated.
    d. require emergency treatment.

    ANS: B   DIF: I   OBJ: 48-1.5

21. redness and swelling : the inflammatory response ::
    a. increased blood flow : AIDS
    b. inflammatory response : membrane attack complex
    c. neutrophils : autoimmune disease
    d. message to the brain : temperature response
    e. macrophages : immune system failure

    ANS: D   DIF: II   OBJ: 48-1.5

22. Where are the cells of the immune system produced in adults?
    a. lymph nodes   c. thymus
    b. mucous membranes.   d. bone marrow

    ANS: D   DIF: I   OBJ: 48-2.1

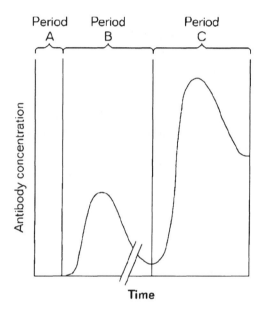

23. Refer to the illustration above. During which time period would the first antibodies to the pathogen be produced?
    a. "Period A"   c. "Period C"
    b. "Period B"   d. None of the above

    ANS: B   DIF: I   OBJ: 48-2.1

24. Refer to the illustration above. Which time period would be characterized by the most rapid division of B cells?
    a. "Period A"   c. "Period C"
    b. "Period B"   d. None of the above

    ANS: C   DIF: I   OBJ: 48-2.3

25. Antibodies
   a. prevent diseases caused by vaccines.
   b. are produced by bacteria that infect animals.
   c. help destroy microbes that invade the body.
   d. cause viruses to infect bacterial cells.

   ANS: C   DIF: I   OBJ: 48-2.1

26. Once stimulated by antigens on the surface of macrophages, helper T cells may
   a. stimulate cytotoxic T cells to attack viruses directly.
   b. stimulate B cells to divide and develop into plasma cells.
   c. repair macrophages.
   d. cause fever.

   ANS: B   DIF: I   OBJ: 48-2.2

27. The role of helper T cells in immune responses is to
   a. secrete interleukin-1.
   b. stimulate macrophages to initiate an "alarm signal."
   c. initiate the activities of neutrophils.
   d. activate two different types of immune system cells.

   ANS: D   DIF: I   OBJ: 48-2.2

28. Cytotoxic T cells recognize cells that have been infected by viruses
   a. only after the infected cells have been ingested by macrophages.
   b. because the infected cells have viral proteins on their surfaces.
   c. when the infected cells have been coated with complement.
   d. at the same time that neutrophils release their toxins into damaged tissue.

   ANS: B   DIF: I   OBJ: 48-2.2

29. All of the following are white blood cells that are involved in immune responses *except*
   a. B cells.   c. macrophages.
   b. T cells.   d. megakaryocytes.

   ANS: D   DIF: I   OBJ: 48-2.3

30. Which of the following pairs is *incorrectly* associated?
   a. cytotoxic T cells—attack and kill infected cells
   b. helper T cells—activate killer T cells and B cells
   c. B cells—engulf cells that are infected with microbes
   d. macrophages—consume pathogens and infected cells

   ANS: C   DIF: I   OBJ: 48-2.3

31. When B cells encounter a pathogen, they
   a. secrete interleukin-2, which stimulates cytotoxic T cells.
   b. divide and produce large amounts of antibody.
   c. initiate an inflammatory response.
   d. attack the cell by making a hole in its membrane.

   ANS: B   DIF: I   OBJ: 48-2.3

32. A few B cells that have encountered a pathogen
    a. become killer T cells.
    b. are ingested by macrophages.
    c. have viral protein on their cell membrane surface.
    d. become memory cells.

    ANS: D   DIF: I   OBJ: 48-2.3

33. B cells
    a. sometimes remain in the blood for years.
    b. secrete antibodies.
    c. are stimulated by helper T cells.
    d. All of the above

    ANS: D   DIF: I   OBJ: 48-2.3

34. After the initial immune response subsides, B cells that patrol body tissues for long
    periods of time
    a. are called helper T cells.   c. are called memory cells.
    b. develop into phagocytes.   d. cannot react to the original antigen.

    ANS: C   DIF: I   OBJ: 48-2.3

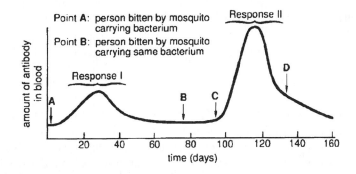

35. Refer to the illustration above. The most likely reason for "Response II" being greater
    than "Response I" in the diagram is that
    a. more bacteria entered at point "C" than at point "A."
    b. memory cells were produced in "Response I."
    c. antibodies from "Response I" still remained in the blood.
    d. macrophages increased their production of antibodies.

    ANS: B   DIF: I   OBJ: 48-2.3

36. pathogenic bacteria and viruses : enemies to humans ::
    a. B cells and T cells : mucous membrane cells
    b. helper T cells and cytotoxic T cells : skin cells
    c. cytotoxic T cells and macrophages : pathogens
    d. cytotoxic T cells and B cells : white blood cells

    ANS: D   DIF: II   OBJ: 48-2.3

Modern Biology Assessment Item Listing
457

37. macrophages : helper T cells ::
    a. cytotoxic T cells : macrophages
    b. helper T cells : cytotoxic T cells and B cells
    c. B cells : cytotoxic T cells and macrophages
    d. mucous membrane cells : helper T cells and B cells

    ANS: B   DIF: II   OBJ: 48-2.3

38. Vaccines are effective in preventing disease because they
    a. interfere with the release of suppressor T cells.
    b. are antibodies directed against specific pathogens.
    c. contain specific B cells and T cells.
    d. trigger antibody formation.

    ANS: D   DIF: I   OBJ: 48-2.4

39. Secondary exposure to a pathogen
    a. results in very rapid production of antibodies.
    b. stimulates memory cells to divide quickly.
    c. may result in destruction of the pathogen before a person knows he or she is infected.
    d. All of the above

    ANS: D   DIF: I   OBJ: 48-2.4

40. All vaccines are produced from killed or weakened
    a. phagocytes.   c. antigens.
    b. pathogens.   d. allergens.

    ANS: B   DIF: I   OBJ: 48-2.4

41. John and James are identical twins. During the summer following their fifteenth birthday, they went on a vacation and stayed in a cabin with two of their cousins. One of the cousins came down with chicken pox in the middle of the vacation. Chicken pox is caused by a virus. Two weeks later, John came down with chicken pox. James, however, never developed any symptoms of the disease. Which of the following is the best explanation for the different responses John and James had to exposure to the same disease?
    a. John and James are not really identical twins. James inherited an immunity to chicken pox but John did not.
    b. Even though John and James are identical twins, they produce different kinds of immune system cells. James had cytotoxic T cells that could recognize and destroy the chicken pox viruses, while John did not.
    c. James had been exposed to chicken pox at an earlier age and developed the disease. His body produced memory cells that protected him from further infections of the disease. John did not get exposed to chicken pox at an earlier age.
    d. James had a cold at the time he was exposed to the chicken pox virus. The cold virus had stimulated his body to produce lots of B cells, which were then also able to recognize and bind to the chicken pox viruses. John did not have a cold at the time he was exposed to the chicken pox.

    ANS: C   DIF: II   OBJ: 48-2.4

42. A misdirected immune system response against a harmless antigen is called
    a. an autoimmune disease.
    b. a secondary immune reaction.
    c. an allergic reaction.
    d. a vaccination reaction.

    ANS: C   DIF: I   OBJ: 48-2.5

43. Autoimmune diseases occur when
    a. cells release antihistamine.
    b. a person is infected with HIV.
    c. the body manufactures "anti-self" antibodies.
    d. a person receives a blood transfusion of the wrong type.

    ANS: C   DIF: I   OBJ: 48-2.5

44. An autoimmune disease in which the immune system attacks myelinated nerves is
    a. multiple sclerosis.
    b. rheumatoid arthritis.
    c. Graves' disease.
    d. lupus erythematosus.

    ANS: A   DIF: I   OBJ: 48-2.5

45. Which of the following is true about the release of histamine from cells in the nasal passages?
    a. It occurs during an allergic reaction.
    b. It causes nearby capillaries to swell.
    c. It may cause increased secretion by mucous membranes.
    d. All of the above

    ANS: D   DIF: I   OBJ: 48-2.5

46. Which of the following describes the actions of HIV?
    a. HIV attacks and cripples the immune system.
    b. HIV invades macrophages and helper T cells.
    c. HIV kills large numbers of helper T cells.
    d. All of the above

    ANS: D   DIF: I   OBJ: 48-3.1

47. Scientists think that practically everyone infected with HIV
    a. can be cured with vaccines.
    b. will die of AIDS within one year of diagnosis of the virus.
    c. will live a normal life if they don't smoke and if they eat a balanced diet.
    d. will eventually develop AIDS.

    ANS: D   DIF: I   OBJ: 48-3.1

48. A person infected with HIV may
    a. develop the disease called AIDS.
    b. have viruses reproducing in helper T cells.
    c. be more susceptible to a variety of pathogens.
    d. All of the above

    ANS: D   DIF: I   OBJ: 48-3.1

Modern Biology Assessment Item Listing
459

49. HIV causes AIDS by attacking and destroying
    a. helper T cells.
    b. B cells.
    c. neutrophils.
    d. antibodies.

    ANS: A   DIF: I   OBJ: 48-3.1

50. The debilitating effects of AIDS are due to inability of the immune system to
    a. activate B cells and cytotoxic T cells.
    b. produce antibodies against pathogens.
    c. recognize and destroy infected cells.
    d. All of the above

    ANS: D   DIF: I   OBJ: 48-3.1

51. HIV can be transmitted
    a. through sexual intercourse with an infected person.
    b. by breast-feeding.
    c. by sharing contaminated hypodermic needles and syringes.
    d. All of the above

    ANS: D   DIF: I   OBJ: 48-3.2

52. Which of the following is used to determine whether a person has been infected with HIV?
    a. determining the person has had sexual intercourse with an infected person
    b. determining whether the person has antibodies to HIV in his or her blood
    c. determining whether the person has AIDS
    d. determining whether the person is an intravenous drug user

    ANS: B   DIF: II   OBJ: 48-3.2

53. Which of the following explains why HIV evolves rapidly?
    a. The genes that code for its surface proteins mutate rapidly.
    b. Each new chemical used in treatment induces mutations in the virus.
    c. Its DNA mutates rapidly when the virus enters human body cells.
    d. All of the above

    ANS: A   DIF: I   OBJ: 48-3.3

COMPLETION

1. Sweat is protective because it contains lysozyme, a(n) _____ that attacks the cell walls of many bacteria.

    ANS: enzyme   DIF: I   OBJ: 48-1.2

2. Moist epithelial layers that line internal body surfaces and that are barriers to many pathogens are called _____.

    ANS: mucous membranes   DIF: I   OBJ: 48-1.2

3. The _____ acts as a barrier to keep foreign organisms and viruses out of the body.

   ANS: skin DIF: I OBJ: 48-1.2

4. At the site of a splinter, redness, swelling, and an increase in temperature would be signs of a(n) _____ response.

   ANS: inflammatory DIF: I OBJ: 48-1.3

5. _____ are white blood cells that travel throughout the body, killing bacteria one at a time by ingesting them.

   ANS: Macrophages DIF: I OBJ: 48-1.4

6. Immune surveillance by _____ cells is one of the body's most potent defenses against cancer.

   ANS: natural killer DIF: I OBJ: 48-1.4

7. Moderate _____, occurring in the early phases of an infection and caused by the release of interleukin-1, inhibits the growth of pathogens and stimulates macrophage action.

   ANS: fever DIF: I OBJ: 48-1.5

8. _____ are defensive proteins found in the body of an organism that label infectious microbes for destruction before they can cause disease.

   ANS: Antibodies DIF: I OBJ: 48-2.1

9. An "alarm signal" is emitted by macrophages in the form of a protein called _____, which activates helper T cells.

   ANS: interleukin-1 DIF: I OBJ: 48-2.2

10. Interleukin-2 is produced by _____ cells.

    ANS: helper T DIF: I OBJ: 48-2.2

11. B cells produce proteins called _____ that can mark pathogens for destruction.

    ANS: antibodies DIF: I OBJ: 48-2.3

12. After a primary exposure to a pathogen, the bloodstream contains _____ cells that can be specifically recalled to defend against that particular pathogen.

    ANS: memory DIF: I OBJ: 48-2.4

13. _____ is the process by which a dead or disabled pathogen (or proteins from that pathogen) is introduced into the body so that an immune response results without an actual infection.

ANS: Vaccination   DIF: I   OBJ: 48-2.4

14. _____ is a chemical released from mast cells during an allergic reaction.

ANS: Histamine   DIF: I   OBJ: 48-2.5

15. A disease in which the body's immune system attacks its own body cells is called a(n) _____ disease.

ANS: autoimmune   DIF: I   OBJ: 48-2.5

16. A(n) _____ is a misdirected immune system response against a harmless antigen.

ANS: allergy   DIF: I   OBJ: 48-2.5

17. _____ causes AIDS.

ANS: HIV   DIF: I   OBJ: 48-3.1

18. The most effective treatment for AIDS is now considered to be the administration of _____ antiviral drugs to patients.

ANS: three/several different   DIF: I   OBJ: 48-3.3

ESSAY

1. Describe three components of the first line of defense that the body uses to prevent infections. Write your answer in the space below.

ANS:
The skin prevents a pathogen from entering the body. In addition, oils and sweat produced by glands in the skin make the skin's surface acidic and create an environment unfavorable to pathogens. Sweat also contains enzymes that digest bacterial walls. Tears and saliva are other forms of chemical warfare that defend the body. Mucous membranes line internal body surfaces that are exposed to the environment. They secrete mucus, which is a sticky substance for trapping pathogens. Once pathogens are trapped, cilia lining the respiratory tract sweep them up to the pharynx, where they are swallowed and travel to the stomach, which contains destructive enzymes. Inflammatory responses result in the destruction of pathogens that gain entry through minor wounds. During inflammation, chemical alarm signals mobilize chemical and temperature changes and attract phagocytes to the injury.

DIF: I   OBJ: 48-1.3

2. Imagine that a potential pathogen has been able to get through the skin, the first line of body defense. What four steps does the body use as a second line of defense to prevent the pathogen from initiating a major infection? Write your answer in the space below.

ANS:
There are four steps that serve as a second line of defense against infection. (1) Cells such as macrophages, neutrophils, and natural killer cells can destroy invading microbes or cells that have been invaded by the microbes. (2) Complement consists of proteins that interact when they encounter cell membranes of bacteria or fungi, causing the membranes to puncture, thus destroying them. (3) Localized infection initiates an inflammatory response that suppresses infection and speeds healing. (4) Fever is initiated by macrophages that send a message to the brain, resulting in an elevation of body temperature. This temperature increase interferes with the ability of bacteria to grow and reproduce.

DIF: II   OBJ: 48-1.5

3. Briefly describe how a cell that has been infected by a virus can be recognized and destroyed. Write your answer in the space below.

ANS:
Macrophages contact infected cells and release an "alarm signal" called interleukin-1. This protein activates helper T cells that secrete another protein, interleukin-2. This substance, in turn, stimulates cytotoxic T cells, which bind to the infected cell using surface receptor molecules that recognize traces of viral protein on the surface of the infected cell. This interaction causes damage to the cell membrane of the infected cell, resulting in its destruction.

DIF: I   OBJ: 48-2.1

4. What is the function of memory cells in immune response? Write your answer in the space below.

ANS:
After primary immune response, some B and T cells capable of recognizing a particular antigen remain in circulation. If the individual is again exposed to the same antigen, these cells will begin to divide rapidly, forming a new generation of antibody-producing cells.

DIF: I   OBJ: 48-2.4

5. HIV is a fatal infection, but victims are not always killed by the virus itself. They generally die from other diseases that a healthy individual could resist successfully. Explain why this is true. Write your answer in the space below.

ANS:
The human immunodeficiency virus (HIV) disables the immune system of the infected person, making the individual susceptible to other pathogens. HIV destroys the immune system by attacking helper T cells, without which the immune system is unable to stimulate B cells or killer T cells.

DIF: I   OBJ: 48-3.1

TRUE/FALSE

1. A fatty acid that has as many hydrogen atoms as possible is called a saturated fatty acid.

   ANS: T   DIF: I   OBJ: 49-1.1

2. Proteins consist of many simple sugars bonded together.

   ANS: F   DIF: I   OBJ: 49-1.1

3. Carbohydrates are obtained mostly from oils, margarine, and butter.

   ANS: F   DIF: I   OBJ: 49-1.2

4. According to most authorities, a well-balanced diet has more fat than protein.

   ANS: T   DIF: I   OBJ: 49-1.2

5. Proteins are the body's main source of fuel.

   ANS: F   DIF: I   OBJ: 49-1.4

6. The liver stores fat-soluble nutrients and regulates the levels of food molecules in the blood.

   ANS: T   DIF: I   OBJ: 49-2.1

7. The liver is part of the digestive system.

   ANS: T   DIF: I   OBJ: 49-2.1

8. In the first stage of digestion, proteins are broken down by pepsins in the stomach.

   ANS: F   DIF: I   OBJ: 49-2.2

9. Bile is a chemical secreted by the small intestine.

   ANS: F   DIF: I   OBJ: 49-2.4

10. Almost all lipids are digested in the small intestine.

    ANS: T   DIF: I   OBJ: 49-2.4

11. The synthesis of hydrochloric acid in the stomach is regulated by the hormone ulcerin.

    ANS: F   DIF: I   OBJ: 49-2.4

12. Some nutrients are absorbed in the large intestine.

    ANS: T   DIF: I   OBJ: 49-2.5

13. Urea is a highly toxic nitrogenous waste.

    ANS: F   DIF: I   OBJ: 49-3.1

14. The skin can be considered an excretory organ.

    ANS: T   DIF: I   OBJ: 49-3.1

15. The kidneys filter out toxins, urea, water, and mineral salts from the blood.

    ANS: T   DIF: I   OBJ: 49-3.1

16. The functional units of the kidneys are called nephrons.

    ANS: T   DIF: I   OBJ: 49-3.2

17. The first stage of urine formation is called reabsorption.

    ANS: F   DIF: I   OBJ: 49-3.3

18. Nitrogenous waste is removed from the blood by a process called filtration.

    ANS: T   DIF: I   OBJ: 49-3.4

19. The ureter is a muscular sac that stores urine.

    ANS: F   DIF: I   OBJ: 49-3.5

MULTIPLE CHOICE

1. Nutrients provide the body with the energy and materials it needs for
   a. growth.   c. repair.
   b. maintenance.   d. All of the above

   ANS: D   DIF: I   OBJ: 49-1.1

2. All essential amino acids
   a. must be obtained from the foods we eat.
   b. are made in our body.
   c. are found in gelatin.
   d. None of the above

   ANS: A   DIF: I   OBJ: 49-1.1

3. carbohydrates : energy ::
   a. fats : bone   c. fats : protein
   b. amino acids : enzymes   d. fats : muscle

   ANS: B   DIF: II   OBJ: 49-1.1

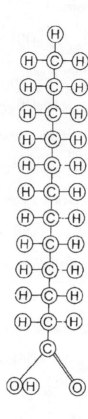

4. Refer to the illustration above. Most of the energy in the molecule shown is stored in the
   a. carbon-oxygen bonds.   c. oxygen-hydrogen bonds.
   b. carbon-hydrogen bonds.   d. carbon-oxygen double bond.

   ANS: B   DIF: I   OBJ: 49-1.1

5. Refer to the illustration above. The structure shown is most likely a portion of a
   a. fat molecule.   c. protein molecule.
   b. carbohydrate molecule.   d. amino acid molecule.

   ANS: A   DIF: I   OBJ: 49-1.1

6. Vitamin K
   a. is stored in fatty tissue.   c. is found in green, leafy vegetables.
   b. assists with blood clotting.   d. All of the above

   ANS: D   DIF: I   OBJ: 49-1.3

7. Vitamins are organic compounds that
   a. help activate enzymes during chemical reactions.
   b. provide energy for metabolism.
   c. help form cell membranes.
   d. are not obtained from food.

   ANS: A   DIF: I   OBJ: 49-1.3

8. Excessive amounts of vitamins such as vitamins A, D, E, and K
   a. lead to excellent health.
   b. can be harmful.
   c. present no problem since they are not stored in the body.
   d. prevent beriberi.

   ANS: B   DIF: I   OBJ: 49-1.3

9. Brain cells and red blood cells receive most of their energy directly from
   a. proteins.   c. glucose.
   b. cellulose.   d. deoxyribose.

   ANS: C   DIF: I   OBJ: 49-1.4

10. Most of the body's energy needs should be supplied by dietary
    a. carbohydrates.   c. vitamins.
    b. fats.   d. proteins.

    ANS: A   DIF: I   OBJ: 49-1.4

11. The first portion of the small intestine is the
    a. colon.   c. duodenum.
    b. esophagus.   d. rectum.

    ANS: C   DIF: I   OBJ: 49-2.1

12. The pharynx is
    a. located in the colon.   c. also called the voice box.
    b. located in the back of the throat. d. None of the above

    ANS: B   DIF: I   OBJ: 49-2.1

13. Which of the following provides a passage for both food and air?
    a. esophagus   c. pharynx
    b. trachea   d. duodenum

    ANS: C   DIF: I   OBJ: 49-2.1

14. The function of the digestive system is to
    a. chemically break down food.   c. absorb nutrient materials.
    b. mechanically break apart food.   d. All of the above

    ANS: D   DIF: I   OBJ: 49-2.1

15. small intestine : large intestine ::
    a. large intestine : small intestine   c. esophagus : stomach
    b. tomach : large intestine   d. small intestine : esophagus

    ANS: C   DIF: II   OBJ: 49-2.1

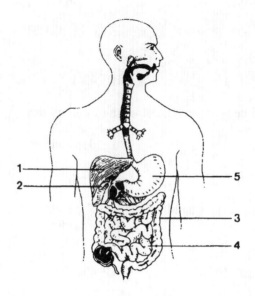

16. Refer to the illustration above. What is the name of structure "5"?
    a. liver
    b. stomach
    c. duodenum
    d. ileum

    ANS: B   DIF: I   OBJ: 49-2.1

17. Refer to the illustration above. Most of the end products of digestion are absorbed into
    the circulatory system from which structure?
    a. structure "1"
    b. structure "2"
    c. structure "3"
    d. structure "4"

    ANS: D   DIF: I   OBJ: 49-2.5

18. Chemical digestion occurs as a result of the action of
    a. hydrochloric acid.
    b. pepsin.
    c. saliva.
    d. All of the above

    ANS: D   DIF: I   OBJ: 49-2.2

19. The wavelike contractions of muscle that move food through the digestive system are
    called
    a. peristalsis.
    b. voluntary contractions.
    c. mechanical digestion.
    d. involuntary digestion.

    ANS: A   DIF: I   OBJ: 49-2.3

20. Enzymes in saliva begin the chemical digestion of
    a. fat.
    b. protein.
    c. carbohydrates.
    d. vitamins.

    ANS: C   DIF: I   OBJ: 49-2.4

21. Pepsin and hydrochloric acid in the stomach begin the digestion of
    a. protein.   c. fats.
    b. starch.   d. carbohydrates.

    ANS: A   DIF: I   OBJ: 49-2.4

22. Bile
    a. breaks down globules of fat into tiny droplets.
    b. is stored in the liver.
    c. is produced by the gall bladder.
    d. All of the above

    ANS: A   DIF: I   OBJ: 49-2.4

23. Fat molecules are broken down into fatty acids by
    a. emulsifiers.   c. sphincters.
    b. amylases.   d. lipases.

    ANS: D   DIF: I   OBJ: 49-2.4

24. Most enzymes and chemicals secreted by the upper end of the small intestine come from
    a. villi.   c. the liver and pancreas.
    b. saliva.   d. the large intestine.

    ANS: C   DIF: I   OBJ: 49-2.4

25. pancreas : enzymes for small intestine ::
    a. stomach : saliva   c. liver : bile
    b. stomach : proteins from amino acids   d. liver : hydrochloric acid

    ANS: C   DIF: II   OBJ: 49-2.4

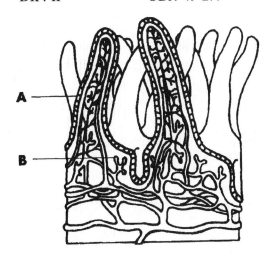

26. Refer to the illustration above. Structure "A" in the diagram is a
    a. villus.   c. ureter.
    b. nephron.   d. urethra.

    ANS: A   DIF: I   OBJ: 49-2.5

27. Refer to the illustration above. This structure is found in the
    a. kidney.
    b. esophagus.
    c. small intestine.
    d. tongue.

    ANS: C   DIF: I   OBJ: 49-2.5

28. Refer to the illustration above. This structure allows for an increase in
    a. nutrient absorption area.
    b. mechanical digestion.
    c. acid production.
    d. bile production.

    ANS: A   DIF: I   OBJ: 49-2.5

29. Refer to the illustration above. Structure "B" in the diagram is
    a. a passageway for bile to flow into the stomach.
    b. a capillary.
    c. found only in the duodenum.
    d. a nephron.

    ANS: B   DIF: I   OBJ: 49-2.5

30. The villi of the small intestine allow for an increase in the rate of
    a. nutrient absorption.
    b. cellulose digestion.
    c. acid production.
    d. bile production.

    ANS: A   DIF: I   OBJ: 49-2.5

31. Urea is formed in the
    a. cells.
    b. lungs.
    c. kidneys.
    d. liver.

    ANS: D   DIF: I   OBJ: 49-3.1

32. Because of their crucial function, kidneys receive large amounts of
    a. food.
    b. blood.
    c. oxygen.
    d. carbon dioxide.

    ANS: B   DIF: I   OBJ: 49-3.2

33. The kidneys play a major role in maintaining
    a. the proper breathing rate.
    b. the proper glucose levels in the blood.
    c. homeostasis by removing urea, water, and other wastes from the blood.
    d. the concentration of digestive enzymes in the blood.

    ANS: C   DIF: I   OBJ: 49-3.2

34. The basic functional unit of the kidney is the
    a. villus.
    b. nephron.
    c. ureter.
    d. urethra.

    ANS: B   DIF: I   OBJ: 49-3.2

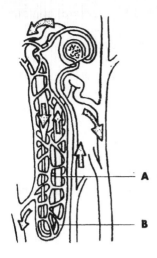

35. Refer to the illustration above. The structure shown in the diagram is known as a
   a. villus.
   b. nephron.
   c. ureter.
   d. urethra.

   ANS: B   DIF: I   OBJ: 49-3.3

36. Refer to the illustration above. At the location labeled "B,"
   a. filtration is taking place.
   b. water and solutes are moving back into the blood.
   c. red blood cells are moving out of the blood.
   d. red blood cells are forced back into the blood.

   ANS: A   DIF: I   OBJ: 49-3.3

37. Refer to the illustration above. The structure shown in the diagram is the basic unit of the
   a. esophagus.
   b. pancreas.
   c. kidney.
   d. liver.

   ANS: C   DIF: I   OBJ: 49-3.3

38. glomerulus : baseball ::
   a. loop of Henle : stop sign
   b. renal tubule : pitcher's mound
   c. renal tubule : baseball scoreboard
   d. Bowman's capsule : baseball glove

   ANS: D   DIF: II   OBJ: 49-3.3

39. The filtrate removed from the blood by the kidneys might contain
   a. salts, amino acids, glucose, and urea.
   b. ammonia, red blood cells, and minerals.
   c. fat, urea, and water.
   d. salts, urea, and plasma.

   ANS: A   DIF: I   OBJ: 49-3.4

40. Urine, when compared with the initial filtrate, contains
    a. more glucose.
    b. less water, fewer minerals, and more urea.
    c. decomposed red blood cells.
    d. concentrated amino acids.

    ANS: B   DIF: I   OBJ: 49-3.4

41. Ammonia is converted to urea because
    a. urea is less toxic to the body.
    b. urea can be converted to a nutrient.
    c. the nitrogenous wastes in urea can be recycled and do not need to be excreted.
    d. All of the above

    ANS: A   DIF: I   OBJ: 49-3.4

42. The first stage of urine formation is called
    a. filtration.   c. reabsorption.
    b. bladder inflation.   d. nephrosis.

    ANS: A   DIF: I   OBJ: 49-3.4

43. Which of the following filtrates is *not* reabsorbed in significant quantities back into the
    bloodstream by the nephrons?
    a. glucose   c. urea
    b. ions   d. water

    ANS: C   DIF: I   OBJ: 49-3.4

44. Urine leaves the body through the
    a. ureter.   c. bladder.
    b. urethra.   d. intestine.

    ANS: B   DIF: I   OBJ: 49-3.5

45. ureter : urinary bladder ::
    a. urinary bladder : ureter   c. urinary bladder : urethra
    b. urethra : urinary bladder   d. Loop of Henle : vena cava

    ANS: C   DIF: II   OBJ: 49-3.5

COMPLETION

1. Brain cells and red blood cells rely almost entirely on _____ for
   energy.

   ANS: glucose   DIF: I   OBJ: 49-1.4

2. The major building blocks of body tissue are supplied by foods containing
   _____.

   ANS: protein   DIF: I   OBJ: 49-1.4

3. The amino acids that humans are unable to manufacture are called
_____ amino acids.

    ANS: essential   DIF: I   OBJ: 49-1.4

4. The mouth, esophagus, stomach, small intestine, and large intestine are the main organs
of the _____ system.

    ANS: digestive   DIF: I   OBJ: 49-2.1

5. The large intestine is also known as the _____.

    ANS: colon   DIF: I   OBJ: 49-2.1

6. Digestion is completed in the _____, where most nutrients are
absorbed.

    ANS: small intestine   DIF: I   OBJ: 49-2.1

7. The semisolid mixture of food, acid, and enzymes in the stomach is known as
_____.

    ANS: chyme   DIF: I   OBJ: 49-2.3

8. The _____ sends enzymes through a duct into the first part of the
small intestine.

    ANS: pancreas   DIF: I   OBJ: 49-2.3

9. Indigestible material such as fiber is briefly stored and compacted in the
_____.

    ANS: large intestine   DIF: I   OBJ: 49-2.3

10. Starches are broken down into sugar molecules by enzymes called
_____.

    ANS: amylases   DIF: I   OBJ: 49-2.4

11. When digestive enzymes eat through part of the stomach lining, they produce a(n)
_____.

    ANS: ulcer   DIF: I   OBJ: 49-2.4

12. Hydrochloric acid is secreted by cells in the _____ found on the
stomach's inner wall.

    ANS: gastric pits   DIF: I   OBJ: 49-2.4

13. Pepsin and hydrochloric acid in the stomach begin the digestion of
    _____.

    ANS: proteins   DIF: I   OBJ: 49-2.4

14. Each kidney contains over 1 million functional units called _____.

    ANS: nephrons   DIF: I   OBJ: 49-3.2

15. The kidneys play a major role in maintaining _____.

    ANS: homeostasis   DIF: I   OBJ: 49-3.4

16. Urine produced in the kidneys passes into the bladder through tubes called
    _____.

    ANS: ureters   DIF: I   OBJ: 49-3.5

PROBLEM

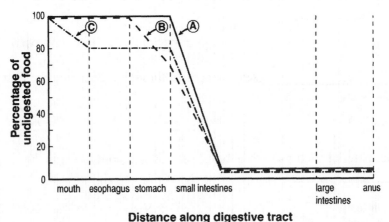

Distance along digestive tract

[Note: Values are approximate.]

1. The graph above shows the progress of digestion as carbohydrates, fats, and proteins pass through the human digestive tract. The horizontal axis indicates the relative distance along the digestive tract, from the mouth to the anus. The vertical axis indicates the percentage of undigested food remaining as the food moves down through the digestive tract. The percentages of undigested carbohydrate, fat, and protein are shown separately, but they are identified only as "A," "B," and "C." Correctly identify which of the graph lines shows carbohydrate digestion, which shows fat digestion, and which shows protein digestion. Write your answer in the space below.

   ANS: "A" is fat, "B" is protein, and "C" is carbohydrate.

   DIF: III   OBJ: 49-2.4

2. The chart below shows the composition of three different body fluids taken from a person. These are identified as fluids "A," "B," and "C." A number of substances are listed in the far left column of the table. The presence of one of these substances in a fluid is indicated by a "+" in the appropriate column. The absence of one of these substances from a fluid is indicated by a "–." Write your answer in the space below.

Substance	Fluid A	Fluid B	Fluid C
Water	+	+	+
Blood cells	–	–	+
Proteins	–	–	+
Hormones	–	–	+
Amino acids	+	–	+
Urea	+	+	+
Glucose	+	–	+
Sodium	+	+	+
Other ions	+	+	+

Write your answers to the following in the spaces below.
a. Which fluid, "A," "B," or "C," is blood? Justify your choice.
b. Which fluid, "A," "B," or "C," is filtrate from nephrons of the kidney? Justify your choice.
c. Which fluid, "A," "B," or "C," is urine? Justify your choice.
d. Which fluid, "A," "B," or "C," would you expect to be the most concentrated? (have the least amount of water in a given volume)

ANS:
a. "C" must be blood because it is the only one of the fluids that has blood cells in it.
b. "A" must be filtrate in the nephrons because it contains glucose and amino acids, which are reabsorbed from the filtrate before urine leaves the body. "A" could not be blood because it does not contain blood cells.
c. "B" must be urine because it contains only water, urea, sodium, and other ions. Both blood and nephron filtrate would contain additional substances.
d. "B"

DIF: III   OBJ: 49-3.1

ESSAY

1. A strict vegetarian consumes no meat or other foods derived from animals, such as eggs or milk. What dietary problems might a strict vegetarian encounter? Write your answer in the space below.

ANS:
Individual plant foods may not contain sufficient amounts of all of the essential amino acids. Strict vegetarians must carefully plan their diet so that plant foods lacking or low in some amino acids are eaten with other plant foods that are high in those amino acids. A strict vegetarian who simply abstains from all animal-derived foods may show symptoms of vitamin B_{12} deficiency.

DIF: II   OBJ: 49-1.2

2. Describe the chemical phase of digestion that occurs in the mouth. Write your answer in the space below.

ANS:
In the mouth, salivary glands release saliva, which is a mixture of water, mucus, and the enzyme salivary amylase. The salivary amylase begins the chemical digestion of starch.

DIF: I   OBJ: 49-2.2

3. The structure of proteins makes it difficult for the body to digest them. How does the body solve the problem of digesting proteins? Write your answer in the space below.

ANS:
Almost all proteins are chains of amino acids that are either folded into tight balls or wound together into tough fibers. Enzymes cannot get at the individual protein chains. The human body solves this problem by carrying out protein digestion in two steps. First, hydrochloric acid in the stomach is used to unfold large proteins into single polypeptide strands; then enzymes in the small intestine, called proteases, attack the individual protein strands, cutting them into smaller fragments.

DIF: I   OBJ: 49-2.3

4. Identify the major wastes excreted by humans, and briefly describe how each is eliminated from the body. Write your answer in the space below.

ANS:
The major waste products excreted by humans are carbon dioxide, urea, and water. Carbon dioxide and some water are excreted by the lungs during exhalation. The kidneys remove water and urea (and some salts) from the blood to form urine, which is voided from the body through the urethra.

DIF: I   OBJ: 49-3.1

5. Explain how the kidneys play a role in maintaining homeostasis in the body. Write your answer in the space below.

ANS:
The kidneys regulate the amounts of substances like salts, minerals, and other chemicals that are retained in the blood or excreted in the urine. In addition, the kidneys regulate the concentration of substances in the blood by adjusting the total amount of water in the body to keep the concentration nearly constant. Kidneys also remove urea and other waste products from the body.

DIF: I   OBJ: 49-3.4

CHAPTER 50—NERVOUS SYSTEM AND SENSE ORGANS

TRUE/FALSE

1. The elongated extension of a neuron that receives impulses from the cell body is called an axon.

   ANS: T   DIF: I   OBJ: 50-1.1

2. The basic unit of the nervous system is the nerve cell, or neuron.

   ANS: T   DIF: I   OBJ: 50-1.1

3. Most of the activity of the cerebrum occurs in its gray matter.

   ANS: T   DIF: I   OBJ: 50-1.2

4. Cerebrospinal fluid in the brain and spinal cord is made up of cells that provide ATP for nerve-cell function.

   ANS: F   DIF: I   OBJ: 50-1.3

5. The peripheral nervous system carries all the messages back and forth between the central nervous system and the rest of the body.

   ANS: T   DIF: I   OBJ: 50-2.1

6. Motor nerves that conduct impulses to skeletal muscles under our conscious control make up the limbic system.

   ANS: F   DIF: I   OBJ: 50-2.2

7. Emotions are controlled by the sympathetic division of the autonomic nervous system.

   ANS: F   DIF: I   OBJ: 50-2.3

8. A spinal reflex is an involuntary response that requires the spinal cord but not the brain.

   ANS: T   DIF: II   OBJ: 50-2.4

9. In some neurons, a form of supporting cell called a myelin sheath wraps around the axon.

   ANS: T   DIF: I   OBJ: 50-3.1

10. Myelin sheaths slow down nerve impulses by forcing them to jump from node to node.

    ANS: F   DIF: I   OBJ: 50-3.1

11. The inside of a resting neuron has a positive charge.

    ANS: F   DIF: I   OBJ: 50-3.3

12. Neurons communicate with other cells by sending neurotransmitters across synapses.

    ANS: T   DIF: I   OBJ: 50-3.4

13. Neurotransmitters are chemical messengers that carry nerve impulses across the synapse.

    ANS: T   DIF: I   OBJ: 50-3.4

14. Most of the pain receptors in the body are located in the brain.

    ANS: F   DIF: I   OBJ: 50-4.1

15. Photoreceptors that produce sharp images are called rods.

    ANS: F   DIF: I   OBJ: 50-4.2

16. Rods are receptor cells used in bright light for detail and color.

    ANS: F   DIF: I   OBJ: 50-4.2

17. Your ears help you maintain your balance.

    ANS: T   DIF: I   OBJ: 50-4.3

18. We hear by detecting vibrations in the ground.

    ANS: F   DIF: I   OBJ: 50-4.3

19. Taste buds, which are located on the surface of the tongue, are stimulated when a chemical dissolved in saliva binds to chemoreceptors in the taste buds.

    ANS: T   DIF: I   OBJ: 50-4.4

MULTIPLE CHOICE

1. The central nervous system consists of
   a. the brain and spinal cord.
   b. spinal nerves only.
   c. the brain stem and cerebellum.
   d. the cerebrum and spinal cord.

   ANS: A   DIF: I   OBJ: 50-1.1

2. The gray matter of the brain consists of
   a. cell bodies of neurons.
   b. only synapses.
   c. myelin.
   d. nodes.

   ANS: A   DIF: I   OBJ: 50-1.2

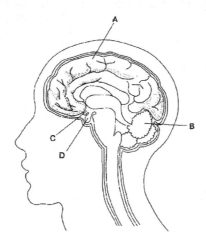

3. Refer to the illustration above. Structure "B" in the diagram is the
   a. reticular formation.
   b. brain stem.
   c. cerebellum.
   d. cerebrum.

   ANS: C   DIF: I   OBJ: 50-1.2

4. Refer to the illustration above. The gray matter of the brain in the diagram is found in
   a. "A."
   b. "B."
   c. "C."
   d. "D."

   ANS: A   DIF: I   OBJ: 50-1.2

5. limbic system : processing sensations such as pain and hunger ::
   a. cerebellum : balance and posture
   b. brain stem : nerve connections for consciousness
   c. hypothalamus : connecting the brain to the spinal cord
   d. reticular formation : activities related to the body temperature and blood pressure

   ANS: A   DIF: II   OBJ: 50-1.2

6. Which part of the spinal cord contains the cell bodies of neurons?
   a. gray matter
   b. dorsal root
   c. ventral root
   d. white matter

   ANS: A   DIF: II   OBJ: 50-1.4

7. Which part of the spinal cord contains motor neurons?
   a. gray matter
   b. dorsal root
   c. ventral root
   d. All of the above

   ANS: C   DIF: II   OBJ: 50-1.4

8. Information is carried from the central nervous system to a muscle or gland by
   a. sensory neurons.
   b. afferent neurons.
   c. reticular neurons.
   d. motor neurons.

   ANS: D   DIF: I   OBJ: 50-1.5

9. Sensory neurons transmit messages
   a. from the central nervous system to a muscle or gland.
   b. from the brain to the spinal cord.
   c. from the environment to the spinal cord or brain.
   d. within the brain.

   ANS: C   DIF: I   OBJ: 50-1.5

10. Motor neurons transmit messages
    a. from the environment to the brain.
    b. from the environment to the spinal cord.
    c. from the spinal cord to the brain.
    d. from the central nervous system to a muscle or gland.

    ANS: D   DIF: I   OBJ: 50-1.5

11. The peripheral nervous system
    a. is not linked to the central nervous system.
    b. provides pathways to and from the central nervous system.
    c. consists of the cerebellum and spinal cord.
    d. is composed of only motor neurons.

    ANS: B   DIF: I   OBJ: 50-2.1

12. The autonomic nervous system controls
    a. reflexes.
    b. voluntary movement.
    c. involuntary functions of the internal organs.
    d. locomotion.

    ANS: C   DIF: I   OBJ: 50-2.2

13. The "fight-or-flight" response involves activity of the
    a. autonomic nervous system.
    b. sympathetic nervous system.
    c. peripheral nervous system.
    d. All of the above

    ANS: D   DIF: I   OBJ: 50-2.3

14. A reflex
    a. may involve two or three neurons.
    b. is not under conscious control.
    c. is not learned.
    d. All of the above

    ANS: D   DIF: I   OBJ: 50-2.4

15. Extensions that receive input at one end of a neuron's body are called
    a. axons.
    b. cell bodies.
    c. synapses.
    d. dendrites.

    ANS: D   DIF: I   OBJ: 50-3.1

16. Nodes of Ranvier
    a. strengthen axons.
    b. slow the nerve impulse.
    c. occur in diseased axons.
    d. are gaps in the myelin sheath.

    ANS: D   DIF: I   OBJ: 50-3.1

17. The myelin sheath
    a. transmits impulses from one neuron to another.
    b. insulates the synapses.
    c. nourishes the neurons.
    d. insulates the axons.

    ANS: D   DIF: I   OBJ: 50-3.1

18. synapse : two neurons ::
    a. neuron : two cell bodies
    b. cell body : two axons
    c. synapse : cell body and axon
    d. axon : cell body and synapse

    ANS: D   DIF: II   OBJ: 50-3.1

19. The sodium-potassium pump
    a. rebuilds axon fibers.
    b. restores resting potential.
    c. creates a stimulus.
    d. is found only in the peripheral nervous system.

    ANS: B   DIF: I   OBJ: 50-3.2

20. Which statement about the resting potential of a neuron is *true*?
    a. There are many times more sodium ions outside the neuron membrane than inside.
    b. Sodium ions are in balance inside and outside the neuron's membrane.
    c. There are fewer potassium ions inside the neuron membrane than outside.
    d. Potassium and sodium ions are equal on both sides of the neuron's membrane.

    ANS: A   DIF: I   OBJ: 50-3.2

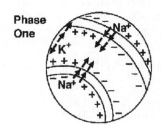
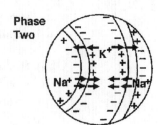
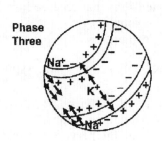

Phase One   Phase Two   Phase Three

21. Refer to the illustration above. When a neuron is at rest,
    a. sodium ions are found mostly on the outside of the cell.
    b. potassium ions are found mostly on the inside of the cell.
    c. the inside of the cell is negatively charged.
    d. All of the above

ANS: D   DIF: I   OBJ: 50-3.2

22. Refer to the illustration above. The diagrams indicate that a nerve impulse
    a. moves from the inside to the outside of an axon.
    b. moves from the outside to the inside of an axon.
    c. is the movement of an action potential along a neuron.
    d. moves slowly.

ANS: C   DIF: I   OBJ: 50-3.3

23. Refer to the illustration above. When an impulse moves down the axon,
    a. sodium ions first rush out of the cell.
    b. a small part of the axon momentarily reverses its polarity.
    c. the resting potential of the cell does not change.
    d. potassium ions are pumped into the axon.

ANS: B   DIF: I   OBJ: 50-3.3

24. Refer to the illustration above. An action potential may be described as
    a. an electrical impulse.
    b. an electromagnetic message.
    c. a chemical message.
    d. a chemical change occurring in the brain.

ANS: A   DIF: I   OBJ: 50-3.3

25. Electrical changes in a neuron create
    a. a stimulus.   c. an action potential.
    b. an electrical shock.   d. light and sound.

ANS: C   DIF: I   OBJ: 50-3.3

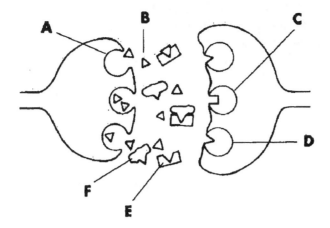

26. Refer to the illustration above. In the diagram, label "B" indicates a
    a. neurotransmitter molecule.
    b. neuromodulator molecule.
    c. receptor protein molecule.
    d. psychoactive drug molecule.

    ANS: A   DIF: I   OBJ: 50-3.3

27. Refer to the illustration above. If neurotransmitters could not be cleared out of a synapse after transmitting a message,
    a. a second neuron would continue to be stimulated for an indefinite period of time.
    b. the first neuron could not pass on its impulse.
    c. neuromodulators would be formed in the synapse.
    d. the neurotransmitter would mimic the effect of a psychoactive drug.

    ANS: A   DIF: I   OBJ: 50-3.4

28. Neurotransmitters are
    a. electrical impulses.
    b. found only in neurons with myelin sheaths.
    c. released at synapses.
    d. produced by muscles.

    ANS: C   DIF: I   OBJ: 50-3.4

29. Some neurotransmitters cross a synaptic cleft and open sodium channels in the membrane of the postsynaptic neuron, causing
    a. inhibition of impulses in the neuron.
    b. the death of the neuron.
    c. initiation of an impulse in the neuron.
    d. the formation of protein receptors in the neuron.

    ANS: C   DIF: I   OBJ: 50-3.4

30. When a nerve impulse reaches a synapse, neurotransmitters
    a. become enzymes in the space between the neurons.
    b. are released into the synaptic cleft.
    c. cover the membrane of the axon.
    d. cause the cell body of the next neuron to enlarge.

    ANS: B   DIF: I   OBJ: 50-3.4

31. The layer of photoreceptors and other neurons at the back of the eye is called the
    a. retina.   c. iris.
    b. cochlea.   d. optic nerve.

    ANS: A   DIF: I   OBJ: 50-4.2

32. Dim-light vision is sensed by the
    a. cones.   c. cornea.
    b. lens.   d. rods.

    ANS: D   DIF: I   OBJ: 50-4.2

33. The sharpest images occur in a section of the retina that contains many
    a. blood vessels.   c. cones.
    b. rods.   d. glands.

    ANS: C   DIF: I   OBJ: 50-4.2

34. iris : amount of light entering the eye ::
    a. pupil : amount of light entering the eye
    b. cornea : shape of the lens
    c. lens : point of focus on the retina
    d. retina : movement of iris muscle

    ANS: C   DIF: II   OBJ: 50-4.2

35. Sensory receptors essential for balance are located in the
    a. sclera.   c. cochlea of the inner ear.
    b. eardrum.   d. semicircular canals.

    ANS: D   DIF: I   OBJ: 50-4.3

36. Hair cells in the semicircular canals detect
    a. motion of the head.   c. the direction of gravity.
    b. loudness.   d. the direction of sounds.

    ANS: A   DIF: I   OBJ: 50-4.3

37. Ears
    a. function to detect sounds.
    b. maintain your balance and sense of where you are in space.
    c. detect only internal stimuli.
    d. Both a and b

    ANS: D   DIF: I   OBJ: 50-4.3

38. Specialized hearing receptors are found in the
    a. cornea.
    b. semicircular canals.
    c. cochlea.
    d. cerebellum.

    ANS: C   DIF: I   OBJ: 50-4.3

39. When we hear,
    a. sound waves enter the ear canal and strike the eardrum.
    b. the fluid in the cochlea moves.
    c. the auditory nerve carries nerve impulses to the brain.
    d. All of the above

    ANS: D   DIF: I   OBJ: 50-4.3

COMPLETION

1. Nerves that control breathing, swallowing, heartbeat, and the diameter of the blood vessels are found in the _____.

    ANS: brain stem   DIF: I   OBJ: 50-1.2

2. The thalamus, hypothalamus, and cells deep within the gray matter of the brain make up the _____ system, which helps regulate emotions.

    ANS: limbic   DIF: I   OBJ: 50-1.2

3. The brain and spinal cord are surrounded by three protective layers collectively called the _____.

    ANS: meninges   DIF: I   OBJ: 50-1.3

4. Ventral-root axons carry information to _____ and _____, while dorsal-root axons carry information to the _____ system.

    ANS: muscles; glands; central nervous   DIF: I   OBJ: 50-1.4

5. All of the nervous system outside the spinal cord and brain is known as the _____ nervous system.

    ANS: peripheral   DIF: I   OBJ: 50-2.1

6. The division of the autonomic nervous system that controls stimulation of internal organs during routine conditions is called the _____ nervous system.

    ANS: parasympathetic   DIF: I   OBJ: 50-2.3

7. A sudden, involuntary movement in response to a stimulus is called a(n) _____.

    ANS: reflex   DIF: I   OBJ: 50-2.4

8. A(n) _____ is the basic unit of communication of the nervous system.

ANS: neuron   DIF: I   OBJ: 50-3.1

9. Cytoplasmic extensions called _____ allow a neuron to receive information simultaneously from many different sources.

ANS: dendrites   DIF: I   OBJ: 50-3.1

10. Some axons are surrounded by an insulating structure called a(n) _____.

ANS: myelin sheath   DIF: I   OBJ: 50-3.1

11. A neuron transmits a nerve impulse as a wave of _____.

ANS: positive charge   DIF: I   OBJ: 50-3.3

12. The electrical charge across the membrane of a neuron is caused by different concentrations of _____ and _____ ions inside and outside the cell.

ANS: sodium, potassium   DIF: I   OBJ: 50-3.3

13. Messages are carried across synapses by _____.

ANS: neurotransmitters   DIF: I   OBJ: 50-3.4

14. The junction of a neuron with another neuron or muscle cell is called a(n) _____.

ANS: synapse   DIF: I   OBJ: 50-3.4

15. Sensory receptors that respond to tissue damage are called _____ receptors.

ANS: pain   DIF: I   OBJ: 50-4.1

16. Peripheral nerve cells that receive information from both internal and external stimuli are called _____.

ANS: receptors   DIF: I   OBJ: 50-4.1

17. The _____ is the light-sensing portion of the eye.

ANS: retina   DIF: I   OBJ: 50-4.2

18. When light enters the eye, it activates photoreceptors called _____ and _____.

ANS: rods, cones   DIF: I   OBJ: 50-4.2

19. The amount of light entering the eye is controlled by the _____.

    ANS: iris   DIF: I   OBJ: 50-4.2

20. When light enters the eye, it first passes through the _____.

    ANS: cornea   DIF: I   OBJ: 50-4.2

21. The _____ is a small, snail-shaped structure lined with hair cells.

    ANS: cochlea   DIF: I   OBJ: 50-4.3

22. The specialized hearing receptors found in the cochlea are _____ cells.

    ANS: hair   DIF: I   OBJ: 50-4.3

23. A(n) _____ is a globular cluster of cells specialized to detect the four basic types of chemicals found in foods.

    ANS: taste bud   DIF: I   OBJ: 50-4.4

ESSAY

1. Meningitis is an inflammation of the meninges of the central nervous system usually due to a bacterial or viral infection. Why is meningitis a dangerous disease? Write your answer in the space below.

    ANS:
The meninges contain tissues that nourish and protect the central nervous system. They also contain cerebrospinal fluid, which cushions the brain and spinal cord and transports substances to the cells in these organs. Any disease agent that enters the cerebrospinal fluid could be transported to and infect any cells of the central nervous system. These cells are vital to body functioning and cannot be replaced.

    DIF: III   OBJ: 50-1.3

2. Explain why you cannot hold your breath indefinitely. Write your answer in the space below.

    ANS:
The autonomic nervous system carries messages to muscles and glands that usually work without our noticing, and enables the nervous system to govern homeostasis within the body. We have involuntary control over some functions, such as breathing, that are regulated by the autonomic nervous system. Any voluntary control of the autonomic nervous system that endangers life disturbs the homeostasis of the brain tissue, causing unconsciousness. Then the autonomic nervous system takes over and restores normal functioning—in this case, breathing.

    DIF: I   OBJ: 50-2.2

3. How is a signal from one neuron transferred to another neuron? Write your answer in the space below.

ANS:
When a nerve impulse gets to the end of an axon, its message must cross the synapse. Messages are carried across synapses by chemical transmitters called neurotransmitters. Neurotransmitters are found in vesicles of axons. When a nerve impulse reaches an axon terminal, it causes the vesicles to release neurotransmitters into the synapses. The neurotransmitters diffuse across the synapses and bind to receptors in the membrane of the postsynaptic cell.

DIF: I   OBJ: 50-3.4

4. Briefly describe how sensory receptors help you maintain posture and keep your balance. Write your answer in the space below.

ANS:
Inside our bodies we have pressure receptors in the joints, tendons, and muscles that detect movement and degree of stretch. These receptors help control how we move and how we maintain our balance. Receptors in the inner ear signal the direction of gravity and the speed and direction of movements to the brain, enabling us to maintain a vertical posture.

DIF: I   OBJ: 50-4.4

TRUE/FALSE

1. An endocrine gland secretes its product directly into the blood.

   ANS: T   DIF: I   OBJ: 51-1.1

2. Organs and glands that produce most of the hormones in the body are called endocrine glands.

   ANS: T   DIF: I   OBJ: 51-1.1

3. Hormones travel throughout the body in the bloodstream and can affect any cell.

   ANS: F   DIF: I   OBJ: 51-1.2

4. Amino acid-based hormones are lipid-soluble, while steroid hormones are water-soluble.

   ANS: F   DIF: I   OBJ: 51-1.3

5. Steroid hormones act from outside the cell by means of second messengers.

   ANS: F   DIF: I   OBJ: 51-1.3

6. Amino acid-based hormones pass through the cell membrane.

   ANS: F   DIF: I   OBJ: 51-1.3

7. Steroid hormones directly influence the activity of the genes in their target cells.

   ANS: T   DIF: I   OBJ: 51-1.3

8. Prostaglandins function as hormones and are transported throughout the body in the bloodstream.

   ANS: F   DIF: I   OBJ: 51-1.4

9. The pancreas is both an endocrine and an exocrine gland.

   ANS: T   DIF: I   OBJ: 51-2.1

10. Luteinizing hormone (LH) initiates ovulation in females.

    ANS: T   DIF: I   OBJ: 51-2.1

11. Antidiuretic hormone (ADH) causes the muscles of the uterus to contract during childbirth.

    ANS: F   DIF: I   OBJ: 51-2.1

12. In females, the ovaries produce the hormones estrogen and progesterone.

ANS: T DIF: I OBJ: 51-2.1

13. The ovary is the source of follicle-stimulating hormone (FSH).

ANS: F DIF: I OBJ: 51-2.1

14. The hypothalamus is controlled by the pituitary gland.

ANS: F DIF: I OBJ: 51-2.2

15. A goiter is the result of futile attempts by the thyroid gland to make thyroxine when the person is suffering from an iodine deficiency.

ANS: T DIF: I OBJ: 51-2.3

16. The inability of cells to take glucose from blood and tissue fluids is called diabetes mellitus.

ANS: T DIF: I OBJ: 51-2.3

17. Antagonistic hormones have opposite effects on the same biological function.

ANS: T DIF: I OBJ: 51-3.1

18. Negative feedback mechanisms are regulated by the level of a nonhormonal compound, such as glucose, in the blood, while positive feedback systems are regulated by the level of a hormone in the blood.

ANS: F DIF: I OBJ: 51-3.2

19. In the human endocrine system, hormone levels are commonly regulated by negative feedback.

ANS: T DIF: I OBJ: 51-3.3

20. When sufficient levels of testosterone are present in a male's bloodstream, production is inhibited by a negative-feedback system.

ANS: T DIF: I OBJ: 51-3.4

MULTIPLE CHOICE

1. Hormones are
   a. chemicals that stimulate nerve cells during times of stress.
   b. the same as electrical nerve impulses.
   c. transported to their targets by the bloodstream.
   d. neurons along which messages travel.

ANS: C DIF: I OBJ: 51-1.1

2. All endocrine glands secrete hormones
   a. directly into the bloodstream.
   b. that go to the pituitary gland.
   c. that affect target cells near the gland.
   d. that are lipid molecules.

   ANS: A   DIF: I   OBJ: 51-1.1

3. Hormones are essential to maintaining homeostasis mainly because
   a. they catalyze specific chemical reactions in brain cells.
   b. the body requires them for digesting food.
   c. they cause specific responses in specific targets.
   d. they act faster than nerve impulses.

   ANS: C   DIF: I   OBJ: 51-1.2

4. In order for a hormone to work,
   a. it must reach its target cell.
   b. it must bind to a receptor protein.
   c. its message must cross a cell membrane.
   d. All of the above

   ANS: D   DIF: I   OBJ: 51-1.2

5. Which of the following would *not* be influenced by cyclic AMP?
   a. activation of enzymes within a target cell
   b. inhibition of the chemical activities within a target cell
   c. action of steroid hormones
   d. amplification of the effect of a peptide hormone

   ANS: C   DIF: I   OBJ: 51-1.2

6. When an amino acid-based hormone attaches to a target cell,
   a. it binds to a receptor in the cytoplasm.
   b. it passes through the cell membrane.
   c. a series of chemical reactions forms a "second messenger."
   d. the hormone is converted into a steroid.

   ANS: C   DIF: I   OBJ: 51-1.2

7. If an amino acid-based hormone acts as a "first messenger," then _____ sometimes acts as a "second messenger."
   a. steroid hormone
   b. cyclic AMP
   c. receptor protein
   d. glucagon

   ANS: B   DIF: I   OBJ: 51-1.2

8. When a hormone molecule bonds with a receptor protein,
   a. the receptor protein changes shape.
   b. the activity or amounts of enzymes in the cell change.
   c. the chemical reactions inside the cell change.
   d. All of the above

   ANS: D   DIF: I   OBJ: 51-1.2

9. All of the following are steroid hormones *except*
   a. progesterone.
   b. estrogen.
   c. epinephrine.
   d. testosterone.

   ANS: C   DIF: I   OBJ: 51-1.3

10. All of the following are nonendocrine chemical signal molecules *except*
   a. steroids.
   b. neuropeptides.
   c. neurotransmitters.
   d. prostaglandins.

   ANS: A   DIF: I   OBJ: 51-1.3

11. Which of the following is an example of an amino acid-based hormone?
   a. receptor protein
   b. estrogen
   c. glycogen
   d. glucagon

   ANS: D   DIF: I   OBJ: 51-1.3

12. Refer to the illustration above. Which of the hormones shown would activate the receptor protein on the right?
   a. Hormone "A"
   b. Hormone "B"
   c. Hormone "C"
   d. Hormone "D"

   ANS: A   DIF: I   OBJ: 51-1.3

13. Refer to the illustration above. If a hormone attached to the receptor protein shown in the diagram, the receptor protein would
   a. detach and move into the cytoplasm.
   b. change its shape.
   c. change the shape of the hormone.
   d. become a phospholipid molecule.

   ANS: B   DIF: I   OBJ: 51-1.3

14. Refer to the illustration above. If one of the steroid hormones in the diagram were able to activate a cell containing the receptor protein,
   a. the hormone would first have to be chemically converted into a different shape.
   b. a receptor molecule for the steroid would have to be somewhere in the cell membrane.
   c. a receptor molecule for the steroid would have to be found in the cell's cytoplasm.
   d. None of the above

   ANS: C   DIF: I   OBJ: 51-1.3

15. The polarity of amino acid-based hormones prevents them from entering cells. Therefore, these hormones
    a. send messages from outside the cell.
    b. are carried into the cell by channel proteins.
    c. combine with steroid hormones in order to activate cells.
    d. cannot dissolve in polar molecules.

    ANS: A   DIF: I   OBJ: 51-1.3

16. Since steroid hormones are lipids, they
    a. attach only to lipid receptor molecules.
    b. cannot enter the target cell.
    c. activate only fat cells.
    d. pass through the lipid bilayer of cell membranes.

    ANS: D   DIF: I   OBJ: 51-1.3

17. A substance that functions by affecting the activities of genes in a target cell is a
    a. prostaglandin.   c. peptide hormone.
    b. steroid hormone.   d. second messenger.

    ANS: B   DIF: I   OBJ: 51-1.3

18. A hormone receptor protein found inside the cytoplasm of a cell may
    a. attach to cyclic AMP.   c. synthesize DNA.
    b. combine with a steroid hormone.   d. act as a second messenger.

    ANS: B   DIF: I   OBJ: 51-1.3

19. Modified lipids that tend to accumulate in areas of tissue disturbance or injury are
    a. endorphins.   c. neuromodulators.
    b. enkephalins.   d. prostaglandins.

    ANS: D   DIF: I   OBJ: 51-1.4

20. Prostaglandins
    a. are transported throughout the body through the blood.
    b. are produced by the hypothalamus.
    c. act locally.
    d. are not considered hormones since they function very differently from them.

    ANS: C   DIF: I   OBJ: 51-1.4

21. Which of the following are mismatched?
    a. oxytocin—hypothalamus   c. glucagon—pancreas
    b. insulin—pancreas   d. thyroxine—pituitary gland

    ANS: D   DIF: I   OBJ: 51-2.1

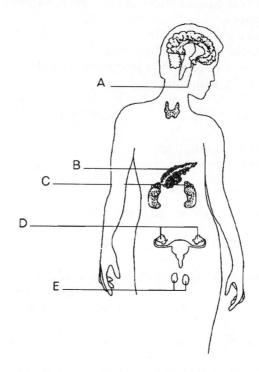

22. Refer to the illustration above. The gland that produces the hormone insulin is
    a. gland "A."
    b. gland "B."
    c. gland "C."
    d. gland "D."

    ANS: B   DIF: I   OBJ: 51-2.1

23. Refer to the illustration above. The gland in the diagram that is stimulated during emergency situations (causing the "flight-or-fight" response) is
    a. gland "A."
    b. gland "B."
    c. gland "C."
    d. gland "D."

    ANS: C   DIF: I   OBJ: 51-2.1

24. Refer to the illustration above. The pituitary gland is indicated in the diagram by
    a. gland "A."
    b. gland "B."
    c. gland "C."
    d. gland "D."

    ANS: A   DIF: I   OBJ: 51-2.2

25. Refer to the illustration above. Development and maintenance of female sexual characteristics are mainly stimulated by secretions of
    a. gland "A."
    b. gland "B."
    c. gland "C."
    d. gland "D."

    ANS: D   DIF: I   OBJ: 51-2.3

26. Refer to the illustration above. Growth hormone is produced by
    a. gland "A."
    b. gland "B."
    c. gland "C."
    d. gland "D."

    ANS: A   DIF: I   OBJ: 51-2.3

27. Refer to the illustration above. Diabetes mellitus is associated with a defect in the functioning of
    a. gland "A."
    b. gland "B."
    c. gland "C."
    d. gland "D."

    ANS: B   DIF: I   OBJ: 51-2.3

28. Refer to the illustration above. Testosterone is produced by
    a. gland "A."
    b. gland "B."
    c. gland "E."
    d. All of the above

    ANS: C   DIF: I   OBJ: 51-2.3

29. The body's normal metabolic rate is regulated by
    a. thyroxine.
    b. epinephrine.
    c. estrogen.
    d. prolactin.

    ANS: A   DIF: I   OBJ: 51-2.1

30. Which of the following are mismatched?
    a. oxytocin—uterus
    b. ADH—kidneys
    c. parathyroid hormone—bones
    d. insulin—hypothalamus

    ANS: D   DIF: I   OBJ: 51-2.1

31. Which of the following organs contain(s) cells that have an endocrine function?
    a. brain
    b. stomach
    c. small intestine
    d. All of the above

    ANS: D   DIF: I   OBJ: 51-2.1

32. Thyroxine
    a. stimulates cell metabolism and growth.
    b. slows growth of its target cells.
    c. stimulates synthesis of DNA.
    d. All of the above

    ANS: A   DIF: I   OBJ: 51-2.1

33. epinephrine : initial reaction to stress ::
    a. norepinephrine : changes in blood pressure
    b. aldosterone : readiness to "fight"
    c. aldosterone : readiness for "flight"
    d. ACTH : blood calcium level

    ANS: D   DIF: II   OBJ: 51-2.1

34. Hormones produced by the anterior pituitary
    a. are regulated by secretions from the hypothalamus.
    b. control the activity of other endocrine glands.
    c. are produced as the result of stimulation by releasing hormones.
    d. All of the above

    ANS: D   DIF: I   OBJ: 51-2.2

35. The posterior lobe of the pituitary gland
    a. secretes releasing hormones that stimulate the anterior lobe of the pituitary gland.
    b. produces and secretes certain steroid hormones.
    c. stores and releases hormones made in the hypothalamus.
    d. is responsible for producing and secreting seven peptide hormones.

    ANS: C   DIF: I   OBJ: 51-2.2

36. The adrenal medulla is different from other endocrine glands in that it
    a. is stimulated to release its hormones by the nervous system.
    b. produces only steroid hormones.
    c. secretes ACTH.
    d. does not release its hormones into the bloodstream.

    ANS: A   DIF: I   OBJ: 51-2.2

37. All of the following are produced by the pituitary gland *except*
    a. prolactin.   c. oxytocin.
    b. growth hormone.   d. parathyroid hormone.

    ANS: D   DIF: I   OBJ: 51-2.2

38. endocrine glands : hormones ::
    a. neurons : neurotransmitters   c. all cells : neurotransmitters
    b. neurons : hormones   d. all cells : hormones

    ANS: A   DIF: II   OBJ: 51-2.2

39. Scientists once thought that the pituitary gland was the regulatory center of the
    endocrine system. They now think that a structure in the brain, the hypothalamus, acts
    as this regulatory center. Which of the following does not provide information
    supporting this new conclusion?
    a. The hypothalamus can send nerve signals to other parts of the brain.
    b. The hypothalamus produces and secretes hormones.
    c. Hormones produced by the hypothalamus stimulate or inhibit the release of other
        hormones by the pituitary gland.
    d. Blood vessels that connect the hypothalamus with the pituitary gland have been found.

    ANS: A   DIF: III   OBJ: 51-2.2

40. An increase in which hormone raises the blood sugar level?
    a. glucagon   c. oxytocin
    b. insulin   d. ADH

    ANS: A   DIF: I   OBJ: 51-2.3

41. The islets of Langerhan in the pancreas are responsible for
    a. production of epinephrine and norepinephrine.
    b. making hormones that regulate blood sugar levels.
    c. regulating calcium levels in the blood and in the bones.
    d. controlling the amount of iodine that reaches the thyroid gland.

    ANS: B   DIF: I   OBJ: 51-2.3

42. When the level of calcium in the blood drops,
    a. one should immediately drink at least two eight-ounce glasses of milk.
    b. the parathyroid glands secrete a hormone that causes the release of calcium from bone into the blood.
    c. the thyroid gland releases calcium into the blood.
    d. All of the above

    ANS: B   DIF: I   OBJ: 51-2.3

43. In a person with diabetes mellitus, even though blood glucose levels may be high,
    a. glycogen is stored in large quantities.   c. cells do not receive glucose.
    b. insulin levels still increase.   d. None of the above

    ANS: C   DIF: I   OBJ: 51-2.3

44. Low levels of thyroxine cause the disease known as
    a. hypothyroidism.   c. hyperthyroidism.
    b. diabetes mellitus.   d. gigantism.

    ANS: A   DIF: I   OBJ: 51-2.3

45. Hypothyroidism can cause
    a. nervousness.   c. increased blood sugar.
    b. weight loss.   d. lack of energy.

    ANS: D   DIF: I   OBJ: 51-2.3

46. Individuals with Type II diabetes
    a. may require daily injections of insulin.
    b. exhibit especially low levels of insulin in their blood.
    c. have an abnormally low number of insulin receptors on their cell membranes.
    d. All of the above

    ANS: D   DIF: I   OBJ: 51-2.3

47. Parathyroid hormone is important for survival because it
    a. stimulates the body's metabolic rate.
    b. regulates the amount of calcium in the blood.
    c. causes the heart to contract and pump blood.
    d. increases the excretion of calcium by the kidneys.

    ANS: B   DIF: I   OBJ: 51-2.3

48. A goiter results from a lack of
   a. iodine.
   b. insulin.
   c. ADH.
   d. sodium ions.

   ANS: A   DIF: I   OBJ: 51-2.3

49. parathyroid gland : parathyroid hormone ::
   a. thyroid gland : thyroxine
   b. pancreas : estrogen
   c. pituitary gland : insulin
   d. adrenal gland : FSH

   ANS: A   DIF: II   OBJ: 51-2.3

50. increase in blood sugar level : glucagon release ::
   a. calcitonin production : low blood calcium level
   b. ADH production : high blood calcium level
   c. hyperthyroidism : overproduction of thyroxine
   d. hypothyroidism : overproduction of thyroxine

   ANS: C   DIF: II   OBJ: 51-2.3

51. In negative feedback, the
   a. last step stimulates the first step.
   b. first step inhibits the last step.
   c. last step inhibits the first step.
   d. All of the above

   ANS: C   DIF: I   OBJ: 51-3.2

52. Which of the following structures produces releasing hormones?
   a. thyroid gland
   b. anterior pituitary
   c. hypothalamus
   d. posterior pituitary

   ANS: C   DIF: I   OBJ: 51-3.3

53. When the levels of thyroid hormones in the blood are low, which of the following series of events follows?
   a. The hypothalamus secretes TSH release-inhibiting hormone, the anterior pituitary stops secreting TSH, and the thyroid stops secreting thyroid hormones.
   b. The hypothalamus secretes TSH release-inhibiting hormone, the anterior pituitary secretes TSH, and the thyroid secretes thyroid hormones.
   c. The hypothalamus secretes TSH-releasing hormone, the anterior pituitary stops secreting TSH, and the thyroid stops secreting thyroid hormones.
   d. The hypothalamus secretes TSH-releasing hormone, the anterior pituitary secretes TSH, and the thyroid secretes thyroid hormones.

   ANS: D   DIF: I   OBJ: 51-3.4

54. Which of the following inhibits the secretion of LH-releasing hormone from the hypothalamus?
   a. high cAMP levels
   b. high testosterone levels
   c. low estrogen levels
   d. low LH-releasing hormone levels

   ANS: B   DIF: II   OBJ: 51-3.4

COMPLETION

1. Hormones affect only the appropriate _____ cells.

   ANS: target   DIF: I   OBJ: 51-1.2

2. Hormones that activate specific genes within a target cell are called
   _____.

   ANS: steroids   DIF: I   OBJ: 51-1.3

3. Fat-soluble lipid hormones, similar in structure to cholesterol, are
   _____.

   ANS: steroids   DIF: I   OBJ: 51-1.3

4. _____ hormones remain outside their target cells, while
   _____ hormones carry out their function from within their target
   cells.

   ANS: Amino acid-based; steroid   DIF: I   OBJ: 51-1.3

5. Cyclic AMP is a molecule that amplifies the effect of a hormone by acting as a(n)
   _____ in cells that are activated by amino acid-based hormones.

   ANS: second messenger   DIF: I   OBJ: 51-1.3

6. A steroid hormone combines with a receptor protein to form a(n)
   _____ complex, which enters the nucleus of a cell and binds to DNA.

   ANS: hormone-receptor   DIF: I   OBJ: 51-1.3

7. High levels of calcium in the blood stimulate the production of
   _____, a hormone that causes more calcium to be deposited in bone
   tissue, thus lowering the blood-calcium level.

   ANS: calcitonin   DIF: I   OBJ: 51-2.1

8. A hormone that enables the cells of certain tissues to take in glucose molecules is
   _____.

   ANS: insulin   DIF: I   OBJ: 51-2.1

9. The _____, a structure of the brain, controls much of the endocrine
   activity of the body by regulating the secretions of the pituitary gland.

   ANS: hypothalamus   DIF: I   OBJ: 51-2.2

10. The part of the brain that may be considered the "master switchboard of the endocrine
    system" is the _____.

    ANS: hypothalamus   DIF: I   OBJ: 51-2.2

11. The gland that produces oxytocin is the _____.

     ANS: posterior pituitary   DIF: I   OBJ: 51-2.2

12. The glands responsible for regulating blood levels of calcium ions are the

     _____.

     ANS: parathyroid glands   DIF: I   OBJ: 51-2.3

13. _____ is a steroid hormone that is produced by the adrenal cortex in response to stress.

     ANS: Cortisol   DIF: I   OBJ: 51-2.3

14. Epinephrine and norepinephrine are produced by the adrenal _____.

     ANS: medulla   DIF: I   OBJ: 51-2.3

15. A condition that results from the inability of cells to take glucose from blood and tissue fluids is called _____.

     ANS: diabetes mellitus   DIF: I   OBJ: 51-2.3

16. A swollen thyroid gland is called a(n) _____.

     ANS: goiter   DIF: I   OBJ: 51-2.3

17. The _____ glands secrete a hormone that regulates the level of calcium in the bloodstream.

     ANS: parathyroid   DIF: I   OBJ: 51-2.3

18. Secretion of epinephrine during stressful times causes an increase of _____ in the bloodstream.

     ANS: glucose   DIF: I   OBJ: 51-3.1

19. An increase in blood glucose stimulates the release of the hormone _____, and a decrease in blood glucose stimulates the release of the hormone _____.

     ANS: insulin; glucagon   DIF: I   OBJ: 51-3.1

20. Glandular production of a hormone that circulates in the blood and inhibits the release of more of the same hormone from the producing gland is known as _____ feedback.

     ANS: negative   DIF: I   OBJ: 51-3.2

21. A hormone that increases the body's metabolic rate is _____.

     ANS: thyroxine   DIF: I   OBJ: 51-3.3

ESSAY

1. Why does a hormone affect only a target cell? Write your answer in the space below.

   ANS:
   Only target cells have receptors that bind the hormone.

   DIF: I   OBJ: 51-1.2

2. Compare the action mechanisms of amino acid-based hormones and steroid hormones. Write your answer in the space below.

   ANS:
   Amino acid-based hormones attach to receptor proteins on the surface of a target cell, causing the production of cyclic AMP within the cell. Cyclic AMP in turn activates enzymes within the cell; thus, the cell is "turned on." Steroid hormones enter the cell, where they combine with receptor proteins in the cytoplasm. The combined hormone and receptor molecules enter into the cell's nucleus, where they activate specific genes on the DNA molecules.

   DIF: I   OBJ: 51-1.3

3. Explain why the cells of a patient with diabetes mellitus starve due to lack of glucose even though blood glucose levels are higher than normal. Write your answer in the space below.

   ANS:
   In a diabetes patient, the pancreas does not make enough insulin. Insulin stimulates the cells to take glucose from the bloodstream. In the absence of insulin, even though there may be plenty of glucose in the blood, cells are unable to absorb it. Therefore, the cells cannot conduct cellular respiration, and they starve.

   DIF: I   OBJ: 51-2.3

CHAPTER 52—REPRODUCTIVE SYSTEM

TRUE/FALSE

1. Sperm are produced and mature in the testes.

   ANS: F DIF: I OBJ: 52-1.1

2. Semen contains sugars to provide energy for sperm cells.

   ANS: T DIF: I OBJ: 52-1.1

3. Testosterone is produced by the testes.

   ANS: T DIF: I OBJ: 52-1.3

4. The urethra is the tube that carries semen during ejaculation.

   ANS: T DIF: I OBJ: 52-1.4

5. The uterus is a pear-shaped organ made of three muscular layers.

   ANS: F DIF: I OBJ: 52-2.1

6. The lower part of the uterus is a ring of strong muscles known as the cervix.

   ANS: T DIF: I OBJ: 52-2.1

7. An ovum is a mature egg cell.

   ANS: T DIF: I OBJ: 52-2.2

8. The fallopian tubes are the organs responsible for producing eggs.

   ANS: F DIF: I OBJ: 52-2.3

9. The ovary is the source of follicle-stimulating hormone (FSH).

   ANS: F DIF: I OBJ: 52-2.3

10. After puberty, FSH stimulates one egg to resume the maturation process each month.

    ANS: F DIF: I OBJ: 52-2.4

11. The lining of the uterus begins to thicken and become spongy in preparation to receive the embryo in the four or five days after the egg is released from the ovary.

    ANS: F DIF: I OBJ: 52-2.4

12. Fertilization usually takes place in the fallopian tubes.

    ANS: T DIF: I OBJ: 52-3.1

13. The entry of an embryo into the uterine wall is called fertilization.

    ANS: F   DIF: I   OBJ: 52-3.1

14. Ectoderm, mesoderm, and endoderm form during the first trimester of pregnancy.

    ANS: T   DIF: I   OBJ: 52-3.2

15. Immediately after fertilization, a human embryo rapidly increases in size.

    ANS: F   DIF: I   OBJ: 52-3.2

16. A In the placenta, fetal blood mixes directly with maternal blood.

    ANS: F   DIF: I   OBJ: 52-3.3

MULTIPLE CHOICE

1. A sperm cell consists of a tail used for locomotion, a midpiece containing mitochondria, and a head that contains
   a. semen.
   b. RNA.
   c. DNA.
   d. mucus.

    ANS: C   DIF: I   OBJ: 52-1.1

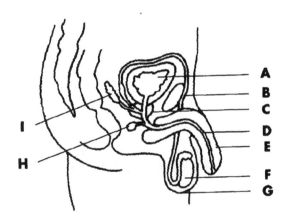

2. Refer to the illustration above. Sperm are produced in
   a. "A."
   b. "C."
   c. "F."
   d. "H."

    ANS: C   DIF: I   OBJ: 52-1.2

3. Refer to the illustration above. The structure that connects the epididymis to the urethra is labeled
   a. "A."
   b. "H."
   c. "I."
   d. "B."

    ANS: D   DIF: I   OBJ: 52-1.4

4. Refer to the illustration above. The tube that carries urine during excretion and semen during ejaculation is labeled
   a. "A."
   c. "B."
   b. "H."
   d. "D."

   ANS: D   DIF: I   OBJ: 52-1.4

5. Which of the following structures of the male reproductive system is *not* located outside the abdominal cavity?
   a. testis
   c. seminal vesicle
   b. epididymis
   d. urethra

   ANS: C   DIF: I   OBJ: 52-1.2

6. The testes
   a. produce sperm.
   c. are suspended in the scrotum.
   b. produce male hormones.
   d. All of the above

   ANS: D   DIF: I   OBJ: 52-1.3

7. Production of sperm and testosterone is regulated by luteinizing hormone and follicle-stimulating hormone, which are produced by
   a. the testes.
   c. the bulbourethral gland.
   b. the hypothalamus.
   d. the pituitary gland.

   ANS: D   DIF: I   OBJ: 52-1.3

8. ovary : egg production ::
   a. ovary : sperm production
   b. female reproductive system : sperm production
   c. testes : sperm production
   d. ovary : fertilization

   ANS: C   DIF: II   OBJ: 52-1.3

9. The process by which sperm leave the male's body is called
   a. secretion.
   c. diffusion.
   b. ejaculation.
   d. locomotion.

   ANS: B   DIF: I   OBJ: 52-1.4

10. The muscular structure in which the fetus develops is the
    a. vagina.
    c. cervix.
    b. fallopian tube.
    d. uterus.

    ANS: D   DIF: I   OBJ: 52-2.1

11. The fallopian tubes
    a. secrete estrogen.
    b. produce eggs.
    c. extend from the ovaries to each side of the uterus, through which the egg travels.
    d. All of the above

    ANS: C   DIF: I   OBJ: 52-2.1

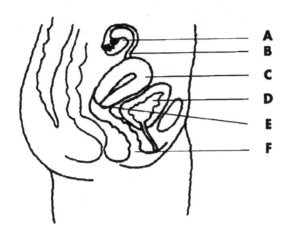

12. Refer to the illustration above. The structure labeled "C" in the diagram is
    a. a fallopian tube.   c. the uterus.
    b. the urethra.   d. a ureter.

    ANS: C   DIF: I   OBJ: 52-2.1

13. Refer to the illustration above. Eggs mature in the structure labeled
    a. "A."   c. "D."
    b. "F."   d. "E."

    ANS: A   DIF: I   OBJ: 52-2.3

14. Refer to the illustration above. Fertilization usually occurs in the structure labeled
    a. "A."   c. "C."
    b. "F."   d. "B."

    ANS: D   DIF: I   OBJ: 52-2.3

15. The strong ring of muscles at the entrance to the uterus is called the
    a. vagina.   c. cervix.
    b. vulva.   d. diaphragm.

    ANS: C   DIF: I   OBJ: 52-2.1

Modern Biology Assessment Item Listing
505

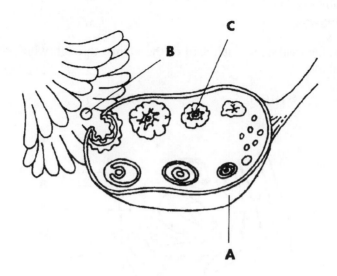

16. Refer to the illustration above. In the diagram, the structure labeled "B" is
    a. a sperm cell.
    b. a follicle cell.
    c. an egg cell.
    d. the cervix.

    ANS: C   DIF: I   OBJ: 52-2.1

17. Refer to the illustration above. The structure labeled "A" in the diagram is
    a. a follicle.
    b. an egg cell.
    c. the uterus.
    d. an ovary.

    ANS: D   DIF: I   OBJ: 52-2.1

18. Refer to the illustration above. The structure labeled "C" in the diagram is a(n)
    a. immature follicle.
    b. follicle beginning to break down.
    c. mature egg.
    d. immature egg.

    ANS: B   DIF: I   OBJ: 52-2.4

19. Sperm and eggs are both
    a. haploid.
    b. diploid.
    c. tetraploid.
    d. None of the above

    ANS: A   DIF: I   OBJ: 52-2.2

20. In which of the following ways are mature human sperm and eggs similar?
    a. They both have the same number of chromosomes in their nuclei.
    b. They are both the same size.
    c. They are both equipped with a flagellum that provides motility.
    d. They are both produced after ovulation.

    ANS: A   DIF: I   OBJ: 52-2.2

21. Female gametes are called
    a. sperm.
    b. ova.
    c. fallopia.
    d. follicles.

    ANS: B   DIF: I   OBJ: 52-2.2

22. Eggs are produced in the
    a. ovaries.
    b. fallopian tubes.
    c. uterus.
    d. vagina.

    ANS: A   DIF: I   OBJ: 52-2.3

23. The ruptured follicle left in the ovary after ovulation develops into a
    a. corpus luteum.
    b. zygote.
    c. chorion.
    d. cervix.

    ANS: A   DIF: I   OBJ: 52-2.4

24. If no embryo arrives after the uterus has prepared to receive it,
    a. birth will occur later than the usual nine months.
    b. the lining of the uterus stays intact in preparation for another embryo.
    c. the lining of the uterus is expelled from the body.
    d. None of the above

    ANS: C   DIF: I   OBJ: 52-2.4

25. Menopause is the time at which
    a. adult sex characteristics first appear.
    b. eggs are produced.
    c. menstruation begins.
    d. females cease to release eggs.

    ANS: D   DIF: I   OBJ: 52-2.4

26. During implantation,
    a. the follicle matures.
    b. the embryo attaches itself to the uterine wall.
    c. the sperm reaches the egg.
    d. menstruation occurs.

    ANS: B   DIF: I   OBJ: 52-3.1

27. The attachment of an embryo into the uterine wall is known as
    a. implantation.
    b. development.
    c. labor.
    d. fertilization.

    ANS: A   DIF: I   OBJ: 52-3.1

28. The embryo is formed
    a. in the ovary.
    b. during the third trimester of pregnancy.
    c. at fertilization.
    d. when the fertilized egg divides.

    ANS: D   DIF: I   OBJ: 52-3.2

29. Cells produced by division of the fertilized egg give rise to the
    a. embryo.
    b. placenta.
    c. umbilical cord.
    d. All of the above

ANS: A   DIF: I   OBJ: 52-3.2

30. Drinking alcohol, smoking, or using other drugs during pregnancy can cause
    a. birth defects in babies.
    b. small or sick babies.
    c. mental retardation.
    d. All of the above

ANS: D   DIF: I   OBJ: 52-3.2

31. The structure that exchanges substances between mother and fetus is the
    a. yolk sac.
    b. fallopian tube.
    c. placenta.
    d. mature follicle.

ANS: C   DIF: I   OBJ: 52-3.3

32. During the fetal period,
    a. the mother's blood flows into the fetus through the umbilical cord.
    b. the infant's lungs absorb oxygen from the amniotic fluid.
    c. digestion occurs independently of the mother.
    d. the blood of the fetus absorbs oxygen and gets rid of carbon dioxide through the placenta.

ANS: D   DIF: I   OBJ: 52-3.3

33. Embryonic cells are organized into the major organ systems
    a. during the sixth month.
    b. by the end of the first trimester.
    c. during the second trimester.
    d. just before birth.

ANS: B   DIF: I   OBJ: 52-3.3

34. Pregnancy is often divided into three 3-month periods known as
    a. quarters.
    b. fetal development.
    c. trimesters.
    d. ovarian cycles.

ANS: C   DIF: I   OBJ: 52-3.3

COMPLETION

1. The testes are suspended in the _____.

ANS: scrotum   DIF: I   OBJ: 52-1.2

2. In the testes, sperm are produced in tubes called _____.

ANS: seminiferous tubules   DIF: I   OBJ: 52-1.3

3. The inner wall of the uterus is called the _____.

ANS: endometrium   DIF: I   OBJ: 52-2.1

4. The strong ring of muscles at the lower opening of the uterus is called the
   _____.

   ANS: cervix   DIF: I   OBJ: 52-2.1

5. The release of an egg from an ovary is called _____.

   ANS: ovulation   DIF: I   OBJ: 52-2.4

6. The immature eggs found in a female at birth are arrested in the
   _____ stage of the first meiotic division.

   ANS: prophase   DIF: I   OBJ: 52-2.4

7. Clusters of cells that surround an immature egg are called _____.

   ANS: follicles   DIF: I   OBJ: 52-2.4

8. The _____ cycle of the female is usually about 28 days long.

   ANS: menstrual   DIF: I   OBJ: 52-2.4

9. The part of the female reproductive system that is lost each month as menstrual flow is
   the lining of the _____.

   ANS: uterus   DIF: I   OBJ: 52-2.4

10. The entry of an embryo into the uterine wall is called _____.

    ANS: implantation   DIF: I   OBJ: 52-3.1

11. The duct joining the ovary and the uterus is the _____, where
    fertilization takes place.

    ANS: fallopian tube   DIF: I   OBJ: 52-3.1

12. Cleavage produces a ball of cells called the _____.

    ANS: blastocyst   DIF: I   OBJ: 52-3.1

13. The period of rapid division of an egg immediately after fertilization is called
    _____.

    ANS: cleavage   DIF: I   OBJ: 52-3.1

14. Following implantation, a membrane called the _____ encloses the
    embryo.

    ANS: amnion   DIF: I   OBJ: 52-3.2

15. Nutrients, oxygen, and wastes including carbon dioxide, are transferred between the mother and embryo through the _____.

ANS: placenta   DIF: I   OBJ: 52-3.3

16. Pregnancy is often divided into three 3-month periods known as _____.

ANS: trimesters   DIF: I   OBJ: 52-3.3

ESSAY

1. Describe the structure of a sperm cell and explain how it is adapted for its function. Write your answer in the space below.

ANS:
A sperm cell consists of a head with very little cytoplasm and a long tail. Digestive enzymes in the head enable a sperm cell to penetrate an egg. Located between the head and tail is the midpiece that contains mitochondria which supply the tail with ATP containing the energy that the sperm cell needs to swim through a female's reproductive system to an egg. Swimming is accomplished by rapid movement of the tail, while the head contains genetic information.

DIF: I   OBJ: 52-1.1

2. Why must so many sperm be ejaculated for fertilization to take place? Write your answer in the space below.

ANS:
Although millions of sperm may be ejaculated, sperm are very small and must travel a long distance to reach the egg. The sperm must enter the uterus through the opening of the cervix and travel to the fallopian tube, where fertilization occurs. Usually only one of the fallopian tubes contains an egg. Most sperm never leave the vagina.

DIF: I   OBJ: 52-1.4

3. Describe the path of an unfertilized egg from the place where it is produced to the site where it leaves the body with menstrual flow. Write your answer in the space below.

ANS:
An egg is produced and stored in the ovaries. When the egg matures, the follicle, which has formed around the egg, moves to the wall of the ovary, ruptures, and releases the egg. Tiny fingerlike projections draw the egg from the ovary to the fallopian tube. The egg moves through the fallopian tube to the uterus, and then enters the uterus. If the egg has not been fertilized, it disintegrates in the uterus and along with the thickened lining of the uterus, is shed as a bloody discharge at menstruation.

DIF: I   OBJ: 52-2.2

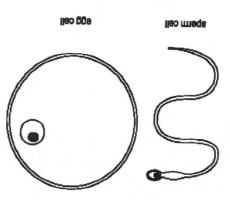

sperm cell   egg cell

4. Refer to the illustration above. (Note: These drawings are not to scale. An egg cell is very much larger than a sperm cell.) Write your answers to the following in the spaces below.
   a. Describe three ways in which these two cells differ from each other.
   b. Relate the differences you noted in part "a" of this question to the activities carried out by these two cells.
   c. Identify one way in which these two cells differ from each other that cannot be seen using a microscope.
   d. Identify one thing that these two cells have in common with each other that cannot be seen using a microscope.
   e. Which part(s) of the sperm cell will enter the egg cell and become part of the zygote?

ANS:
   a. Possible answers: (1) The egg cell is much larger than the sperm cell. (2) The sperm cell has a flagellum while the egg cell does not. (3) The sperm cell has much less cytoplasm in it than the egg cell does. (4) The sperm cell has a distinct head and tail.
   b. Possible answers: (1) The egg cell contains the organelles and food reserves that the zygote will need in order for it to divide and develop into an embryo. The sperm cell carries only a few mitochondria, that enable it to move, and no food reserves (these are supplied in the semen). (2) Sperm cells are deposited in the vagina of the human female and must swim up into a fallopian tube in order to reach a ripe egg. The egg cell does not have to move itself; it is propelled down the fallopian tube to the uterus by cilia. (3) The sperm cell must swim a long distance inside the female reproductive tract. If it carried much cytoplasm, it wouldn't be able to swim as far or as fast. (4) The head end of the sperm cell contains the nucleus, which will enter the egg cell. The tail end of the sperm cell propels it in the female reproductive tract.
   c. Possible answers: (1) The sperm cell has completed meiosis, while the egg cell has not. (2) The sperm cell has been alive only a few months, while the egg cell has been alive since the woman carrying it was an embryo herself.
   d. Possible answers: (1) Both are haploid cells. (2) Both have 23 chromosomes.
   e. only the nucleus

DIF: III   OBJ: 52-2.3

5. Describe the effect of estrogen on the uterine lining and on the pituitary gland. Write your answer in the space below.

ANS: Estrogen causes the uterine lining to thicken and stimulates the anterior pituitary to release luteinizing hormone (LH), which in turn causes the maturation of the ovum.

DIF: I   OBJ: 52-2.4

6. Julie was about 6 weeks pregnant. She was very excited about having a baby, as was her husband. However, her husband, Jim, was very concerned about Julie's habit of drinking some kind of alcoholic drink every day. Jim told her that he thought she should stop drinking because it could affect the health of their baby. Julie told him "the alcohol can't possibly hurt the baby. The baby has a completely separate circulatory system from mine, so alcohol in my blood can't even get into the baby." What error has Julie made in her reasoning? Write your answer in the space below.

ANS:
Julie has made an error in reasoning that her circulatory system is completely separate from her baby's. While it is true that the mother's blood does not flow directly into the baby, many substances flow from the mothers blood into the baby's through the placenta. Substances such as nutrients and oxygen are vital for the embryo's survival and growth. Substances such as alcohol can cause great harm to the developing baby.

DIF: I   OBJ: 52-3.2

7. What are the functions of the placenta? Write your answer in the space below.

ANS:
The placenta works to exchange substances between the mother and the developing fetus. The mother's body must carry out the processes of digestion, respiration, and excretion for the fetus. Oxygen and nutrients pass from the mother to the fetus and waste products pass from the fetus to the mother through the placenta.

DIF: I   OBJ: 52-3.3

8. Explain why the first trimester of pregnancy is such a critical time of development. Write your answer in the space below.

ANS:
Most of the major developmental events (for example, organ formation) occur during early pregnancy. Most miscarriages occur during this period. Fetal alcohol syndrome is due to alcohol use by pregnant women, especially during early pregnancy. Exposure to mutagens or drugs at this stage can cause serious damage to the embryo.

DIF: I   OBJ: 52-3.3

9. Describe the development that occurs in a fetus from the end of the first trimester to the end of the third trimester. Write your answer in the space below.

ANS:
By the end of the first trimester, all of the major body organs have differentiated, and the sex of the fetus has been established. During the second and third trimesters, the fetus grows rapidly as its organs finish developing and become functional. By the end of the third trimester, the fetus is able to exist outside its mother's body.

DIF: I   OBJ: 52-3.3

TRUE/FALSE

1. All drugs used today are synthetic versions of naturally occurring substances or synthesized compounds that have no known naturally occurring counterpart.

    ANS: F   DIF: I   OBJ: 53-1.1

2. Drugs classified as prescription drugs are also known as over-the-counter drugs.

    ANS: F   DIF: I   OBJ: 53-1.1

3. Nonprescription drugs cannot be obtained unless they are prescribed by a physician.

    ANS: F   DIF: I   OBJ: 53-1.1

4. Generally, drugs that are proteins are taken orally.

    ANS: F   DIF: I   OBJ: 53-1.2

5. Drugs that are naturally occurring or synthetic versions of human hormones are used as hormone replacements.

    ANS: T   DIF: I   OBJ: 53-1.3

6. Drugs that treat mental disorders are not available because these disorders are not caused by chemical imbalances.

    ANS: F   DIF: I   OBJ: 53-1.3

7. A drug can decrease the effectiveness of another drug but cannot enhance its effectiveness.

    ANS: F   DIF: I   OBJ: 53-1.4

8. Nonprescription drugs are harmless in excessive amounts, but prescription drugs may be harmful in excessive amounts and therefore can only be obtained by a physician's order.

    ANS: F   DIF: I   OBJ: 53-1.5

9. Nicotine is a depressant found in tobacco.

    ANS: F   DIF: I   OBJ: 53-2.1

11. More than 90 percent of all lung cancer deaths can be attributed to smoking.

    ANS: T   DIF: I   OBJ: 53-2.2

10. Nicotine can cause addiction, and the tars formed by burning cigarettes can cause disease.

    ANS: T   DIF: I   OBJ: 53-2.2

12. Smoking during pregnancy doubles the risk of miscarriage or the death of an infant.

ANS: T   DIF: I   OBJ: 53-2.3

13. A person who drinks alcohol but hasn't eaten recently will experience reduced effects of the alcohol compared with a person who has just eaten.

ANS: F   DIF: I   OBJ: 53-2.5

14. In pregnant women, alcohol diffuses through the placenta and enters the fetus's bloodstream.

ANS: T   DIF: I   OBJ: 53-2.5

15. There is no established safe level of alcohol intake during pregnancy.

ANS: T   DIF: I   OBJ: 53-2.6

16. Alcoholism is an addiction to alcohol.

ANS: T   DIF: I   OBJ: 53-2.5

17. As a person develops tolerance to a drug, the lethal dose increases.

ANS: F   DIF: I   OBJ: 53-3.1

18. Tolerance is an emotional effect of long-term drug use.

ANS: F   DIF: I   OBJ: 53-3.1

19. Addiction to psychoactive drugs is a physiological response because addiction involves interactions of drug molecules and nerve cell membranes.

ANS: T   DIF: I   OBJ: 53-3.2

20. Withdrawal is the set of symptoms experienced by a drug addict in response to absence of the drug.

ANS: T   DIF: I   OBJ: 53-3.3

21. Enkephalins are neurotransmitters released by the body in response to pain.

ANS: T   DIF: I   OBJ: 53-3.4

22. Narcotics are addictive because of their ability to mimic enkephalins.

ANS: T   DIF: I   OBJ: 53-3.4

23. Cocaine acts by blocking serotonin reabsorption at synapses.

ANS: F   DIF: I   OBJ: 53-3.5

MULTIPLE CHOICE

1. Which of the following is the best definition of a drug?
   a. a chemical used to treat a medical condition
   b. a synthetic or naturally occurring chemical that has biological activity
   c. a chemical that has medicinal value but is often used inappropriately
   d. a chemical that affects the structure or function of part of the human body

   ANS: D   DIF: I   OBJ: 53-1.1

2. Drugs classified as prescription drugs
   a. are also known as over-the-counter drugs.
   b. are the only drugs that do no require a specific dose.
   c. are safer than nonprescription drugs.
   d. require a physician's prescription.

   ANS: D   DIF: I   OBJ: 53-1.1

3. Which of the following methods of drug administration might have the most rapid effect?
   a. ingestion
   b. injection into a vein
   c. skin application
   d. placement under the tongue

   ANS: B   DIF: II   OBJ: 53-1.2

4. Drugs can be administered
   a. by injection.
   b. nasally.
   c. orally.
   d. All of the above

   ANS: D   DIF: I   OBJ: 53-1.2

5. Which of the following counteractive drugs is *incorrectly* matched with what it counteracts?
   a. antihistimine—allergic response
   b. anti-inflammatory—swelling
   c. antacid—hypertension
   d. antibiotic—bacteria

   ANS: C   DIF: II   OBJ: 53-1.3

6. Taking a drug that contains calcium will interfere with the effectiveness of
   a. birth control pills.
   b. anti-fungal drugs.
   c. antihistamines.
   d. tetracycline.

   ANS: D   DIF: I   OBJ: 53-1.4

7. The overuse of antibiotics has resulted in
   a. a number of deaths.
   b. the development of antibiotic-resistant bacteria.
   c. the discovery of many additional benefits of antibiotics.
   d. All of the above

   ANS: B   DIF: II   OBJ: 53-1.5

8. When tobacco is inhaled, nicotine
   a. is absorbed into the bloodstream through the mouth and lungs.
   b. is transported throughout body.
   c. increases blood pressure and heart rate.
   d. All of the above

   ANS: D   DIF: I   OBJ: 53-2.1

9. Tars
   a. cause an increase in heart rate.
   b. paralyze cilia.
   c. are neurotransmitters.
   d. All of the above

   ANS: B   DIF: I   OBJ: 53-2.1

10. Which of the following body systems is affected by long-term tobacco use?
    a. circulatory system
    b. excretory system
    c. digestive system
    d. All of the above

    ANS: D   DIF: I   OBJ: 53-2.2

11. Which of the following is *not* a possible risk factor associated with smoking?
    a. cirrhosis
    b. high blood pressure
    c. lung cancer
    d. peptic ulcers

    ANS: A   DIF: I   OBJ: 53-2.2

12. Smoking causes
    a. lung cancer.
    b. cancer of the mouth and larynx.
    c. stains on the teeth.
    d. All of the above

    ANS: D   DIF: I   OBJ: 53-2.2

13. Drinking alcohol, smoking, or using other drugs during pregnancy can cause
    a. birth defects in babies.
    b. small or sick babies.
    c. mental retardation.
    d. All of the above

    ANS: D   DIF: I   OBJ: 53-2.3

14. The harmful effects of smoking on a fetus are due to
    a. tars.
    b. nicotine.
    c. high blood pressure in the mother.
    d. emphysema in the mother.

    ANS: B   DIF: I   OBJ: 53-2.3

15. Stimulants and depressants are named for their effects on
    a. the respiratory system.
    b. the digestive system.
    c. behavior.
    d. the central nervous system.

    ANS: D   DIF: I   OBJ: 53-2.4

16. Which of the following is *not* an effect of a depressant drug?
a. impaired coordination
b. slowed reaction time
c. increased heart rate
d. decreased respiration rate

ANS: C   DIF: I   OBJ: 53-2.4

17. Which of the following does *not* affect blood alcohol concentration?
a. body weight
b. gender
c. rate of alcohol consumption
d. deciding not to be affected by alcohol

ANS: D   DIF: I   OBJ: 53-2.5

18. Excessive alcohol consumption is associated with all of the following *except*
a. fatty liver.
b. cirrhosis.
c. emphysema.
d. hepatitis.

ANS: C   DIF: I   OBJ: 53-2.6

19. Fetal alcohol syndrome
a. results when babies are allowed to drink alcohol.
b. is a cluster of physical and mental defects associated with exposure of a fetus to alcohol.
c. is likely to occur only when pregnant women become drunk.
d. All of the above

ANS: B   DIF: I   OBJ: 53-2.6

20. Which of the following definitions is *incorrect?*
a. An effective dose is a dose that causes a desired effect.
b. A lethal dose is a dose that results in death.
c. Withdrawal is a response to the lack of a drug.
d. Tolerance means that decreasing amounts are needed to be effective.

ANS: D   DIF: I   OBJ: 53-3.1

21. When a drug blocks removal of a neurotransmitter for a prolonged period,
a. receptors across the synapse are flooded with excess neurotransmitter.
b. the receiving nerve lowers the number of its receptors in the synapse.
c. the only way to maintain normal functioning of the nerve pathway is to continue taking the drug.
d. All of the above

ANS: D   DIF: I   OBJ: 53-3.2

22. Narcotics affect the nervous system's control of pain perception by
a. blocking dopamine reabsorption.
b. binding to muscle.
c. inhibiting the neurotransmitter norepinephrine.
d. mimicking enkephalins.

ANS: D   DIF: I   OBJ: 53-3.2

23. When an addict stops taking the drug that has caused the addiction, the body will not function normally until
a. the number of receptor proteins in the affected synapses has had time to readjust.
b. the amount of the drug being used has been reduced to a safe level.
c. methadone has been prescribed by a physician.
d. All of the above

ANS: A   DIF: I   OBJ: 53-3.3

24. Cocaine is a
a. mimic.   c. degrader.
b. reuptake inhibitor.   d. All of the above

ANS: B   DIF: II   OBJ: 53-3.3

25. Cocaine
a. affects the central nervous system by changing the activity of synapses.
b. prevents reuptake of dopamine.
c. overstimulates nerve pathways.
d. All of the above

ANS: D   DIF: I   OBJ: 53-3.5

COMPLETION

1. A(n) _____ is a chemical compound that affects the structure of a body part or the functioning of a biological process.

ANS: drug   DIF: I   OBJ: 53-1.1

2. Reye's syndrome may develop in children who have flulike symptoms or chickenpox and who are given _____.

ANS: aspirin   DIF: I   OBJ: 53-1.4

3. Overuse of acetaminophen can result in damage to the _____.

ANS: liver   DIF: I   OBJ: 53-1.5

4. _____ are complex mixtures of chemicals and smoke particles produced by burning tobacco.

ANS: Tars   DIF: I   OBJ: 53-2.1

5. Drugs that decrease the activity of the central nervous system are known as _____.

ANS: depressants   DIF: I   OBJ: 53-2.4

6. _____ is a measurement of the amount of alcohol in the blood.

ANS: Blood alcohol concentration   DIF: I   OBJ: 53-2.5

Modern Biology Assessment Item Listing

7. Most psychoactive drugs are _____ and are thus potentially harmful.

   ANS: addictive   DIF: I   OBJ: 53-3.2

8. Natural pain relievers released by the human body in response to pain and stress are called
   _____.

   ANS: enkephalins   DIF: I   OBJ: 53-3.2

9. Amphetamines, caffeine, and cocaine are psychoactive drugs that are categorized as
   _____.

   ANS: stimulants   DIF: I   OBJ: 53-3.4

10. Drugs that affect the functioning of the central nervous system are called
    _____.

   ANS: psychoactive drugs   DIF: I   OBJ: 53-3.2

11. A _____ is a pain relieving drug that also induces sleep.

   ANS: narcotic   DIF: I   OBJ: 53-3.4

PROBLEM

1. Julie was about 6 weeks pregnant. She was very excited about having a baby, as was her husband. However, her husband, Jim, was very concerned about Julie's habit of drinking some kind of alcoholic drink every day. Jim told her that he thought she should stop drinking because it could affect the health of their baby. Julie told him "the alcohol can't possibly hurt the baby. The baby has a completely separate circulatory system from mine, so alcohol in my blood can't even get into the baby." What error has Julie made in her reasoning? Write your answer in the space below.

   ANS:
   Julie has made an error in reasoning that her circulatory system is completely separate from her baby's. While it is true that the mother's blood does not flow directly into the baby, many substances flow from the mothers blood into the baby's through the placenta. Substances such as nutrients and oxygen are vital for the embryo's survival and growth. Substances such as alcohol can cause great harm to the developing baby.

   DIF: I   OBJ: 53-2.6

ESSAY

1. Colds are caused by viruses. Explain why an antibiotic would not be an effective treatment for a cold. Write your answer in the space below.

   ANS:
   Antibiotics are specifically used to treat bacterial infections. They are ineffective against viruses.

   DIF: I   OBJ: 53-1.5

2. Describe the effects of nicotine on the body. Write your answer in the space below.

ANS:
Nicotine is a stimulant that causes an increase in heart rate and blood pressure and a decrease in blood circulation to the hands and feet.

DIF: I   OBJ: 53-2.1

3. Explain why addiction to mood-altering drugs is said to have a physiological basis. Write your answer in the space below.

ANS:
Some drugs cause excessive amounts of neurotransmitter to be present in synapses for long periods of time. This results in a decreased number of receptors on the post-synaptic membrane and a less sensitive nerve pathway. The only way a person who is addicted can maintain normal functioning of the nerve pathway is to continue taking the drug.

DIF: I   OBJ: 53-3.2

4. How do enkephalins prevent pain messages in the body? Write your answer in the space below.

ANS:
When enkephalins bind to receptor proteins in spinal neurons, they block action potentials from reaching the brain, where they would be interpreted as pain.

DIF: I   OBJ: 53-3.2

5. Describe the action of cocaine at the synapse and the effects of long-term use on receptors. Write your answer in the space below.

ANS:
Cocaine prevents the reuptake of dopamine from the synapse. The trapped dopamine repeatedly stimulates neurons. Neurons adjust to the presence of cocaine by decreasing their number of dopamine receptors. This causes neurons to become less and less sensitive, requiring more and more cocaine for stimulation.

DIF: I   OBJ: 53-3.5